Methods in Neurosciences

Volume 2

Cell Culture

Methods in Neurosciences

Edited by

P. Michael Conn

Department of Pharmacology
The University of Iowa
College of Medicine
Iowa City, Iowa

Volume 2
Cell Culture

ACADEMIC PRESS, INC.
Harcourt Brace Jovanovich, Publishers
San Diego New York Boston London Sydney Tokyo Toronto

Front cover photograph (paperback edition only) courtesy of Sean Murphy, Department of Pharmacology, The University of Iowa College of Medicine, Iowa City, Iowa.

Academic Press, Inc.
San Diego, California 92101

United Kingdom Edition published by
Academic Press Limited
24-28 Oval Road, London NW1 7DX

Library of Congress Catalog Card Number: 1043-9471

ISBN   0-12-185253-9   (hardcover)(alk. paper)
ISBN   0-12-185254-7   (paperback)(alk. paper)

Printed in the United States of America
90 91 92 93   9 8 7 6 5 4 3 2 1

Table of Contents

Section VI Cell Lineage

Contributors to Volume 2

Article numbers are in parentheses following the names of contributors. Affiliations listed are current.

RUBEN ADLER (10), Retinal Degenerations Research Center, Retinal Degenerations Laboratories, Wilmer Eye Institute, The Johns Hopkins University, School of Medicine, Baltimore, Maryland 21205

EFRAIN C. AZMITIA (17), Department of Biology, New York University, New York, New York 10003

BARBARA A. BENNETT (21), Department of Physiology and Pharmacology, The Bowman Gray School of Medicine, Wake Forest University, Winston-Salem, North Carolina 27103

MICHAEL E. BERENS (16), Brain Tumor Research Center, Department of Neurosurgery, School of Medicine, University of California, San Francisco, San Francisco, California 94143

ROLF BJERKVIG (15), Department of Pathology, The Gade Institute, University of Bergen, Haukeland Hospital, N-5021 Bergen, Norway

IRA B. BLACK (1), Division of Developmental Neurology, Department of Neurology and Neuroscience, Cornell University Medical College and The New York Hospital, New York, New York 10021

LIANE BOLOGA (11), Institute of Anatomy, University of Fribourg, CH-1700 Fribourg, Switzerland

E. PETER BOSCH (4), Division of Neurochemistry and Neurobiology, Department of Neurology, The University of Iowa, College of Medicine, Iowa City, Iowa 52242

JANE E. BOTTENSTEIN (5), Marine Biomedical Institute and Department of Human Biological Chemistry & Genetics, The University of Texas Medical Branch at Galveston, Galveston, Texas 77550

P. MICHAEL CONN (13), Department of Pharmacology, The University of Iowa, College of Medicine, Iowa City, Iowa 52242

STANLEY M. CRAIN (6), Departments of Neuroscience and of Physiology and Biophysics, Albert Einstein College of Medicine of Yeshiva University, Bronx, New York 10461

CHERYL F. DREYFUS (1), Division of Developmental Neurology, Department of Neurology and Neuroscience, Cornell University Medical College and The New York Hospital, New York, New York 10021

GARY R. DUTTON (7), Department of Pharmacology, The University of Iowa, College of Medicine, Iowa City, Iowa 52242

LAURA FACCI (2), Department of CNS Research, Fidia Research Laboratories, 35031 Abano Terme, Italy

ANNIE FAIVRE-BAUMAN (23), Groupe de Neuroendocrinologie Cellulaire et Moléculaire URA 1115, Collège de France, Centre National de la Recherche Scientifique (CNRS), 75231 Paris Cédex 05, France

MUHAMMAD FAROOQ (12), Department of Neurology, Albert Einstein College of Medicine of Yeshiva University, Bronx, New York 10461

PAUL C. GOLDSMITH (16), Reproductive Endocrinology Center, Department of Obstetrics, Gynecology and Reproductive Sciences, School of Medicine, University of California, San Francisco, San Francisco, California 94143

JAMES R. HANSEN (13), Department of Pediatrics, The University of Iowa, College of Medicine, Iowa City, Iowa 52242

NORBERT HERSCHKOWITZ (11), Department of Pediatrics, University of Bern, CH-3010 Bern, Switzerland

SAMUEL F. HUNTER (5), Department of Pharmacology & Toxicology, The University of Texas Medical Branch at Galveston, Galveston, Texas 77550

MARCUS JACOBSON (25), Department of Anatomy, University of Utah Medical School, Salt Lake City, Utah 84132

RICHARD M. KRIS (22), Rorer Biotechnology Incorporated, King of Prussia, Pennsylvania 19406

KINYA KURIYAMA (8), Department of Pharmacology, Kyoto Prefectural University of Medicine, Kawaramachi-Hirokoij, Kamikyo-Ku, Kyoto 602, Japan

OLE DIDRIK LAERUM (15), Department of Pathology, The Gade Institute, University of Bergen, Haukeland Hospital, N-5021 Bergen, Norway

MEI LEE (22), Department of Biochemistry, The George Washington University Medical Center, Washington, D.C. 20037

ALBERTA LEON (2), Department of CNS Research, Fidia Research Laboratories, 35031 Abano Terme, Italy

JON E. LEVINE (20), Section of Biological Sciences, Department of Neurobiology and Physiology, Northwestern University, Evanston, Illinois 60208

RAMON LIM (4), Division of Neurochemistry and Neurobiology, Department of Neurology, The University of Iowa, College of Medicine, Iowa City, Iowa 52242

DARIA MILANI (2), Department of CNS Research, Fidia Research Laboratories, 35031 Abano Terme, Italy

TERRY W. MOODY (22), Department of Biochemistry, The George Washington University Medical Center, Washington, D.C. 20037

MARIANA MORRIS (21), Department of Physiology and Pharmacology, The Bowman Gray School of Medicine, Wake Forest University, Winston-Salem, North Carolina 27103

SEAN MURPHY (3), Department of Pharmacology, The University of Iowa, College of Medicine, Iowa City, Iowa 52242

WILLIAM T. NORTON (12), Department of Neurology, Albert Einstein College of Medicine of Yeshiva University, Bronx, New York 10461

SEITARO OHKUMA (8), Department of Pharmacology, Kyoto Prefectural University of Medicine, Kawaramachi-Hirokoij, Kamikyo-Ku, Kyoto 602, Japan

JOHN S. RAMSDELL (19), Division of Molecular and Cellular Endocrinology, Department of Anatomy and Cell Biology, Medical University of South Carolina, Charleston, South Carolina 29425

RUSSELL P. SANETO (9), Department of Cell Biology and Anatomy, Oregon Health Sciences University, Portland, Oregon 97201

ABRAHAM SHAHAR (14), Section of Electron Microscopy, Department of Virology, Israel Institute for Biological Research (IIBR), 70450 Ness-Ziona, Israel

STEPHEN D. SKAPER (2), Department of CNS Research, Fidia Research Laboratories, 35031 Abano Terme, Italy

JULIE STALEY (22), Department of Biochemistry, The George Washington University Medical Center, Washington, D.C. 20037

GUNTHER S. STENT (24), Department of Molecular & Cell Biology, University of California, Berkeley, Berkeley, California 94720

FRANK J. STROBL (20), Section of Biological Sciences, Department of Neurobiology and Physiology, Northwestern University, Evanston, Illinois 60208

DUNCAN K. STUART (24), Department of Molecular & Cell Biology, University of California, Berkeley, Berkeley, California 94720

DAVID K. SUNDBERG (21), Department of Physiology and Pharmacology, The Bowman Gray School of Medicine, Wake Forest University, Winston-Salem, North Carolina 27103

ANDRÉE TIXIER-VIDAL (23), Groupe de Neuroendocrinologie Cellulaire et Moléculaire URA 1115, Collège de France, Centre National de la Recherche Scientifique (CNRS), 75231 Paris Cédex 05, France

GINO TOFFANO (2), Fidia Research Laboratories, 35031 Abano Terme, Italy

C. DOMINIQUE TORAN-ALLERAND (18), Department of Anatomy and Cell Biology and Center for Reproductive Sciences, College of Physicians and Surgeons of Columbia University, New York, New York 10032

STEVEN A. TORRENCE (24), Department of Molecular & Cell Biology, University of California, Berkeley, Berkeley, California 94720

Preface

It is appropriate that an early volume in the *Methods in Neurosciences* series deal with cell culture techniques. The ability to assess the response of neural cells (and targets of neurally derived substances) is an important goal of studies in the neurosciences. The means to measure responses in a chemically defined medium (and away from the influences of other tissues) has been a positive feature of the use of cell cultures and is the major reason that it is so central to this field.

In describing methods, the authors have been encouraged to identify shortcuts not included in earlier publications and to include comparisons among similar techniques in order that the reader be able to make appropriate decisions when selecting methods. Much of the material presented is published for the first time.

General techniques (Section I: General Approaches to Preparation of Cell Cultures) that can be adapted to many different systems as well as means for the purification of cells for culture (Section II: Purification of Cell Types) have been included as have procedures appropriate for large-scale isolation (Section III: Bulk Isolation), for functionally esoteric uses (Section IV: Special Approaches) which may be easily adapted to other systems, for assessing differentiated function (Section V: Functional Assessment), and for tracing lineage (Section VI: Cell Lineage).

Although some topics could not be covered due to space limitations or prior commitments of some of the invited authors, the sampling offered is broad and sufficiently referenced to enable the reader to identify methods that will be readily adaptable to many systems.

Particular thanks go to the authors for making time in their schedules to participate, for meeting deadlines, and for maintaining high standards of quality. Also, thanks are due to the staff of Academic Press for their help and for the timely publication of this material.

P. MICHAEL CONN

Methods in Neurosciences
Edited by P. Michael Conn

Section I

General Approaches to Preparation of Cell Cultures

[1]   Multiple Approaches to Brain Culture

Cheryl F. Dreyfus and Ira B. Black

Introduction

It may appear paradoxical to employ culture approaches in the brain sciences, which, after all, are ultimately concerned with the genesis of mentation and behavior. How can *in vitro* models, singularly lacking in behavioral output, inform study of the brain? The mammalian central nervous system (CNS), composed of heterogeneous cells and systems, and exhibiting multiple levels of complexity and organization, would seem to defy such simplistic, reductionistic avenues. In fact, however, the profound complexity and heterogeneity demand the simplifying strategies that typify cell and tissue culture. The judicious, parallel use of *in vivo* and *in vitro* techniques has provided insights unobtainable through either method alone. The resolution provided by culture models is now beginning to indicate how cell and molecular biology underlies systems and behavioral function.

Culture approaches are particularly powerful in this regard, since different systems may be developed to approximate an enormous range of complexities. Preparations vary from extremely complex, interacting systems of neurons to the culture of single, identified cells. Indeed, a prime problem facing the neuroscientist concerns the choice of an optimal model to address the particular problem under investigation. To help the uninitiated, as well as the experienced neuroscientist in the choice of *in vitro* systems, we describe both complex and relatively simple culture systems. However, the field of cell culture is so vast that we can hardly provide even a cursory survey of all available approaches. Rather, we have adopted a different strategy in the present brief review.

We describe exemplars of the most complex, heterogeneous, "life-like" cultures, and those representing the most simplified and highly defined. Our goal is to present the spectrum, allowing the reader to choose the most appropriate system. Initially, we characterize complex explant cultures that largely preserve cytoarchitectonic, synaptic, and gross anatomic relations. We proceed to indicate how complex systems can then be dissected into component parts, allowing rigorous characterization of individual elements. Finally, we describe reconstitution methods that allow investigation of the interaction of defined cellular and molecular components. This treatment tacitly acknowledges that each particular method has both strengths and limitations, and that no single method is wholly adequate.

This seemingly self-evident truism bears special emphasis in the area of neural culture. The more simplified the culture system, the further from the *in vivo* CNS situation, the greater the potential for irrelevance, and the greater the interpretative difficulty. The more complex the culture system, the greater the approximation of the *in vivo* situation, and the more difficult the control of cellular and molecular variables. The tension between controllability and relevance and simplicity and complexity should not be confounded with issues of rigor. Different systems are simply suited to address different questions, and no one system addresses them all. It is apparent that a number of approaches have to be employed simultaneously to study most problems in neurobiology.

Nevertheless, this brief review must, of necessity, omit description of entire areas of neural culture. Space restrictions do not permit description of neoplastic cell lines, transformed lines, various reaggregate techniques and the whole area of *in vivo* culture, or grafting, which are important examples of approaches that have provided critical insights. The reader is referred to a number of reviews of these areas (1–10).

Organotypic Explant Culture

One of the earliest techniques developed is also one of the most complex, the culture of intact fragments of neural tissue. Maximow used the term "organotypic" in 1925, which emphasizes the degree of preservation of normal, *in vivo*, cellular, and systems relations. In many instances, synaptic interactions are maintained, allowing analysis of interactions of very different cellular elements that are simply inaccessible *in vivo*. Moreover, explants are dynamic, growing areas of brain that undergo synaptogenesis and myelinogenesis, and that generate spontaneous action potentials (11–17). These properties result in the development of neural systems that exhibit appropriate synaptic specificity ultrastructurally, and normal chemical and pharmacological characteristics. These astounding observations attest to the power of the technique, and simultaneously constitute a remarkable set of scientific insights. Simply stated, many aspects of specificity, selectivity, and sensitivity, the hallmarks of neural function, can be reproduced in culture. Explantation provides accessibility for molecular, cellular, and systems analysis. Several specific examples may help illustrate the potential for examination of diverse areas of the nervous system.

Cerebellar explants develop normal architectural arrangements of cortical laminae and deep nuclei (13, 18–20), permitting detailed characterization of interactions in this critically important model of motor control and mapping functions. Explants of hypothalamus, the governor of vegetative life, exhibit the development of appropriate peptidergic neurons (21–23), allowing detailed, chronic biochemical (23, 24) and electrophysiological (25) approaches. The locus coeruleus (26–33), which appears to subserve arousal and attention, and the substantia nigra (34–36), which degenerates in Parkinson's disease, express catecholaminergic phenotypic traits in culture, permitting analysis of underlying molecular genetic mechanisms. In one final example, the hippocampus, which has been implicated in memory mechanisms, displays functional, synaptic networks in culture (11) and pyramidal and granule cells develop normal dendritic arborizations (13). Explantation of virtually any area of the CNS allows definition of the cell and systems biology of a variety of specific neural functions.

It is apparent that explant culture is particularly well-suited for study of interacting systems and nuclei within the local environment, but divorced from the confounding variables of the whole organism. The preservation of normal cellular relationships approximates aspects of *in vivo* conditions in an accessible, simplified form. Mechanisms underlying systems development and function can be conveniently examined in the explant environment, and extensive investigation indicates that explants faithfully reflect growth *in vivo*. Nevertheless, fidelity to the *in vivo* situation is purchased at the expense of complexity: frequently, elucidation of specific cellular and molecular mechanisms requires the use of simplified, dissociated cell culture, as detailed below.

Growth and Maintenance: General Considerations

A number of specialized techniques have been developed to grow and maintain organotypic cultures. One approach that we have successfully employed involves modification of the original methods of Maximow (37). This technique permits the growth and differentiation of selected brain regions for extended periods of at least 4–5 weeks. Prolonged viability allows observation of the lengthy processes of development and maintenance of neural systems. For example, we have used this approach to document the development of neurons from areas as diverse as the substantia nigra (36), basal forebrain (38), and striatum (39). In particular, we have defined the differentiation of catecholaminergic neurons of the locus coeruleus (28, 32). In organotypic culture the neurons express an array of noradrenergic phenotypic traits, including the high-affinity norepinephrine uptake system, the biosynthetic enzymes tyrosine monooxygenase and dopamine β-monooxygenase, and the transmitter itself, norepinephrine. Moreover, the culture preparation has permitted manipulations that have begun to define the molecular mechanisms governing the development of normal phenotypic expression. The locus neurons also extend neurites in culture and make functional, synaptic connections with appropriate central targets such as the hippocampus (28, 30). Consequently, neuronal subsystems develop and are maintained in organotypic culture, allowing analysis of a range of problems from selective survival to neurite guidance to trophic interactions.

Successful growth of the cultures involves the use of a number of specialized techniques. To assist the uninitiated, we describe a typical·procedure for culture of coeruleal explants that can be conveniently adapted to other brain regions (see Fig. 1).

Experimental Animals

Pregnant rats or mice, or neonates, are sacrificed by exposure to CO_2 vapor. Pregnant animals are sterilized by immersion in 80% (v/v) ethanol for 10 min. Fetuses are removed from the gravid uterus under sterile conditions, and placed in a 60-mm petri dish containing Hanks' balanced salt solution [(BSS) 10 ml]. Neonates are sterilized in 80% ethanol and rinsed twice in BSS.

Dissection and Tissue Preparation

Fetuses or neonates in BSS on ice are moved to an EdgeGard laminar flow hood for dissection. Using a dissecting microscope, the brain is removed with fine forceps (Roboz #5), scalpel blades (#11), and curved forceps (Roboz #7), and freed of adherent meninges. In the case of the locus coeruleus, the rostral pons (1 mm³) is dissected from the brain and placed in a petri dish of BSS to await transfer to collagen-coated coverslips. The immature tissue is particularly friable, requiring great care in the dissection procedure. Buffered solutions are required to maintain viability during the dissection procedure, and solution volume varies with brain area. Inadequate liquid volume leads to tissue dehydration, but excess volume renders dissection of a freely floating section impossible. Although dissections are routinely performed by hand, recent reports have described use of the McIlwain tissue chopper or Vibratome for the preparation of slices of reproducible thickness (40).

Brain sections are transferred to round, collagen-coated coverslips (#3 thickness, 22 mm diameter; Corning, Corning, NY). While it is possible to transfer tissue using a large-bore pipette, we prefer to use #7 curved forceps that permit controlled placement of explants on the substrate. This is particularly important in establishing cocultures of different areas (see below). Collagen substrate is prepared from rat tail collagen that is depolymerized in acetic acid [0.1% (v/v)] (37, 41) and photoreconstituted (42).

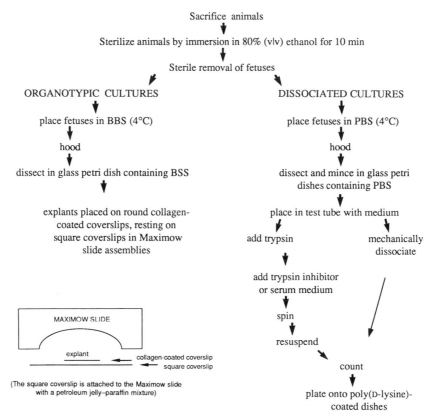

FIG. 1   A simplified flow diagram of the organotypic and dissociated culture procedures.

Culture Preparation

Explanted tissue is maintained in lying drop preparations (37). Brain sections on coverslips are placed either within a Maximow depression slide chamber or in multiwell dishes (6-well dishes; Corning). In our experience, brain tissue survives longer (at least 5 versus 2 weeks) in Maximow chambers. However, the Maximow technique is cumbersome, requiring repeated assembly and disassembly of chambers to allow feeding. If experiments permit growth for 14 days or less, use of multiwell dishes may well be preferable. Chambers are maintained in a water-jacketed, 34.5°C incubator (NAPCO, Tualatin, OR). To ensure proper pH for initial growth, explants are exposed to CO_2 gas for the first two feedings, prior to sealing of the chamber. Subsequent gassing is unnecessary. Multiwell dishes are maintained in a humidified, CO_2 incubator at 37°C (Forma Scientific, Marietta, OH).

Culture Maintenance

Explants are washed in BSS and fed once or twice weekly, depending on brain region. Care tends to be customized to the area grown. For example, the locus coeruleus is initially fed without a wash, but is subsequently washed before each feeding. Two feedings per week is optimal for the locus. All explants are grown in a complex medium, consisting of Eagle's minimum essential medium with Earle's salts and glutamine [50% (v/v); Cat. #320-1095AG, GIBCO, Grand Island, NY], glucose (600 mg %), chick embryo extract [10% (v/v)], heat-inactivated (56°C, 30 min) horse serum [33% (v/v); Cat. #12-44977, Hazelton Biologics, Lenexa, KS], and achromycin with ascorbic acid (1.2 μg/ml; Lederle, Pearl River, NY). The volume of medium, 50–100 μl, is critical. This volume apparently allows the tissue to "condition" the medium optimally, resulting in survival for weeks. In turn, the prolonged survival period fosters the formation of complex cellular interrelationships, which may be analyzed in detail.

Glassware Preparation

Meticulous preparation of glassware is critical to the entire culture endeavor (see Ref. 37 for detail). Although plasticware is employed whenever possible, round and square coverslips, petri dishes for dissection, and Maximow chambers must be made of glass for optimal results. Coverslips are cleaned in concentrated nitric acid and rinsed well in double-distilled or Millipore-filtered water before sterilization. Initially, new glassware is soaked in 10% (v/v) HCl and washed in a 0.4% (w/v) solution of metasilicate (Cat. #S-408-500, Fisher Scientific, Fairlawn, NJ). It is then transferred to hydrochloric acid (1% concentration). Acid is removed by rinsing well in deionized and distilled water. Routine cleaning of the glassware does not include the initial soak in HCl, but otherwise is the same.

Coculture Preparation

In summary, explant culture permits detailed examination of neuronal populations and systems growing in a preserved microenvironment, but isolated from other CNS and organism influences. In addition, the explant paradigm allows investigation of interactions among diverse brain areas (13, 30, 43). For example, the locus innervates cocultured hippocampus, a normal target *in vivo*, forming functional synaptic connections (28). Explant approaches conveniently allow study of such interactions.

Multiple cocultures are grown on the same coverslip. Areas are dissected, as described, and placed approximately 0.5 mm apart on the collagen-coated coverslip. Tissue is allowed to attach for 5–10 min and then gently fed a small quantity of nutrient medium. Numerous neuritic connections extend between cocultured areas within 1 week.

Dissociated Cell Cultures

Introduction

While the use of explant culture represents a convenient simplifying strategy, the presence of heterogeneous populations of cells in a complex microenvironment exposed to complicated medium makes analysis at the single-cell or molecule level extremely difficult. To approach this level of resolution, dissociated cell culture usually is required. However, dissociated cell preparations are diverse, varying from heterogeneous populations grown in undefined medium to highly purified subpopulations cultured in fully defined medium. Different approaches present different advantages and difficulties. To capture the range of potentials, we begin with some of the most complex preparations, proceed to simplified approaches, and, finally, describe reconstitution experiments. The approaches are complementary, ultimately allowing resolution of intrinsic cellular information and epigenetic signals that regulate function (see Fig. 1).

Mixed Neuron-Support Cell Cultures in Serum-Containing Medium

In general terms, dissociates are employed to examine specific interactions of defined populations, and resolve epigenetic regulation and intrinsic cellular information. In most instances, the goal is to elucidate molecular mechanisms underlying neural and glial development and function. The most complex of the dissociated systems consists of mixed neuron-support cell preparations. For example, we have grown the locus coeruleus region, including the coeruleal catecholaminergic neurons with the full complement of local nonneuronal cells (44). In this instance, no attempt is made to purify populations; cultures are composed of neurons, glia, and endothelial cells, as a minimum.

The dissociates are conveniently maintained (34, 45, 46) for weeks. Our cultures are optimally grown in Eagle's minimum medium with Earle's salts and 2 mM L-glutamine (Cat. #320-1095AG, GIBCO), heat-inactivated fetal calf serum [7.5% (v/v); Cat. #12-103-77, Hazelton], glucose (6 mg/ml), penicillin (0.5 U/ml), and streptomycin (0.5 μg/ml; Cat. #600-5145AE, GIBCO) (34). The preparation permits the ongoing study of specific cellular interactions and allows characterization of the actions of exogenous agents.

Dissociates: General Procedures

Dissection and Dissociation

Fetal or neonatal brain tissue such as the locus region is removed from rats, as described for explants. Animals are placed in phosphate-buffered saline (PBS) on ice, the brain region is dissected in the PBS, and tissue is transferred to a 35-mm glass petri dish containing 2 ml of ice-cold nutrient medium. Tissue is minced into pieces of approximately 2 mm^3, which are transferred with medium into a sterile plastic tube (15 ml; Falcon Plastics, Oxnard, CA) for mechanical dissociation. Fetal tissue is easily dissociated by trituration in medium 20 times, using a sterile, long-necked Pasteur pipette, followed by additional trituration 20 times with a fire-polished pipette. In the case of, for example, the locus, this procedure yields neurons that express normal phenotypic characters in culture, including tyrosine monooxygenase, high-affinity norepinephrine uptake, and endogenous norepinephrine.

In many cases, neonatal tissue requires more vigorous techniques due to the presence of dense intercellular material. To maximize cell survival, enzymatic methods are frequently employed to complement mechanical trituration. In one commonly used technique (45, 47), minced tissue is incubated in highly purified trypsin (100 μg/ml, 37°C, in PBS or BSS; Cat. #T-8642, Type X111, Sigma, St. Louis, MO) for 20–30 min (time may vary depending on the tissue). Digestion is terminated by addition of trypsin inhibitor (200 μg/ml; Cat. #T-9003, Type 1-S, Sigma; see Ref. 48) or resuspension of cells in serum-containing medium. Trypsin inhibitor generally is used when cells are to be grown in fully defined medium (see below). Following inhibition, cells are gently centrifuged (1000 rpm, 4°C, 10 min) and resuspended in nutrient medium. Alternatively, papain is used to dissociate fetal as well as neonatal brain regions. Papain (7.3 U/ml; Cat #3126, Worthington Biochemicals, Freehold, NJ; see Ref. 49) is dissolved in cysteine-containing PBS rendered acidic by bubbling with CO_2 gas. Cells are then dissociated by trituration 10 times with a fire-polished pipette. Both methods yield virtually complete dissociation of cells and maximal survival of neurons and support cells.

Culture Preparation

Dissociated cells are counted in a hematocytometer and then plated (in medium) on poly(D-lysine)-coated 35-mm plastic dishes or 24-well dishes (16-mm well diameter; Costar, Cambridge, MA; see Refs. 45, 50–52). [If cultures are to be analyzed autoradiographically, cells are grown on poly(D-lysine)-coated glass coverslips in 35-mm dishes.] Poly(D-lysine) (100 μg/ml; Cat. #P-0899, Sigma) is applied to dishes or wells for approximately 30 min at room temperature, which are then rinsed twice in distilled water. In some cases, 1 ml of medium with fibronectin (10 μg; Cat. #F-4759, Sigma) is added to dishes, and cultures are incubated until plating. Cells may be plated at varying densities. In general, consistently healthy cultures result from plating densities of 1.5×10^6 cells (35-mm dishes) or 0.6×10^6 cells (16-mm wells). However, optimal densities must be established for each brain region and for each experimental paradigm. Dissociates are maintained in a humidified, 5% CO_2 incubator at 37°C and are fed every 5–6 days.

Preparation of Defined Populations

The power of dissociated cultures is more completely realized in the preparation of enriched, or even purified, cellular populations. With defined populations, the locus of action of characterized molecules, and the mechanisms of variegated cellular interactions may be elucidated. Moreover, defined populations constitute bioassay systems for the identification of heretofore uncharacterized putative neuroactive agents. A number of different approaches are available.

Virtually Pure Neuron Culture in Serum-Free Medium

To prepare relatively pure cultures of fetal neurons, tissue is dissociated, as described, but grown in a modification of serum-free medium, described by Bottenstein and Sato (53), using methods modified slightly from those described previously (52, 54). A 1:1 mixture of Ham's F12 medium (Cat. #320-1765, GIBCO) and minimal essential medium with glutamine (GIBCO), supplemented with glucose (6 mg/ml), penicillin (0.5 U/ml), streptomycin (0.5 μg/ml), putrescine hydrochloride (60 μM; Cat. #P-7505, Sigma), progesterone (20 nM; Cat. #P-6149, Sigma), human transferrin (100 μg/ml; Cat. #T2252, Sigma), bovine insulin (25 μg/ml; Cat. #I-5500, Sigma), and selenium (30 nM; Cat. #1657, ICN, Cleveland, OH) is employed. In our experience, dissociates in this medium contain ~5% glial cells after 1 week in culture. Glia require serum to divide and adhere to substrata (35, 55). Consequently, serum-free medium selects for neurons, virtually eliminating glia, from cultured fetal brain dissociates.

Nevertheless, glia are difficult to eliminate by any extant protocol, and this remains an area for future innovation. Currently, many investigators culturing central and peripheral neurons rely on antimitotic agents such as cytosine arabinoside to destroy selectively dividing glial populations. However, antimitotic agents exhibit neuronal toxicity as well and cannot, therefore, be used reliably (56). Recent work suggests that other agents may prove to be preferable in this regard.

Employing the foregoing protocols, brain neurons grow and differentiate in culture, allowing a variety of observations and manipulations (i.e, 33, 57). For example, coeruleal neurons express increasing levels of tyrosine monooxygenase catalytic activity and extend long, ramifying, complex neuritic processes. Such a system may be used to define new growth and trophic factors and to elucidate the roles of added glial and target neuronal populations.

Purification of Neuronal Subpopulations

Increasingly, methods are being developed that allow selection of specific neuronal populations within a brain region. These new approaches allow characterization of intrinsic properties of defined neurons, definition of cell type-specific interactions, and elucidation of cell-specific responses. One approach takes advantage of differences in neuronal sizes within such areas as the cerebellum. Velocity sedimentation (58) and Percoll gradients (59) have been successfully used to separate populations from these areas. There is now a growing need to evolve new methods to purify populations based on other criteria.

Virtually Pure Support Cells in Serum

To begin studying support cell physiology and development (see Ref. 60), and to approach the problem of support cell–neuron interactions, relatively pure support cell populations must be available. Preparative procedures take advantage of the fact that support cells require serum to attach to substratum and proliferate, as indicated above. Consequently, exposure to serum, at least initially, is central to most protocols (55). Neonatal brain tissue is dissected in PBS, dissociated mechanically or enzymatically, and plated in medium containing Eagle's minimum essential medium with glutamine, fetal calf serum (15%), glucose (6 mg/ml), and penicillin–streptomycin. We plate cells in 35- or 60-mm petri dishes and grow them to confluence, a procedure that requires at least 1 week. Cultures may be monitored with a variety of neuron-specific and glial-specific markers to ensure purity of the preparation. For example, in the case of the locus coeruleus, neuron-specific enolase and tyrosine monooxygenase become undetectable after 1 week, indicating that neurons die as support cells continue to undergo mitosis. Within 1 to 2 weeks this procedure yields a virtually pure population of support cells.

Purification of Support Cell Subpopulations

Support cells from specific brain regions may be further purified to obtain astrocyte and oligodenrocyte populations. Procedures primarily take advantage of differential adhesivity to substrates, as well as a number of other distinguishing characteristics (55). For example, astrocytes divide more rapidly than oligodendrocytes, while oligodendrocytes grow well on top of astrocytes.

The purification procedure (55) consists of growing mixed support cell cultures for 9 days in Falcon flasks (75 cm²). Cultures are grown in Eagle's minimum essential medium, 0.1% glutamine, 6 mg/ml glucose, and 15% fetal calf serum, in the absence of antibiotics. Medium is changed three times weekly. Cultures are rinsed on the tenth day with medium, fed 10 ml of fresh medium, and shaken overnight. Suspended cells are collected and filtered through Nitex 35 and Nitex 15 to remove clumps of astrocytes and to dissociate cells of the oligodendrocyte lineage. Cells in the oligodendrocyte filtrate are pelleted and plated in new culture flasks. The procedure may be repeated to increase the purity of the preparation. Oligodendrocyte populations are identified with antibody to the specific surface marker galactocerebroside, which serves to indicate the purity of the cultures.

Astrocytes, which remain attached to the flask surface after shaking, may be further purified. Flasks are rinsed five times with fresh medium, and astrocytes are removed by incubation for 5 min in medium containing 5 mM EDTA. Cells are replated at a density of 30,000/cm². Astrocytes proliferate rapidly and predominate, reducing the relative number of oligodendrocytes that may have been transferred. Purity of the preparation may be ascertained by examining glial fibrillary acidic protein, an astrocyte-specific marker.

Reconstitution in Serum-Free Medium

The availability of purified preparations of neurons and glia allows detailed characterization of cell-specific interactions. To establish neuron–glial cocultures, support cells or oligodendrocytes or astrocytes are initially grown in serum-containing medium. Representative control cultures are examined with the aforementioned markers, to ensure purity. After neurons are no longer detectable in the support cell cultures, coculture may be initiated. A selected group of neurons is plated in serum-free medium on the bed of support cells. Control neuron cultures are grown on poly(D-lysine) in the absence of support cells. In our experience, this protocol succeeds in growing a predominantly neuronal population on the support cell bed. A variety of interactions may be defined, and extensive manipulations may be performed. The purified preparations are particularly valuable in the detection and assay of new growth and trophic factors and in the definition of the molecular basis of neuron–glia interactions.

Afferent Neuron-Target Coculture in Serum-Free Medium

The coculture approach is extremely powerful, allowing examination of neuron–neuron interactions, as well as glia–neuron influences. In fact, this is a convenient and rigorous approach to the study of interactions of afferent neuronal populations and targets in the CNS. For example, we, as well as others (33), are employing this method to investigate interactions of locus coeruleus neurons with target hippocampal neurons. Moreover, in this particular instance, by purifying hippocampal neuron subpopulations the differential effects of pyramidal and granule cells may be evaluated. In parallel studies, purified populations of hippocampal astrocytes and oligodendrocytes may be assessed.

Locus–hippocampal coculture may serve as an example of the nature of the methods employed. Control coeruleal or hippocampal cells are each dissociated in serum-free medium and individually plated in 35-mm petri dishes at a density of 1×10^6 cells/35-mm dish. Alternatively, aliquots of dissociated locus and hippocampus are *simultaneously* plated in the same dish and are shaken gently by hand to mix the two cell groups completely. Neurites rapidly extend between the neurons and influences are evident within 7 days. The procedure is adaptable to a variety of neuron–target interactions in the CNS.

In summary, by dissecting the environment into its component parts, dissociated cultures constitute a powerful approach to study the molecular basis of cell–cell interactions and to define entirely new factors that underly systems formation and function in the CNS. Progressive refinement and dissection of cultures into fundamental, purified elements and subsequent controlled reconstitution allow elucidation of the molecular basis of systems development and function.

Acknowledgments

This work was supported in part by NIH grants HD 23315, NS 10259, NS 20788, and DA 05132 and aided by grants from the Juvenile Diabetes Foundation International, the Bristol Myers Co. Inc., and the March of Dimes Birth Defects Foundation. I. B. Black is the recipient of a McKnight Research Project Award. We acknowledge the valuable assistance of Bettye Mayer, Elise Grossman, Midori Yokoyama, Susana

Cohen, Edward K. O'Malley, Lisa Robinson, David W. Pincus, Dr. Emanuel Di-Cicco-Bloom, and Dr. Joshua E. Adler in the compilation of tissue culture methods described in this manuscript.

References

1. C. Cepko, *Neuron* **1**, 345 (1988).
2. G. D. Fischbach, D. Fambrough, and P. G. Nelson, *Fed. Proc., Fed. Am. Soc. Exp. Biol.* **32**, 1636 (1973).
3. M. V. Edds, D. S. Barkley, and D. M. Fambrough, *Neurosci. Res. Bull.* **10**, 254 (1972).
4. N. W. Seeds, *Proc. Natl. Acad. Sci. U.S.A.* **68**, 1868 (1971).
5. J. Hsiang, S. D. Price, A. Heller, P. C. Hoffman, and B. H. Wainer, *Neuroscience (Oxford)* **26**, 417 (1988).
6. P. Honegger and E. Richelson, *Brain Res.* **109**, 335 (1976).
7. L. Olson, A. Seiger, B. Hoffer, and D. Taylor, *Exp. Brain Res.* **35**, 47 (1979).
8. A. Bjorklund, U. Stenevi, and N. A. Svendgaard, *Nature (London)* **262**, 787 (1976).
9. M. H. Hankin and R. D. Lund, *Brain Res.* **408**, 344 (1987).
10. M. B. Rosenberg, T. Friedman, R. C. Robertson, M. Tuszynski, J. A. Wolff, X. O. Breakfield, and F. H. Gage, *Science* **242**, 1575 (1988).
11. S. M. Crain, *in* "Metabolic Compartmentation and Neurotransmission" (S. Berl, D. D. Clarke, and D. Schneider, eds.), p. 273. Plenum, New York, 1975.
12. M. R. Murray, *in* "Cells and Tissues in Culture: Nervous Tissues *in Vitro*" (E. N. Willmer, ed.), p. 375. Academic Press, New York, 1965.
13. B. H. Gahwiler, *Trends NeuroSci. (Pers. Ed.)* **11**, 484 (1988).
14. P. B. Model, M. B. Bornstein, S. M. Crain, and G. D. Pappas, *J. Cell Biol.* **49**, 363 (1971).
15. W. Hild, *Z. Zellforsch.* **46**, 71 (1957).
16. M. B. Bornstein and M. R. Murray, *J. Biophys. Biochem. Cytol.* **4**, 499 (1958).
17. R. P. Bunge, M. B. Bunge, and E. R. Peterson, *Brain Res.* **6**, 728 (1967).
18. F. J. Seil, *in* "Review of Neuroscience: Cerebellum in Tissue Culture" (D. M. Schneider, ed.), p. 105. Raven, New York, 1979.
19. W. J. Hendelman and K. C. Marshall, *Neuroscience (Oxford)* **5**, 1833 (1980).
20. C. D. Allerand, *J. Comp. Neurol.* **142**, 167 (1971).
21. S. Wray, B. H. Gahwiler, and H. Gainer, *Peptides* **9**, 1151 (1988).
22. A. M. Marson and A. Privat, *Cell Tissue Res.* **203**, 393 (1979).
23. C. D. Toran-Allerand, *Colloq. Int. CNRS* **280**, 759 (1979).
24. K. K. Sakai, B. H. Marks, J. M. George, and A. Koestler, *J. Pharmacol. Exp. Ther.* **190**, 482 (1974).
25. B. H. Gahwiler and J. J. Driefuss, *Brain Res.* **177**, 95 (1979).
26. E. Hosli, U. M. Bucher, and L. Hosli, *Experientia* **31**, 354 (1975).
27. M. Schlumpf, W. J. Shoemaker, and F. E. Bloom, *Proc. Natl. Acad. Sci. U.S.A.* **74**, 4471 (1977).

28. C. F. Dreyfus, M. D. Gershon, and S. M. Crain, *Brain Res.* **161,** 431 (1975).
29. I. Victorov, J. Nguyen-Legros, J. M. Boutry, C. Alvarez, and J. J. Hauw, *Biomedicine* **30,** 161 (1979).
30. K. C. Marshall, R. Y. K. Prin, W. J. Hendelman, and P. G. Nelson, *Science* **213,** 355 (1981).
31. W. J. Hendelman, K. C. Marshall, R. Ferguson, and S. Carriere, *Dev. Neurosci.* **5,** 64 (1982).
32. C. F. Dreyfus, K. A. Markey, M. Goldstein, and I. B. Black, *Dev. Biol.* **97,** 48 (1983).
33. U. di Porzio and M. Estenoz, *Dev. Brain Res.* **16,** 147 (1984).
34. A. Prochiantz, U. di Porzio, A. Kato, B. Berger, and J. Glowinski, *Proc. Natl. Acad. Sci. U.S.A.* **76,** 5387 (1979).
35. U. di Porzio, M. C. Daguet, J. Glowinski, and A. Prochiantz, *Nature (London)* **288,** 370 (1980).
36. W. J. Friedman, C. F. Dreyfus, B. McEwen, and I. B. Black, *J. Neurosci.* **8,** 3616 (1988).
37. M. B. Bornstein, *in* "Tissue Culture: Methods and Applications" (P. F. Kruse and M. K. Patterson, eds.), p. 86. Academic Press, New York, 1973.
38. H. J. Martinez, C. F. Dreyfus, G. M. Jonakait, and I. B. Black, *Brain Res.* **412,** 295 (1987).
39. H. J. Martinez, C. F. Dreyfus, G. M. Jonakait, and I. B. Black, *Proc. Natl. Acad. Sci. U.S.A.* **82,** 7777 (1985).
40. B. H. Gahwiler, *Experientia* **40,** 235 (1984).
41. M. B. Bornstein, *Lab. Invest.* **7,** 134 (1958).
42. E. B. Masurovsky and E. R. Peterson, *Exp. Cell Res.* **76,** 447 (1973).
43. S. M. Crain and E. R. Peterson, *Science* **188,** 275 (1975).
44. L. Robinson, I. B. Black, and C. F. Dreyfus, unpublished observations (1989).
45. G. A. Banker and W. M. Cowan, *Brain Res.* **126,** 397 (1977).
46. J. Hartikka and F. Hefti, *J. Neurosci.* **8,** 2967 (1988).
47. G. D. Fischbach, *Dev. Biol.* **28,** 407 (1972).
48. E. DiCicco-Bloom and I. B. Black, *Proc. Natl. Acad. Sci. U.S.A.* **85,** 4066 (1988).
49. D. M. Lam, *Proc. Natl. Acad. Sci. U.S.A.* **69,** 1987 (1972).
50. E. Yavin and Z. Yavin, *J. Cell Biol.* **62,** 540 (1974).
51. J. E. Bottenstein and G. H. Sato, *Exp. Cell Res.* **129,** 361 (1980).
52. Y. Aizenman and J. de Vellis, *Brain Res.* **406,** 32 (1987).
53. J. E. Bottenstein and G. H. Sato, *Proc. Natl. Acad. Sci. U.S.A.* **76,** 514 (1979).
54. S. D. Skaper, R. Adler, and S. Varon, *Dev. Neurosci.* **2,** 233 (1979).
55. K. D. McCarthy and J. de Vellis, *J. Cell Biol.* **85,** 890 (1980).
56. T. L. Wallace and E. M. Johnson, *J. Neurosci.* **9,** 115 (1989).
57. R. S. Morrison, A. Sharma, J. de Vellis, and R. A. Bradshaw, *Proc. Natl. Acad. Sci. U.S.A.* **83,** 7537 (1986).
58. D. S. Barkley, L. L. Rakic, J. K. Chaffee, and D. L. Wong, *J. Cell. Physiol.* **81,** 271 (1973).
59. M. E. Hatten, *J. Cell Biol.* **100,** 384 (1985).
60. M. C. Raff, *Science* **243,** 1450 (1989).

[2]   Culture and Use of Primary and Clonal Neural Cells

Stephen D. Skaper, Laura Facci, Daria Milani, Alberta Leon, and Gino Toffano

Introduction

The phenomenon of neuronal plasticity represents the capacity of nerve cells to modify their behaviors under the influence of microenvironmentally derived extrinsic agents. Understanding the mechanism(s) underlying neuroplasticity is, certainly, one of the main tasks facing neuroscientists today. The discovery and investigation of nerve growth factor (NGF) (1) documented the existence of molecules (neuronotropic factors) specifically regulating neuronal development.

Neural cell cultures have proved to be a basic and indispensable tool for identifying and purifying substances that influence the differentiation and maturation of the nervous system, for defining their cellular and molecular consequences, and for investigating the mechanisms eliciting these consequences. *In vitro* neural systems also serve to study interdependences between cell types, e.g., neuronal and glial cells, associations believed to occur *in vivo*.

This chapter will describe procedures for preparing and culturing a variety of neural cell types. It is not intended to be all-inclusive, but rather, is based on experiences in our laboratory over a number of years. In this sense, it represents a "hands-on" approach. Advantages and limitations will be discussed, as well as some selected applications of these methods to neurobiological problems.

Clonal Cell Lines

Neural cells have been studied in a variety of *in vitro* systems, from organ cultures, which provide a close approximation to the organization of neural tissue *in situ*, to clonal lines of tumoral cells. Cell lines, for example, provide an advantage of being available in large quantities, and as homogeneous populations (in principle—but not an invariable one). These systems are useful mainly as complements of investigations using normal neural cells.

Neuroblastoma Cells

Probably the most commonly used neuroblastoma line is the mouse C1300 (obtainable from the American Type Culture Collection: CCL 131). These cells can be routinely cultured on a tissue culture plastic surface, in a medium consisting of Dulbecco's modified Eagle's medium (DMEM) supplemented with 2 mM L-glutamine, penicillin (100 U/ml), and 10% (v/v) heat-inactivated fetal calf serum. Heating of serum for culture media use (56°C, 30 min) is done to decomplement it. This medium is suitable for incubation in an atmosphere of 5% CO_2–95% air. Subculture of the cells is carried out by a 10-min exposure (37°C) to 0.5 mM EDTA in phosphate-buffered saline (PBS), pH 7.4, followed by mechanically dislodging, centrifugation (200 g, 5 min, 25°C), and resuspension of the cell pellet in fresh culture medium.

Glioma Cells

The rat C6 glioma cell line (American Type Culture Collection: CCL 107) may be considered as popular as the C1300 neuroblastoma line. C6 cells are cultured under the same conditions as C1300 cells. The same procedures apply when subculturing C6 glioma cells.

Schwannoma Cells

The rat RN22 schwannoma clonal cell line (2) is grown on tissue culture plastic in DMEM supplemented with penicillin/glutamine (as above) and 5% fetal calf serum, 5% newborn calf serum, and 5% horse serum. Culture and maintenance are otherwise as described for neuroblastoma and glioma cells.

Pheochromocytoma Cells

The rat pheochromocytoma cell line PC12 was established to respond to NGF with expression of neuronal properties (3). PC12 cells are grown routinely in tissue culture plastic dishes or flasks in the medium described for neuroblastoma cells. Prior to use, the cell monolayers are washed three times with DMEM. Cells are dislodged into DMEM with a vigorous stream of medium, pipetted up and down to break cell clumps, and filtered through a 20-μm nylon mesh (Nitex).

For bioassay of numerical growth or neurite outgrowth, polyornithine-coated plastic is preferred. PC12 cells rapidly generate clumps on collagen and plastic. With the more adhesive polyornithine surface, cells attach rapidly while still dispersed. As a result, individual cells can be observed over a prolonged period—a necessity if one is to take cell counts to monitor both numerical and neuritic growth. Poly(L-ornithine)-HBr (MW 30,000–45,000; Sigma, St. Louis, MO) is dissolved (0.1 mg/ml) in 15 mM borate buffer, pH 8.4. Exposure of the culture surface for 1–2 hr, followed by washing with water is sufficient for coating.

Cryopreservation of Cells

Because tumoral cell lines are known to undergo genetic changes with prolonged passage in culture, it is advisable to use the cells within a limited number of passages. To accomplish this, stocks of cells can be frozen and recovered for use at the desired passage number. After harvesting, cells are pelleted by centrifugation (200 g, 5 min) and suspended in culture medium containing 20% fetal calf serum and 10% (v/v) dimethyl sulfoxide (DMSO; CRYOSERV Research Industries, Salt Lake City, UT). Freezing vials containing 3–5 × 10^6 cells/ml (1.0–1.5 ml per vial) are placed at −20°C for 2 hr, −80°C overnight, and then in liquid nitrogen. Viability can be maintained for several years. If liquid nitrogen is not available, storage at −80°C is adequate. To reinitiate the culture, an ampoule of frozen cells is thawed in a 37°C water bath, the cell suspension diluted into culture medium containing 10% fetal calf serum, cells pelleted (200 g, 5 min), and redispersed in complete medium.

Uses and Limitations

Cell lines, such as the C6 glioma and RN22 schwannoma, have been employed as sources of trophic and other factors for primary neurons (4–6). Neuroblastoma and glioma cells have also been used to study the influence of genetic defects on neurotransmitter metabolism (7, 8). Using N$_2$A and PC12 clonal lines, effects of glycosphingolipids on neuronal cell differentiation have been examined, both alone (9) and in combination with trophic factors like NGF (10, 11). One limitation, as mentioned already, is that variation can be found within the same cell clone, or even a single culture from it. The tumoral origin of clonal lines makes them subject to genetic instability, and their interactions with trophic or other factors are more difficult to extrapolate to the normal developmental situation.

Primary Neural Cell Cultures: Peripheral Nervous System

Normal neural tissue provides the obvious advantage over clonal cells in that the former allows one to work with the "real" nervous system. Furthermore, different developmental stages, neural organs, or different regions of the same organ which develop asynchronously can be used as source tissue. The following sections describe the culture of selected tissues and cell populations. It is assumed that the reader is already familar with microdissection methods and some developmental biology.

Embryonic Tissues

Chicken embryos are probably the most commonly used experimental animals for *in vitro* studies. Much is known about their development *in vivo*. Chicken embryos also offer practical advantages, such as low cost, availability in large numbers with easy maintenance, and embryos of predetermined stages are obtainable at predictable times. Thus, culture procedures for chicken neurons are the most extensively described to date.

Media and Solutions

    Hanks' balanced salt solution (HBSS)
    Ca^{2+},Mg^{2+}-free HBSS (CMF)
    Hog pancreas trypsin (trypsin), 1:250 (ICN Biochemicals, Cleveland, OH): dissolve in CMF
    Collagenase [0.5% (w/v) (Sigma Type I)]: dissolve in CMF
    DMEM plus 100 U/ml penicillin/2 mM L-glutamine + 10% (v/v) heat-inactivated fetal calf serum (DMEM + FCS10)

Culture Substrata

Tissue culture plastic dishes or multiwell plates are used in all cases. To obtain a highly adhesive collagen substratum, 40 μl (4 μg protein) of reconstituted rat tail collagen is applied to each 35-mm dish (or the proportionate amount for a multiwell), polymerized by 30-min exposure to NH_3 vapors, incubated overnight at 37°C with 1.5 ml of DMEM, with 1 ml of DMEM + FCS10 added 30 min before use (12). A polyornithine (PORN) substratum is obtained by incubating dishes for 1–2 hr at room temperature with 1.5 ml (35-mm dish) of 0.1 mg/ml poly(L-ornithine)-HBr (30,000–45,000 MW; Sigma) in 15 mM borate buffer, pH 8.4, followed by washing twice with water, and incubating overnight at 37°C with 1.5 ml of DMEM. This PORN surface can be modified to one more favorable to neurite growth by treating overnight with a 1 μg/ml solution of laminin (mouse; Bethesda Research Laboratories, Gaithersburg, MD).

Explant Cultures

White Leghorn chicken embryos are used throughout. Dorsal root ganglia (DRG), sympathetic ganglia, or parasympathetic ciliary ganglia are taken between embryonic days 6 and 16 (E6–E16). Ganglia are collected in low-bicarbonate (2.6 mM) DMEM for better control of medium pH during the procedures in air and cleaned of extraneous tissue. Storage medium is removed from one 35-mm culture dish at a time so as to leave only a thin film, and the ganglia positioned at the bottom of the dish. After 15–30 min at 37°C, 2 ml of the desired medium is very gently added to the dish, taking care not to dislodge the ganglia. All cultures are placed in a humidified incubator (37°C) in a 5% CO_2–95% air mixture. Should a laminin substratum be used, it is better to attach the ganglia to the PORN surface first, followed by addition of laminin to the complete culture medium (13). It is more difficult to attach ganglia to a PORN–laminin surface directly.

Monolayer Cultures

The same tissues for explant cultures are also used here. After dissection and cleaning in HBSS, the ganglia are collected in CMF, and centrifuged at 200 g for 5 min (25°C). In the case of ciliary ganglia, there is first a 10-min preincubation in CMF (37°C). The CMF is replaced by 0.08% (w/v) trypsin/CMF (0.25% for sympathetic ganglia), and the ganglia incubated for 20 min (30 min for sympathetic ganglia) at 37°C. For this step, the ratio of ganglia to trypsin volume is important: 40 ganglia/ml. The ganglia are then centrifuged out of the trypsin and washed twice with DMEM + FCS10. Mechanical dispersion is accomplished using a long (9-in.) Pasteur pipette with a 2-ml bulb (tip constricted by flaming; bore opening about 0.5 mm). It may be advisable to coat the Pasteur pipette with a silicone solution (Prosil-28; American Scientific, Orange, CA), to avoid sticking and loss of ganglia. Place the pipette tip against the tube side near the bottom and triturate for 20 strokes. Pressure on the bulb should be controlled to avoid bubbling the suspension. Foaming is detrimental to the cells! Alternatively, dissociation can be performed in DMEM with 1% (w/v) ovalbumin. The presence of some protein is essential to optimize cell yields. At this point, the cells can be counted in a hemacytometer, diluted in culture medium to the desired density and plated. Table I summarizes "average" cell yields for various tissues.

Preparation of Enriched Ganglionic Neurons

In many cases, it is desirable to utilize cultures of purified neurons and not the total ganglionic dissociate (which contains variable proportions of neu-

TABLE I   Neuronal Cell Yields for Different Tissues[a]

Tissue	"Average" cell yields per	
	Tissue unit	Animal
Peripheral nervous system (PNS)		
Chicken DRG		
E8	25×10^3	7.5×10^5
E10	30×10^3	7.5×10^5
E15	35×10^3	7.0×10^5
Mouse DRG		
Newborn	5×10^3	1.0×10^5
Rat DRG		
Newborn	3×10^3	6.0×10^4
Adult	2×10^3	4.0×10^4
Chicken SG		
E12	15×10^3	3.0×10^5
Chicken CG		
E8	20×10^3	4.0×10^4
Central nervous system (CNS)		
Chicken spinal cord		
Lumbar (E4)	2.0×10^5	2.0×10^5
Total (E8)	3×10^6	3.0×10^6
Chicken Cortex		
E8	20×10^6	20×10^6
Rat (E18)		
Hippocampus	2×10^6	2×10^6
Septum	0.5×10^6	0.5×10^6
Striatum	3×10^6	3×10^6
Cortex	6×10^6	6×10^6
Rat cerebellum	20×10^6	20×10^6
(8 days postnatal)		

[a] DRG, Dorsal root ganglia; SG, sympathetic ganglia; CG, ciliary ganglia.

rons and nonneurons, depending on the embryonic stage). After dissociation of the DRG, the cell suspension is diluted to 2.5×10^5 cells/ml with DMEM + FCS10, seeded into tissue culture plastic dishes at 10 ml per 100-mm dish, and incubated at 37°C. Differential attachment of neurons and nonneurons occurs with time and varies with embryo age (14). The best enriched neuronal preparation for E8 ganglia is obtained at 2 hr, with 3 hr being best for E10–E16. Neuronal purity of 80–90% can be obtained, with recoveries varying from 60 to 90%. Similar procedures can also be applied to sympathetic (15) and ciliary ganglionic dissociates (16).

Neonatal and Adult Dorsal Root Ganglia

Rodent (mouse and rat) tissues are also frequently used, being closer to human cells than avian cells. The availability of neurological mutants (especially for the mouse) provides further opportunities to study neuronal survival and differentiation. Their manipulation, however, is more cumbersome than that of chicken embryos. The slower rodent development, on the other hand, makes it possible to use newborn rats or mice for many *in vitro* experiments on such questions.

Neurons

DRG from neonatal ICR Swiss mice (0–2 days) are collected in CMF, incubated in 0.25% trypsin/CMF for 30 min at 37°C, washed twice with DMEM + FCS10, and dispersed in this medium by 30 passes through a flame-constricted siliconized Pasteur pipette. Newborn rat (Wistar) DRG are also collected in CMF, transferred to 0.5% (w/v) collagenase/CMF for 45 min at 37°C, followed by replacing half of the collagenase with an equal volume of 0.25% trypsin/CMF (initial concentration) and incubation continued for 30 min. Ganglia are washed twice with DMEM + FCS10 and dissociated as for mouse DRG (17). Alternatively, washing and dissociation can be done in DMEM + 1% ovalbumin. If desired, a preplating step (to enrich the neuronal population) can be included. A similar procedure can be applied to adult rat DRG (17).

Schwann Cells

This procedure utilizes the neuritic mitogen for selective expansion of Schwann cells in serum-free primary cultures and a secondary culture step involving neuronal removal and additional Schwann cell expansion using a serum mitogen (18).

Neonatal mouse DRG are dissociated as described above, but using Eagle's basal medium (EBM) plus 10% fetal calf serum (EBM + FCS10). Differential preplating leads to an attached neuron–satellite cell fraction (NS). This NS fraction is cultured at 37°C in EBM + FCS10 on highly adhesive collagen with NGF (5 ng/ml). The following day, the culture is switched to EBM + N1 + NGF medium [N1 is a serum replacing supplement (see below)]. After 8 days of neurite-induced expansion of Schwann cells, the medium is shifted to EBM + N1 + FCS10 for 1 day. This step permits Schwann cells to dissociate from neurites and resume proliferation (serum mitogen). The cultures are washed twice with CMF, and a trypsin–collagenase solution in CMF [0.12% (w/v) collagenase (Sigma Type IX)–0.12% (w/v) trypsin] added and aspirated, leaving a film. After 15 min at 37°C, the primary cells are harvested into EBM + N1 + FCS10 and seeded on collagen in 2 ml of this medium at 10,000 cells per 35-mm dish. An average of 70% of the cells in the primary culture can be recovered by this trypsin–collagenase procedure, yielding a plating efficiency of almost 100%. In the absence of NGF, the neurons die off, with serum-induced expansion of Schwann cells over 6 days. Changing these cultures to EBM + N1 medium for 1 day will yield a predominance of Schwann cells having the classical spindle morphology. An average litter of 12 pups will generate a secondary population of 40×10^6 Schwann cells of 98% purity.

Serum-Free Neuronal Cell Cultures

The maintenance and growth *in vitro* of primary neurons using media supplemented with serum presents several problems. These include proliferation of nonneuronal cells, interference with the assessment of the influence of exogenous agents, and the possible action of inhibitory agents not normally encountered by the neuronal cells.

All of the peripheral neural cell types described here can be maintained in a serum-free medium by the chemically defined N1 supplement consisting of insulin ($8.3 \times 10^{-7} M$), transferrin ($6.2 \times 10^{-8} M$), putrescine ($1 \times 10^{-4} M$), progesterone ($2 \times 10^{-8} M$), and selenite ($3 \times 10^{-8} M$) (16, 19–22). Interestingly, the five constituents of the N1 supplement are not all needed; different combinations are, in fact, required by different ganglionic neurons (16, 20, 21) or by neurons of different embryonic ages (21). These various requirements are summarized in Table II.

TABLE II   Differential Requirements for Individual N1 Constituents by Different Primary Peripheral Nervous System Neurons for Their Survival in Serum-Free Culture

Neurons	Insulin	Transferrin	Selenite	Putrescine	Progesterone
Chicken					
Dorsal root (E8–E15)	+	+	−	−	−
Sympathetic (E8)	+	−	+	−	−
Sympathetic (E11)	+	+	+	−	−
Ciliary (E8)	+	−	−	−	−
Mouse					
Dorsal root (newborn)	+	+	−	−	−

Advantages and Limitations

Explant cultures can be used to generate Schwann cells and to study Schwann cell–neurite interactions (23). They were the first cultures used for NGF investigations and are still commonly used in its bioassay (24). Explant cultures have proved useful for studies of factors regulating neurite elongation (13, 25). Since they do not permit direct visualization of the neuronal perikarya inside the explant, monolayer cultures are the preferred *in vitro* system offering maximal access to microscopic observation and control of their environment with minimal intercellular contacts. Monolayer cultures have found application in studying the requirements for, and responses to, trophic factors by neurons and agents modulating such influences (26).

Primary Neural Cell Cultures: Central Nervous System

A major problem in establishing cultures of central nervous system (CNS) neurons suitable for studies like those described for peripheral nervous system (PNS) neurons stems from the marked heterogeneity of CNS tissues. Tissue age and culture conditions can be selected to minimize the presence of nonneuronal elements, but heterogeneity in neuronal subpopulations will remain. Also, many neurons will survive without exogenous trophic support if cell suspensions are seeded at higher densities (e.g., over 30,000 cells/cm^2). By reducing seeding densities to 3,000–5,000 cells/cm^2, cultures with little or no neuronal survival can be obtained, making them amenable for measurement of neuronotrophic factors. The following culture systems have been designed to address these problems.

Avian Cultures

Cerebral Cortex

Tissue from chicken E8 brain is collected in HBSS, incubated first in CMF for 10 min (37°C), followed by 0.08% trypsin/CMF for 20 min (37°C). A ratio of one embryo/tube is maintained throughout. The trypsin is removed, the tissue is washed twice with EBM + 1% ovalbumin and is then dissociated in the same medium (2 ml/tube) using a Pasteur pipette (no constricted tip) with 15 strokes. The cell suspension is counted, is diluted in EBM + N1 (or desired medium), and is plated on a PORN or PORN–laminin substratum.

Lumbar Spinal Cord (E4)

This tissue is populated by essentially one known subset of neurons, namely, motor neurons. Lumbar cord segments from 4-day-old chicken embryos are collected in HBSS (1–2 cords in 5 ml), incubated first for 20 min in CMF at 37°C, then in 0.08% trypsin/CMF for 20 min, washed once in EBM + N1, and triturated by 7 strokes with a constricted-tip Pasteur pipette in fresh medium (2 ml/cord segment). The suspension is counted and diluted into the desired medium for culture plating (5).

Spinal Cord (E8)

Cords from 8-day-old chicken embryos are collected into CMF at 3 cords per 5 ml/tube and are incubated with 0.25% (w/v) trypsin/CMF, 2.5 ml/tube, for 30 min at 37°C. The trypsin is removed, the cords are washed twice with 3 ml of EBM + FCS10, 2 ml of this medium is then added, and the cords are triturated for 20 strokes with a Pasteur pipette (no constricted tip). Dissociates from all tubes are pooled, then counted, diluted, and plated. To limit growth of nonneuronal cells, spinal cord neurons can be cultured in EBM + N1 (27).

Visual System
See Ref. 28.

Rodent Neurons

Hippocampus, Septum, Striatum, Cortex

These brain regions are dissected out from 18-day-old rat fetuses (Sprague-Dawley) into HBSS. Each tissue is incubated for 10 min in CMF at 37°C and then in 0.08% trypsin/CMF (0.25% trypsin for cortex) for another 30 min at 37°C. The tissues are washed twice in EBM + 1% ovalbumin and dissociated in 2 ml of this medium by 20 passes through the constricted tip of a Pasteur pipette (no constriction for cortex). The cell suspensions are diluted with EBM + N1 for subsequent seeding. The average cell yields per tissue are given in Table I. Tissue culture plastic coated with either PORN or PORN/laminin provides a suitable substratum for these cells. Because of the embryonic age, very few glial cells are to be found in these cultures.

Cerebellar Granule Neurons

Granule cells cultures are prepared with a modification of the procedure by Gallo *et al.* (29). Cerebella from 8-day-old rats (Sprague-Dawley) are pooled in Krebs buffer containing 0.5 mM MgSO$_4$ and 0.3% (w/v) bovine serum albumin (solution A, 1 ml/cerebellum). The tissue is minced with a razor blade in a petri dish, is collected (200 g, 1 min), and is incubated in 0.08% trypsin/solution A (1 ml/cerebellum) for 15 min at 37°C with continuous agitation. An equal volume of a solution containing 0.001% (w/v) DNase (No. 104159, Boehringer-Mannheim, Indianapolis, IN), 0.008% (w/v) trypsin inhibitor (Sigma T-9003), and 0.3 mM MgSO$_4$ (in solution A) is added and the tissue is centrifuged at 700 g for 2 min. Then as much supernatant as possible (variable amounts of tissue filaments may be present) is removed, and 2 ml of a solution containing 0.008% DNase, 0.052% trypsin inhibitor, and 1.5 mM MgSO$_4$ (in solution A) is added. The tissue is dissociated by 25 passes with a Pasteur pipette (no constriction), and 3 ml of the preceding solution is added. The cells are triturated another 15 times, 6 ml of solution A containing 0.1 mM CaCl$_2$ and 11.7 mM MgSO$_4$ is added, and the cells are pelleted at 200 g for 7 min, suspended in complete culture medium (EBM supplemented with 2 mM L-glutamine, 100 U/ml penicillin, 50 mg/liter gentamycin, 25 mM KCl, and 10% fetal calf serum), and are counted. Plating is best achieved by coating (on the same day) tissue culture plastic with 10 μg/ml poly(L-lysine)-HBr (70,000–150,000 MW; Sigma P-1274; 1 mg/ml stock in 0.15 M sodium borate, pH 8.4). Other molecular weight ranges for poly(L-lysine) can cause excessive cell clumping. The following day, cytosine arabinoside is added to a final concentration of 10 μM to retard growth of nonneurons. Alternatively, these cells can be cultured serum-free with the N1 supplement.

Astroglial Cells

This procedure is modified from that described by Rudge *et al.* (30). Cerebral hemispheres are removed from 0- to 2-day-old Sprague-Dawley rats, cleaned of their meninges, and collected in CMF (4 hemispheres/10 ml). Each group of four hemispheres is placed in a petri dish and minced thoroughly with a razor blade. Each group of tissue is collected in 10 ml of CMF and is allowed to sit for 5 min. The CMF is replaced with 5 ml of 0.25% trypsin/CMF, the tissue is incubated for 15 min at 37°C, and then 5 ml of 0.25% soybean trypsin inhibitor (Type II-S, Sigma T-9128) is added per tube. After centrifuging at 1000 g for 10 min (37°C), the supernatant is removed, 10 ml of EBM + FCS10 is added, and the tissue is centrifuged again. Then the supernatant is replaced with 4 ml of EBM + FCS10, and the tissue is triturated first 5 times with a 5-ml pipette, then 20 times with a Pasteur pipette. The top 2 ml of medium is removed, 4 ml of medium/tube is added, the mixture is triturated 5 times and the fractions pooled. The tissue suspension is passed through 25-μm Nitex nylon (Millipore). The cells are counted with Trypan

Blue, seeding 2×10^6 dye-negative cells/100-mm culture plastic dish in 10 ml of EBM + FCS10. The culture medium is replaced every 2 days. Yields are typically $6.5–8.5 \times 10^6$ Trypan Blue-excluding cells/brain. Using neonatal rats at more than 2 days of age markedly diminishes cell yields.

Secondary cultures can also be prepared. After 10 days *in vitro*, the confluent primary culture is washed with 10 ml of CMF, 3 ml of 0.25% trypsin/CMF is added and then is removed, leaving a thin film, and is incubated for 15 min at 37°C. The cells are dislodged into 5 ml of EBM + FCS10, are collected, and are centrifuged at 1000 g for 10 min. Each cell pellet from two 100-mm dishes is suspended in 2 ml of EBM + 1% ovalbumin, is diluted, and is counted. These cells can be seeded on culture plastic coated with PORN (0.1 mg/ml in 15 mM borate buffer, pH 8.4) for 2 hr, followed by 10 μg/ml fibronectin (bovine plasma in PBS, Bethesda Research Laboratories) overnight, and can be maintained in EBM.

Advantages and Limitations

CNS neuronal cultures, in general, provide cells in considerably greater numbers and purity than the PNS ganglionic neurons described earlier. These CNS neurons have found widespread use to identify both macromolecular and low molecular weight trophic agents; however, visualizing neuronal subsets within the same culture can be a problem if one is looking for selective CNS trophic factors. One approach to this problem makes use of biochemical markers for specific types of CNS neurons (31). Purified populations of astroglia *in vitro* can be used as a source of neuronotrophic and neurite-promoting activities, and to study trophic and metabolic interactions between themselves and neurons.

Applications

This section describes several examples of how primary neuronal cell cultures can be applied to a quantitative assessment of selected bioactive agents.

Neuronotrophic Factors

Cultures of E8 chicken DRG neurons can, for example, be used to titrate NGF biological activity. Serial dilutions of the NGF sample in culture medium are made in 6-mm-diameter wells of a 96-well test plate that had been previously coated with a PORN/laminin substratum. An equal volume of cell

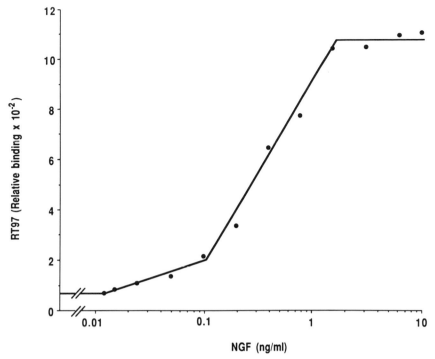

FIG. 1   NGF dose–response curve. Relative binding of monoclonal antibody to human neurofilament RT97 is measured in cultures of E8 chicken dorsal root ganglion neurons maintained for 48 hr with different concentrations of NGF.

suspension is added, and the extent of the neuronal response, in this case survival, is evaluated 24–48 hr later. Although the number of surviving neurons can be counted microscopically, quantitative evaluation of neuronal survival and neurite outgrowth can be carried out using an enzyme-linked immunoadsorbent assay (ELISA) for neurofilament protein with the monoclonal antibody RT97 (32). Figure 1 shows a typical titration curve.

Neuronotoxic Agents

Excitatory amino acid receptor agonists like glutamate, if present in high concentrations and for prolonged periods of time, can kill the same neurons for which they normally serve a transmitter function, hence, the phenomenon of excitotoxicity. Glutamate neurotoxicity is known to occur in a number of neuronal cell types *in vitro*, including cerebellar granule cells (33).

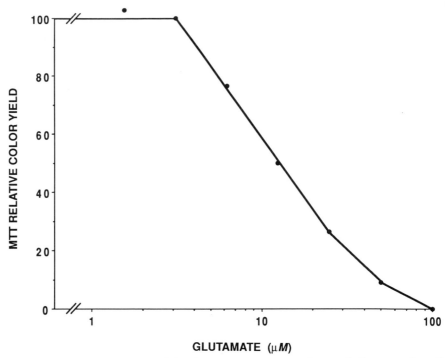

FIG. 2   A glutamate neurotoxicity dose–response curve for cerebellar granule cells maintained for 10 days *in vitro*, using the MTT colorimetric assay. See the text for details. Decreasing MTT color yield reflects decreasing neuronal survival.

This effect can be quantified by measuring the photometric reduction of 3-(4, 5-dimethylthiazol-2-yl)-2, 5-diphenyltetrazolium bromide (MTT) to a blue formazan product (34). Cultures of granule cells (3×10^6/35-mm dish) are incubated for 15 min at room temperature in Mg^{2+}-free medium containing different concentrations of L-glutamate, after which cultures are washed free of glutamate and returned to their original medium for 24 hr. During the final 2 hr, cultures receive an exchange of an equal volume of fresh medium with 0.2 mg/ml MTT. Dye conversion is terminated by adding 1 ml of 2-propanol– 0.08 N HCl per dish. After mixing, 0.15 ml of each sample is transferred to the well of a 96-well microtest plate, and the plate read using an ELISA reader (test wavelength 570 nm, reference wavelength 630 nm). Figure 2 demonstrates such a titration curve.

Cytosolic Free Ca²⁺

Signaling molecules often exert their action via alterations of cell Ca^{2+} homeostasis. The development of Ca^{2+}-sensitive dyes like quin2, fura-2, and indo-1 now permits the study of the action of neuroactive agents on this parameter. For example, monolayers of astroglial cells or granule neurons (described earlier) can be loaded with fura-2 and intracellular free Ca^{2+} concentration ($[Ca^{2+}]_i$) examined by digital fluorescence imaging microscopy. Values of $[Ca^{2+}]_i$ shown in Table III were obtained by measuring the ratio of fluorescence at 350 and 380 nm (35; see Ref. 36 for more details on these techniques). The granule neurons, which display considerable heterogeneity in basal $[Ca^{2+}]_i$, respond to glutamate (1 mM) with large and persistent increases in $[Ca^{2+}]_i$. Astroglia, in contrast, present a more consistent resting $[Ca^{2+}]_i$, with a smaller and largely transient increase in $[Ca^{2+}]_i$ upon glutamate addition (37). While we have considered only changes in perikaryon $[Ca^{2+}]_i$, such dyes can also be used to follow changes in $[Ca^{2+}]_i$ in neurites and growth cones, which are of particular interest when assessing a role for $[Ca^{2+}]_i$ in neuronal development.

Final Remarks

The plasticity of nerve cells is, perhaps, nowhere more evident than in the cultures of neural tissue or cells *in vitro*. Neuronal cultures provide the neuroscientist with a powerful tool for identifying and analyzing extrinsic agents affecting neuronal survival and development, and for investigating the underlying cellular and molecular events. The several types of neural cultures discussed here (clonal cell lines, explants, monolayers) can provide different and complementary views of neural behaviors. Monolayer neuro-

TABLE III   Effect of Glutamate on Cytosolic Free Ca²⁺ in Neural Cells[a]

Time	Granule cell number					Astroglia cell number				
	1	2	3	4	5	1	2	3	4	5
0	100	170	550	200	130	40	50	80	60	100
30 sec	150	520	790	570	315	100	75	260	250	300
5 min	300	530	730	740	220	50	60	90	170	170

[a] Cells were loaded with fura-2/AM and stimulated with 1 mM glutamate, in the presence of Ca^{2+} and Mg^{2+} (for astroglia) or Ca^{2+} only (for granule cells). Values shown are in nanomolar $[Ca^{2+}]_i$.

nal cultures permit the widest opportunities for quantitative analysis of both positive and negative microenvironmentally applied influences, as well as parameters at the single-cell level: the data in Figs. 1 and 2, and Table III illustrate these points well. Hopefully, the description of culture procedures in this volume will further facilitate their application to neurobiological problems.

References

1. R. Levi-Montalcini, *Science* **237,** 1154 (1987).
2. S. E. Pfeiffer, *in* "Tissue Culture of the Nervous System" (G. Sato, ed.), p. 203. Plenum, New York, 1973.
3. L. A. Greene, *Adv. Pharmacol. Ther.* **10,** 197 (1978).
4. S. Varon, S. D. Skaper, G. Barbin, I. Selak, and M. Manthorpe, *J. Neurosci.* **4,** 654 (1984).
5. F. M. Longo, M. Manthorpe, and S. Varon, *Dev. Brain Res.* **3,** 277 (1982).
6. G. E. Davis, M. Manthorpe, E. Engvall, and S. Varon, *J. Neurosci.* **5,** 2662 (1985).
7. S. D. Skaper, G. L. Adelson, and J. E. Seegmiller, *J. Neurochem.* **27,** 1065 (1976).
8. S. D. Skaper and J. E. Seegmiller, *Science* **194,** 1171 (1976).
9. L. Facci, A. Leon, G. Toffano, S. Sonnino, R. Ghidoni, and G. Tettamanti, *J. Neurochem.* **42,** 299 (1984).
10. G. Ferrari, M. Fabris, and A. Gorio, *Dev. Brain Res.* **8,** 215 (1983).
11. R. Katoh-Semba, S. D. Skaper, and S. Varon, *J. Neurosci. Res.* **12,** 299 (1984).
12. R. Adler, M. Manthorpe, and S. Varon, *Dev. Biol.* **69,** 424 (1979).
13. S. D. Skaper, I. Selak, and S. Varon, *J. Neurosci. Res.* **9,** 359 (1983).
14. S. D. Skaper and S. Varon, *Dev. Biol.* **98,** 257 (1983).
15. G. Teitelman, S. Skaper, H. Baker, D. H. Park, T. H. Joh, and R. Adler, *Dev. Brain Res.* **13,** 283 (1984).
16. S. D. Skaper, I. Selak, M. Manthorpe, and S. Varon, *Brain Res.* **302,** 281 (1984).
17. K. Unsicker, S. D. Skaper, G. E. Davis, M. Manthorpe, and S. Varon, *Dev. Brain Res.* **17,** 304 (1985).
18. M. Manthorpe, S. D. Skaper, and S. Varon, *Brain Res.* **196,** 467 (1980).
19. J. E. Bottenstein, S. D. Skaper, S. S. Varon, and G. H. Sato, *Exp. Cell Res.* **125,** 183 (1980).
20. S. D. Skaper, I. Selak, and S. Varon, *J. Neurosci. Res.* **8,** 251 (1982).
21. I. Selak, S. D. Skaper, and S. Varon, *Dev. Brain Res.* **7,** 171 (1983).
22. S. D. Skaper, M. Manthorpe, R. Adler, and S. Varon, *J. Neurocytol.* **9,** 683 (1980).
23. P. M. Wood and R. P. Bunge, *Nature (London)* **256,** 662 (1975).
24. S. D. Skaper and S. Varon, *Exp. Neurol.* **76,** 655 (1982).
25. S. D. Skaper and S. Varon, *Int. J. Dev. Neurosci.* **3,** 187 (1984).
26. S. Varon, S. D. Skaper, and R. Katoh-Semba, *in* "Neuronal Plasticity and

Gangliosides'' (G. Tettamanti, R. Ledeen, K. Sandhoff, Y. Nagai, and G. Toffano, eds.), Vol. 6, p. 215. Liviana Press, Padova, Italy, 1986.

27. S. D. Skaper, R. Adler, and S. Varon, *Dev. Neurosci.* **2,** 233 (1979).
28. R. Adler, this volume [10].
29. V. Gallo, M. T. Ciotti, A. Coletti, F. Aloisi, and G. Levi, *Proc. Natl. Acad. Sci. U.S.A.* **79,** 7919 (1982).
30. J. A. Rudge, M. Manthorpe, and S. Varon, *Dev. Brain Res.* **19,** 161 (1985).
31. G. Ferrari, M.-C. Minozzi, G. Toffano, A. Leon, and S. D. Skaper, *Dev. Biol.* **133,** 140 (1989).
32. P. Doherty, J. G. Dickson, T. P. Flanigan, and F. S. Walsh, *J. Neurochem.* **42,** 1116 (1984).
33. M. Favaron, H. Manev, H. Alho, M. Bertolino, B. Ferret, A. Guidotti, and E. Costa, *Proc. Natl. Acad. Sci. U.S.A.* **85,** 7351 (1988).
34. T. Mosmann, *J. Immunol. Methods* **65,** 55 (1983).
35. G. Grynkyewicz, M. Poenie, and R. Y. Tsien, *J. Biol. Chem.* **260,** 3440 (1985).
36. P. H. Cobbold and T. J. Rink, *Biochem. J.* **248,** 313 (1987).
37. D. Milani, L. Facci, D. Guidolin, A. Leon, and S. D. Skaper, *Glia* **2,** 161 (1989).

[3] Generation of Astrocyte Cultures from Normal and Neoplastic Central Nervous System

Sean Murphy

Astrocytes represent the major cell type in the central nervous system (CNS), but only recently has it become clear that these glial cells perform important and varied roles in the CNS. Situated in and around neurons and their processes, and maintaining close contact via end feet with the vasculature, these cells are implicated in neuronal guidance and in the trophic support of neurons and promotion of local neuritic outgrowth. More specifically, astrocytes might influence the passage of information between neurons through their ability to control local ion and amine/amino acid con-

Methods in Neurosciences, Volume 2

centrations. In addition, these cells display a range of receptors for signal molecules such as neurotransmitters, modulators, and growth factors, and in turn release neuro- and vasoactive amino acids and eicosanoids (1).

It is now also apparent that astrocytes are a heterogeneous class of cells, not just in terms of morphology but in surface properties and also in distribution within the CNS. Astrocytes in white matter (optic nerve, corpus callosum) appear, at least in the rat, to be of two different types. The first (type 1) arises early in development, whereas a later emerging cell (type 2) stems from a distinct progenitor which also gives rise to oligodendroglia (2). These two types of astroglial cell have different properties and appear to play distinct roles. There is also regional and functional heterogeneity with respect to type 1 astrocytes, though the lack of discovery of discriminating antibodies thus far precludes their separation. Thus, the presence of subpopulations of astrocytes in apparently homogeneous cell cultures is an important consideration.

Astrocytes are implicated in a variety of CNS pathologies, including hepatic encephalopathy, seizure, scar formation, and trauma (3). The majority of neoplasms in the CNS arise from astrocytes. These range from well-differentiated astrocytomas (reasonably benign), through anaplastic astrocytomas, to highly malignant and undifferentiated glioblastomas multiforme (4).

The current flurry of interest in astrologlial cells is a result of the discovery of cell-specific antigens in the CNS, and thus the ability to derive well-characterized and homogeneous primary cell cultures. In this chapter, simple, rapid, and highly reproducible methods are described to derive primary cultures of astrocytes from rat and human brain which find use in a variety of studies ranging from cell product analysis through to their transplantation into hosts. Two examples of their utility are briefly described: immunocytochemical screening for agents, which affect astroglial cell proliferation, and quantitation of eicosanoid release by human astrocyte cultures.

Reagents and Materials

Calcium- and magnesium-free Earle's balanced salt solution (EBSS-CMF) and fetal bovine serum (FBS) were from Gibco (Grand Island, NY)

Eagle's minimal essential medium (MEM) containing Earle's salts was obtained from the Cancer Center of The University of Iowa

DNase (from bovine pancreas, chromatographically pure, 2500 Kunitz U/mg), trypsin [from bovine pancreas, salt-free, $1-1.3 \times 10^4$ N_α-benzoyl-L-arginine ethyl ester (BAEE) U/mg], trypsin inhibitor (from soybean, lyophilate, 1 mg inhibits 1–3 mg trypsin), bovine serum albumin [(BSA) fraction V, 96–99% albumin], and poly(D-lysine) hydrobromide (MW 150,000–300,000) were all from Sigma (St. Louis, MO)

Tissue culture plasticware of a variety of sizes was purchased from Costar (Cambridge, MA) and 8-chamber/slides from Nunc (Naperville, IL)

Culture Techniques

The disaggregation method is based on Dutton *et al.* (5). All steps are performed under sterile conditions and at room temperature unless stated otherwise. All solutions are made fresh each day.

For rat astrocyte cultures, routinely two 1- to 2-day-old pups are killed by cervical dislocation and the brains rapidly removed and placed in sterile disaggregation medium (DM; EBSS-CMF containing 14 mM glucose, 0.3% (w/v) BSA, 1.5 mM $MgSO_4$) in a vertical laminar flow hood. The forebrain is removed and cleaned of underlying structures and white matter. The meninges are removed carefully with fine forceps and the tissue is then cut into 0.4-mm cubes with a McIlwain Tissue Chopper. The tissue cubes are dispersed in 10 ml of DM containing 2.5 mg of trypsin in a trypsinization flask, capped, and incubated at 37°C in a shaking water bath for 15 min. The contents of the flask are then poured into a 50-ml plastic centrifuge tube with 10 ml of DM containing 70 μg of DNase and 2 mg of trypsin inhibitor. The tube is centrifuged at 50 g for 5 sec and the tissue cubes resuspended in 2 ml of DM containing 80 μg DNase, 2 mg of trypsin inhibitor, and additional $MgSO_4$ (final concentration 3 mM). The material is triturated gently 10 times with a long Pasteur pipette, the undisrupted blocks allowed to settle, and most of the cell suspension removed to a 15-ml plastic centrifuge tube. The remaining tissue is triturated again, allowed to settle, and the cell suspensions combined. An underlay of 2 ml of DM containing 4% (w/v) BSA is then added and the tube centrifuged at 100 g for 7.5 min. Debris collects at the interface while perikarya form the pellet, which is then resuspended by mild trituration in 1 ml of growth medium. The cell yield is counted using a Coulter Counter equipped with a 140-μm orifice tube for particles with a diameter >5.5 μm (cells) and <5.5 μm (debris). The cells are then dispersed in growth medium (20,000–40,000/ml) which comprises Eagle's MEM with Earle's salts, supplemented with 33 mM glucose, 2 mM glutamine, 100 μg/ml gentamycin, and 10% (v/v) FBS. The cells are seeded at 100 cells/mm^2 onto poly(D-lysine) (50 μg/ml, applied for 30 min and surface left to air-dry) coated plastic. Cultures are maintained at 37°C in a humidified incubator in an atmosphere of 5% CO_2 in air. Every 3 days *in vitro* (DIV) half of the growth medium is replaced until the cultures are confluent (14–18 DIV). This method applies equally well to any region of the rat CNS.

For rat meningeal cell cultures, the meninges removed during the preparation of astrocyte cultures are pooled and incubated for 60 min at 37°C with 2.5 ml of EBSS-CMF containing 5 mg of collagenase (Sigma, type 2). The tissue is then disrupted by trituration and plated out as above.

For human astrocyte cultures, discarded biopsy material (typically, 0.05–0.2 g wet weight) is placed in EBSS-CMF and adhering blood and vessels removed with forceps. The material is then cut into 0.4-mm cubes using the tissue chopper and the same procedure as for rat astrocytes is followed. Alternatively, because the availability of material is not predictable, a simple and rapid method may be used. This involves dispersing the tissue cubes in 3 ml of growth medium (D-valine substituted for L-valine) and dividing this between two T25 flasks. After 1–2 DIV the tissue adheres to the plastic and cells begin to emerge from the "explants." Within 14 DIV the cultures are confluent. The cells can then be replated by first washing in FBS-free growth medium, brief exposure at 37°C to 0.25% (w/v) trypsin containing 0.02% (w/v) EDTA and washing in normal growth medium (containing FBS) to inactivate the trypsin. All routine safety procedures are strictly adhered to when working with human cells; spent medium and contaminated plastic is autoclaved before disposal.

Cell Yield

Table I shows the expected cell yield from neonatal rat cerebral cortex. One rat cortex provides about 12 million cells, and while the yield increases slightly with age, there is a marked increase in the amount of debris. In our

TABLE I Cell Yield from Neonatal Rat Cortex

	Age (days)			
Parameter	All (1–4)	1	2	3–4
10^6 cells/rat	11.81	11.85	10.44	13.80
(SEM)[a]	0.63	0.98	1.12	2.04
Debris (%)	26.63	21.71	29.33	34.30
(SEM)[a]	1.37	1.27	2.03	6.04
n	40	18	12	5

[a] SEM, Standard error of the mean.

Table II Seeding Cells in Routine Culture Preparation

Plasticware	Volume (ml/well)	Seeding (10^3 cells/ml)	Number of cultures from two rats (800 ml of growth medium)
8-chamber/slide	0.4	20	
96-well plate	0.2	20	
24-well plate	1.0	20	15
6-well plate	3.0	35	15
60-mm dish	5.0	40	
T25 flask	7.5	35	10
T75 flask	21.0	35	4

experience, cells derived from pup cortices older than 4 days of age do not show good survival in cultures seeded at low density. However, astrocytes may be prepared from later maturing brain regions (e.g., cerebellum) up to 14 days of age.

Table II contains details of the volume and seeding density for different sizes of plasticware, together with an indication of the numbers of cultures that can be prepared from the cerebral cortices of two neonatal rats.

Viewed under phase contrast in an inverted stage microscope, the cells settle onto the substrate within a few hours. By the next day cells have flattened out and started to divide, though they are sparse until after the first medium change 3 days later. By 10 DIV the cultures cover >50% of the surface and are confluent by 14 DIV. Routinely, confluent cultures are not used until 3 days after the last medium change and can be kept for up to 1 week without changing the medium, or reasonably indefinitely by continued medium changes.

Cell Identification

Cell suspensions from rat cortex are a mixture of neurons, astrocytes, progenitor glial cells, cells derived from the vasculature (smooth muscle and endothelial cells) and from the meninges (fibroblasts), and also microglia. The seeding density and FBS concentration favor the proliferation of astrocytes at the expense of most of the other cell types. At confluence, the cultures are 90–95% astrocytic with contaminating microglia, fibroblasts, and a very few oligodendrocytes. Under phase optics the cultures appear as a monolayer of polygonal cells (astrocytes) with adhering phase-dark and phase-light contaminating cells (oligondendrocytes and microglia). Fibroblasts appear as spindle-shaped cells aligned in parallel arrays and are more common in cultures derived from older animals where removal of the meninges is more difficult and therefore often incomplete. Substituting D- for L-valine in the growth medium will minimize the proliferation of fibroblasts (6). Addition of 5 mM L-leucine methyl ester to the astrocyte cultures at 7 and 14 DIV selectively depletes them of microglia (7). Cultures of cells derived from the meninges serve as useful controls for events which may be related to the properties of the major contaminating cells in the astrocyte cultures.

Probing for cell specific antigens using immunocytochemical or histochemical techniques is the only means to identify unequivocally the purity of these cell cultures (see Table III). Seeding cells at the same relative density onto 8-chamber/slides is useful in this process as these permit a battery of probes to be tested simultaneously.

Antibodies against GFAP (glial fibrillary acidic protein, an intracellular antigen), Gal C (galactocerebroside, cell surface), FN (fibronectin, intracellular), NF (neurofilament protein, intracellular), and smooth muscle actin (intracellular) are widely available (commercially or otherwise). The cell line secreting antibody A_2B_5 (a cell surface marker) is available from the American Type Culture Collection (ATCC) (Rockville, MD). Secondary antibodies conjugated to a number of different fluorochromes, enzymes, or electron-dense material are available from a very wide range of commercial sources. The methods for NSE (nonspecific esterase) and GsA (*Griffonia simplicifolia* agglutinin, from Sigma) detection are routine histochemical procedures (8, 9). While counting $GFAP^+$ cells by immunofluorescence microscopy and expressing these as a proportion of the total number of cells identified by phase contrast will provide a measure of the number of astrocytes in the

TABLE III   Identification of Cell Types in
Mixed Cell Cultures[a]

Cell type	Antigen/probe
Astrocytes	
Type 1	$GFAP^+$
Type 2	$GFAP^+$, $A_2B_5{}^+$
Oligodendrocytes	Gal C^+
Fibroblasts	FN^+, $GFAP^-$
Microglia	NSE^+
Neurons	NF^+
Smooth muscle cells	Smooth muscle actin$^+$
Endothelial cells	GsA^+

[a] +, Positive; −, negative. For some cell types, two criteria have to be met for certain identification.

cultures, this tends to underestimate contamination from other cell types. In addition, this will not provide a measure of type 2 astrocytes in the cultures. Using the method for rat astrocyte cultures described above, some 90–95% of the cells are GFAP[+] (almost entirely type 1), 3–5% are microglia, 2–3% are fibroblasts, and <1% are oligodendrocytes. Neurons are absent (these cells do not survive beyond about 10 DIV) and vascular cells are seen only rarely. In the cultures derived from human astrocytomas the situation is more complex because cells from the less well differentiated tumors, though they may be astrocytic in origin, express little GFAP. Routinely, we find the majority of cells that label are GFAP[+], but frequently there are FN[+] cells in these cultures.

A number of methods have been described for the generation of astrocyte cultures from mouse or rat CNS. These differ not so much in terms of yield, purity, or viability (most result in 85–95% homogeneity), but in the complexity and length of the procedure, and in the subsequent treatment of the cultures. Some methods (10) include a further purification and replating step (resulting in >95% purity), others (11) employ so-called differentiation treatments (e.g., with dibutyryl cAMP). The method described here is inexpensive, takes less than 2 hr, the trypsinization and mechanical disaggregation steps are very mild, and the low seeding density not only favors the propagation of the astrocytes in the cultures but also results in a large number of cultures from few animals. The simplicity of the method means that it is very easily adopted by those producing cell cultures for the first time. Strategies for producing large-scale, homogeneous cultures of type 2 astrocytes are also now being developed (12).

Confluent Rat Astrocyte Cultures

Table IV provides an idea of the expected cell number, DNA content, and protein yield from confluent cultures seeded in a variety of tissue culture plasticware. These data are based on protein assay, DNA determination, and Coulter counting of cells trypsinized from confluent cultures. Thus, starting with a seeding density of 100 cells/mm^2 (approximately 30% of which are viable astrocyes), then at confluence the yield is some 600 astrocytes/mm^2.

Some examples of the utility of cultures seeded into these different sizes of plasticware are the following: 96-well plates, screening potential astrocyte mitogens; 24-well plates, assaying cAMP or release of eicosanoids in response to receptor agonists; 6-well plates, accumulation of inositol phosphates or glycogen in response to receptor agonists; T25 flasks, analysis of secreted metabolites from precursor-labeled cells by TLC and HPLC; T75

TABLE IV   Expected Yield (Approximate) from
Confluent Astrocyte Cultures

Plasticware	Yield		
	Protein (μg)	DNA (μg)	Astrocytes (10^5)
96-well plate	10	0.2	0.25
24-well plate	40	1.0	1.0
6-well plate	200	4.0	5.0
T25 flask or 60-mm dish	400	10.0	12.0
T75 flask	1200	25.0	25.0

flasks, subculturing, preparing membrane fractions, or harvesting conditioned medium.

Use of Specific Antibodies to Quantify Effects of Different Agents on Astrocyte Proliferation

Astrocytes are mitotically active cells and, although in the mature CNS they do not express this property, reentry into the cell cycle is induced following trauma or injury. The mechanism(s) inducing this astrocytosis is not clear and so it is important to discover ways of manipulating astroglial cell division. By double-labeling with antibodies to GFAP and to bromodeoxyuridine (BrdU) incorporated into DNA-synthesizing cells, quantitative estimates can be made of the effects of agents which influence astrocyte proliferation.

Inhibitors of Astrocyte Proliferation

Cell cultures seeded onto 8-chamber slides were fed with 5-fluorodeoxyuridine (FdU; 2 μM) or heparin (10 and 100 μg/ml) at a single dose on day 2 *in vitro*. There were no medium changes. Twenty-four hours before processing for immunocytochemistry, 10 μM BrdU was fed to the cells, and this becomes incorporated into those cells undergoing DNA synthesis. The method which follows is based on that of Yong and Kim (13), and all steps were at room temperature unless specified. The cells were rinsed with phosphate-buffered saline (PBS) and fixed in methanol for 5 min at −20°C. After washing and incubating in PBS containing 50% FBS (to block nonspecific binding), rabbit anti-GFAP (Sigma) was added for 30 min. Cells were again washed and blocked in PBS–FBS and then incubated for 30 min with goat anti-rabbit IgG FITC (Sigma). After washing, the cells were incubated with 2 N HCl for 10 min to denature DNA, rinsed, and incubated with 0.1 M sodium borate (pH 9) for 10 min to neutralize the HCl. The cells were washed and blocked in PBS–FBS and incubated with mouse anti-BrdU (Becton Dickinson, Mountain View, CA) for 30 min. After washing and blocking, goat anti-mouse IgG TRITC was added for 30 min. The slides were mounted in glycerol : PBS (9 : 1) and viewed in a fluorescence microscope equipped with fluorescein and rhodamine optics. Suitable controls (such as the omission of the primary antibodies) were run on the same slide.

Examples of single- and double-labeled astrocytes are shown in Fig. 1a and b. Using a reticule in the eyepiece of the microscope, GFAP$^+$ and GFAP$^+$ BrdU$^+$ cells were counted in selected parts of the grid and averaged over 10 fields chosen randomly. The results are shown in Fig. 2. Considering the data in Fig. 2A, the astrocytes in the untreated cultures doubled in number from 3 to 15 DIV. By 8 DIV the number of astrocytes in the treated cultures was substantially less than in the untreated controls. By 15 DIV, the FdU-treated cultures had <50%, and the heparin-treated cultures 80% (10 μg/ml) and 60% (100 μg/ml) of the untreated controls. The double-labeling procedure provides an explanation for the results of these varied treatments (Fig. 2B). While in the untreated cultures the number of proliferating astrocytes rises between 3 and 8 DIV, all three treatments result in a 75% reduction in the number of proliferating cells. By 11 DIV there are no dividing astrocytes in the FdU-treated cultures, while the number of dividing cells remains fairly constant with the other treatments. At 15 DIV, more dividing cells are seen in the mild as compared with the stronger heparin treatment. Thus FdU and heparin interfere with astrocyte proliferation but do not appear to kill cells.

Astrocyte Growth Arrest and Reinitiation of Cell Cycle

In attempts to derive a model for the astrogliosis that occurs *in situ* when the CNS is damaged, we have first growth-arrested cultured cells and then exposed them to mitogens. To see what proportion of the arrested population reenters the cell cycle, cultures were single- and double-labeled as before with anti-GFAP and anti-GFAP/BrdU. To growth arrest subconfluent cultures, the growth medium was removed and the cells washed with serum-free medium. They were then left for 24 hr in serum-free medium. At this point 10% FBS or insulin-like growth factor (IGF-1) was added and cells processed for immunocytochemistry on each of four successive days. With the readdition of serum, the number of astrocytes increased 6-fold over the

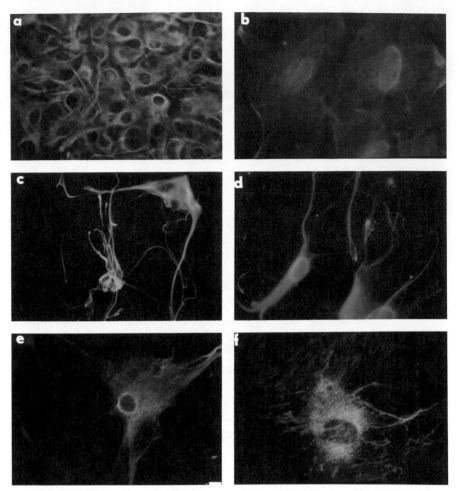

FIG. 1   Identification of cells in rat and human CNS cultures by indirect immuno-fluorescence microscopy. (a) Confluent cultures of astrocytes derived from neonatal rat cortex labeled with rabbit anti-GFAP, followed by goat anti-rabbit IgG conjugated to fluoroscein (FITC). (b) Subconfluent culture of astrocytes derived from neonatal rat cortex incubated with BrdU and then double-labeled with rabbit anti-GFAP/goat anti-rabbit IgG FITC, followed by mouse anti-BrdU/goat anti-mouse IgG conjugated to rhodamine (TRITC). (c) Human astrocytes (19 DIV) cultured from a malignant astrocytoma of the temporal lobe and labeled as in a. (d) Human astrocytes as in c, labeled as in b. (e) Human astrocyte as in c, labeled as in a. (f) Human fibroblast in a culture (24 DIV) from a malignant astrocytoma of the temporal lobe and labeled with rabbit anti-fibronectin, followed by goat anti-rabbit IgG FITC. Bar in e, 15 μm (a and c) and 8 μm (b and d–f).

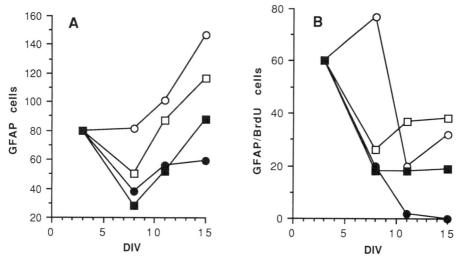

FIG. 2   The effects of mitotic inhibitors on the proliferation of astrocytes in mixed cell cultures. Cells seeded onto 8-chamber/slides were exposed at 2 DIV to heparin or FdU. At various times up to 15 DIV, the cells were incubated with BrdU, and 24 hr later, the cells were labeled with antibodies against GFAP and BrdU. (A) Single- and (B) double-labeled cells were counted using a fluorescence microscope. Values represent the mean of 10 fields. ○, No addition; □, heparin (10 μg/ml); ■, heparin (100 μg/ml); ●, FdU (2 μM).

next 96 hr, while the number of astrocytes in the untreated and IGF-treated cultures remained fairly constant (Fig. 3A). The reason for this difference is not that cells are dying in the absence of serum, but that they are not proliferating (Fig. 3B). After serum withdrawal, less than 10% of the astrocytes are actively synthesizing DNA. With the readdition of serum (but not IGF-1) astrocytes reenter the cell cycle, but not more than 35% of the population is actively synthesizing DNA at any one time. This implies either that growth arrest removes the majority of cells from the cell cycle permanently, or that only a subset of cells can reenter the cell cycle at any time.

Eicosanoid Release from Neoplastic Human Astrocytes

We have shown that cultures of cortical astrocytes derived from the rat synthesize and release a variety of arachidonic acid metabolites, including thromboxane A_2 (14). While ATP, calcium ionophore (A23187), and phorbol esters (such as phorbol myristate acetate) are effective in stimulating the

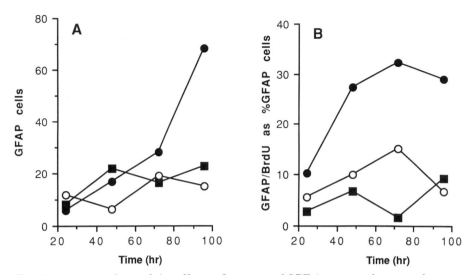

FIG. 3   A comparison of the effects of serum and IGF-1 on growth-arrested astro-cytes. Cells seeded onto 8-chamber/slides were growth arrested at 10 DIV and then exposed to serum or IGF-1. At various times up to 96 hr later, the cells were incubated with BrdU, and 24 hr later, labeled with antibodies against GFAP and BrdU. (A) Single- and (B) double-labeled cells were counted using a fluorescence microscope. Values represent the mean of three trials which differed from one an-other by <20%. $\bigcirc$, No addition; $\bullet$, fetal bovine serum (10%); $\blacksquare$, IGF-1 (3 μg/ml).

release of thromboxane, other predicted effectors, such as the muscarinic receptor agonist carbachol, and norepinephrine are not active. To discover whether astrocytes derived from glial neoplasms display the same proper-ties, we have cultured biopsied human glioma material. The majority of the cells from this material are dividing, GFAP$^+$ cells (Fig. 1c–e; 60–100%, depending on the type of glioma). A large proportion of cells are FN$^+$ (Fig. 1f), some of which are also GFAP$^+$. The coexpression of GFAP with FN is common in cultures derived from neoplastic CNS. The cells which are GFAP$^-$/FN$^+$ could be fibroblastic, but this is unlikely given that the cells are supported in medium containing D-valine, which has been found to minimize fibroblast contamination (6). (It should also be noted that fibroblasts do not synthesize thromboxane A$_2$.) These FN$^+$ cells could still be neoplastic astro-cytes which are not expressing GFAP, as the more malignant gliomas tend to show reduced expression of GFAP. The plasticity of expression of these cell markers in CNS tumors makes the determination of cellular origin equivocal.

Confluent cultures in 24-well plates had the growth medium removed and then were equilibrated in EBSS containing 20 mM glucose for 30 min. The EBSS was replaced, various agents added, and the cells replaced in the incubator. After 30 min, the medium was aspirated and assayed for thromboxane B$_2$ [(TXB$_2$) the stable metabolite of thromboxane A$_2$]. The radioimmunoassay comprised antiserum and unlabeled TXB$_2$ from Sigma and [^{3}H]TXB$_2$ from Amersham (Arlington Heights, IL). The protocol was essentially that provided by Sigma together with the antiserum (separation of bound from free TXB$_2$ is by dextran-coated charcoal), inter- and intraassay variation is <10%, and the assay takes approximately 3 hr. Detection is in the range 2–200 pg and confluent astrocyte cultures in 24-well plates release some 100–1000 pg/well.

Figure 4 shows the effects of various agents on thromboxane release from cell cultures derived from two different malignant astrocytomas from the temporal lobe. It is clear that ATP, but not carbachol, is effective in stimulating thromboxane release. In one tumor, norepinephrine, PMA, and A23187

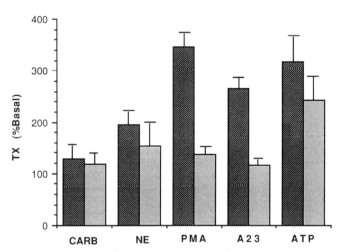

FIG. 4   Release of thromboxane (TX) from human astrocyte cultures derived from malignant astrocytomas of the temporal lobe. Cells seeded in 24-well plates were exposed to a variety of agents for 30 min. The conditioned medium was collected and thromboxane B$_2$ (the stable metabolite of thromboxane A$_2$) was measured by specific radioimmunoassay. The hatched (▨) and stippled (▢) bars represent two different astrocytomas. The values represent the mean (±SEM; $n = 4$) release of thromboxane B$_2$ expressed as percentage of basal release over 30 min. CARB, Carbachol (0.5 mM); NE, norepinephrine (0.5 mM); PMA, phorbol myristate acetate (1 μM); A23, calcium ionophore A23187 (5 μM); ATP, adenosine triphosphate (0.1 mM).

stimulated release 2- to 4-fold, but these agents produced only slight stimulations in cells from the second tumor.

Summary

A rapid, simple, inexpensive, and flexible method for the generation of astrocyte cultures from neonatal rat brain has been presented. The disaggregation steps involve mild trypsinization followed by gentle trituration. Cell yield and low seeding density result in abundant cultures of 90–95% homogeneity within 2–3 weeks, and minor additional steps will push that value closer to 99%. Small to large-scale cultures are useful for experiments requiring single-cell analysis up to bulk preparation of astroglial cell membranes or conditioned medium. The same method, or a truncated version, applies equally well to small amounts of biopsied human CNS.

Acknowledgments

Marc Klosner, Soe Soe Thwin, Greg Welk, and Mark Winter are gratefully acknowledged. The photographs were prepared for publication by Judith Eastburn. Discarded human biopsy specimens were provided by the Division of Neuropathology (Director: Michael N. Hart, MD) of The University of Iowa. Work described in this chapter was supported in part by NS 24621 and Biomedical Research Support Grant RR 05372 from the NIH.

References

1. S. Murphy and B. Pearce, *Neuroscience (Oxford)* **22,** 381 (1987).
2. M. C. Raff and R. H. Miller, *Trends NeuroSci. (Pers. Ed.)* **7,** 469 (1984).
3. S. Federoff and A. Vernadakis (eds.), "Astrocytes," Vol. 3. Academic Press, Orlando, Florida, 1986.
4. J. G. Cairncross, *in* "Astrocytes" (S. Federoff and A. Vernadakis, eds.), Vol. 3, p. 338. Academic Press, Orlando, Florida, 1986.
5. G. R. Dutton, D. N. Currie, and K. Tear, *J. Neurosci. Methods* **3,** 421 (1981).
6. C. Estin and A. Vernadakis, *Brain Res. Bull.* **16,** 723 (1986).
7. D. Giulian and T. J. Baker, *J. Neurosci.* **6,** 2163 (1986).
8. L. S. Kaplow, *in* "Manual of Macrophage Methodology" (H. B. Horscowitz, H. T. Holden, J. A. Bellanti, and A. Ghaffer, eds.), p. 199. Dekker, New York, 1981.
9. E. Whitters, R. L. Schelper, S. A. Moore, and M. N. Hart, *Fed. Proc., Fed. Am. Soc. Exp. Biol.* **465,** 1230 (1987).

10. K. D. McCarthy and J. de Vellis, *J. Cell Biol.* **85,** 890 (1980).
11. B. H. J. Juurlink and L. Hertz, *Dev. Neurosci.* **7,** 263 (1985).
12. M. Noble, K. Murray, P. Stroobant, M. D. Waterfield, and P. Riddle, *Nature (London)* **533,** 560 (1988).
13. V. W. Yong and S. U. Kim, *J. Neurosci. Methods* **21,** 9 (1987).
14. S. Murphy, B. Pearce, J. Jeremy, and P. Dandona, *Glia* **1,** 241 (1988).

[4]   Isolation of Astrocytes and Schwann Cells for Culture

Ramon Lim and E. Peter Bosch

Isolation of Astrocytes from Prenatal Rat Brains

Principle

Astrocytes can be obtained in high yield and high purity (over 95%) if one takes into consideration some special features. First, the developmental stage at which astrocytes are isolated is of prime importance. In rats, the peak genesis of astrocytes spans a period between 4 days prenatal (or 17 days gestation) and 1 day postnatal, a time following neurogenesis but preceding the development of oligodendroglia. Therefore, one good source of astrocytes is fetal rat brain a few days before birth. In our laboratory, we routinely use 18-day-old fetal rats. Next, astrocytes attach rapidly to plastic or glass surfaces without the need of collagen or polycation coating. Therefore, to discourage the attachment of neurons and oligodendroglia, which prefer to adhere to the astrocyte layer than directly to the container surface,

Methods in Neurosciences, Volume 2

it is important to seed the dissociated brain cells on simple tissue culture flasks without these coatings, and to eliminate the still floating neurons and oligodendroglia by changing the medium before these cells have a chance to attach. Third, astrocytes proliferate rapidly in media supplemented with fetal calf serum. Therefore, one should allow time for the astrocytes to overgrow the neurons and oligodendroglia, the former being postmitotic at the specified age, while the latter divide slowly. Fourth, meningeal cells and fibroblasts are difficult to eliminate from astrocytes. However, the former can be excluded by carefully peeling off the meninges before dissociating the brain cells. This also removes the fibroblasts associated with the superficial blood vessels. Fibroblasts associated with the deep vessels cannot be removed by dissection but they do not constitute a large proportion of the cell population (less than 5%). The short duration of culture also prevents the fibroblasts from expanding beyond control. Fifth, under normal culture conditions, microglia do not cause a serious problem of contamination. These phagocytic cells represent less than 5% of the cell population unless culture conditions deteriorate, such as depletion of nutrient or excessive pH and osmotic changes; in these circumstances they proliferate actively. If necessary, microglia can be eliminated by incubating the cell suspension (after trypsinization) with 5 mM L-leucine methyl ester in a defined medium for 2 hr at 37°C (1). However, we found this step unnecessary in our routine procedure. Sixth, ependymal cells, which appear as ciliated flat cells in culture, are very rarely seen. No special precaution needs to be taken to eliminate these cells other than excluding the deeper brain areas adjacent to the ventricles during dissection.

It is advisable for a beginner to estimate the purity of the isolated astrocytes by immunostaining for glial fibrillary acidic protein (GFAP) using an FITC-conjugated secondary antibody. Astrocytes invariably fluoresce strongly, as they contain high levels of GFAP. Rat fibroblasts can be conveniently detected by staining for Thy 1.1 on the cell surface, or for fibronectin in the extracellular matrix. Oligodendrocytes can be identified by immunostaining for galactocerebroside on the cell surface. (For immunofluorescence, it is advisable to grow the cells on glass coverslips.)

Reagents

  Tyrode's salt solution
  Ca^{2+},Mg^{2+}-free Tyrode's salt solution: 8.00 g NaCl, 0.30 g KCl, 0.05 g NaH$_2$PO$_4$ · H$_2$O, 0.025 g KH$_2$PO$_4$, 1.00 g NaHCO$_3$, and 2.00 g glucose per liter solution
  Trypsin solution: 0.25% (w/v) trypsin in Hanks' salt solution
  F12/DMEM nutrient: Ham's F12 nutrient mixed with Dulbecco's modified Eagle's medium at 1 : 1 ratio (v/v)
  Fetal calf serum (FCS)

Procedure

The following procedure, a slight modification of the previously published method (2), is currently used in our laboratory. Eighteen-day-old fetal rats are used as the source material. We find it convenient to use all the fetuses (usually from 10 to 12) from one pregnant rat for each batch of dissociation. First, all the fetuses are removed aseptically from the uteri and placed in ice-cold Tyrode's salt solution. The brains are taken out and the meningeal layer is peeled off with a pair of forceps. The cerebral hemispheres are pooled and diced into small pieces approximately 1 mm in each dimension. After rinsing 15 times with Tyrode's solution, the tissue is rinsed twice with Ca^{2+},Mg^{2+}-free Tyrode's solution and incubated in the same solution for 15 min at 37°C, using about 10 ml for incubation. After decanting the liquid, the tissue is incubated with 10 ml of 0.25% trypsin in isotonic salt solution for 30 min at 37°C. The tissue is rinsed three times with F12/DMEM nutrient containing 20% (v/v) FCS and triturated with a Pasteur pipette in the same solution, using 4 ml for the whole batch. This is followed by passing the cells through a 20-gauge needle attached to a syringe. The dispersed cells are distributed into five 75-cm^2 plastic tissue culture flasks, each containing 15 ml of F12/DMEM supplemented with 20% FCS. This and subsequent cultures are conducted under 5% CO_2 in air and saturated humidity at 37°C. Once seeded, the cells are incubated undisturbed for 48 hr. (At this stage it is critical to minimize any movement as this will encourage the reaggregation of the brain cells into undesirable, large clumps.) At the end of the 2-day period, the medium is decanted and the attached cells are fed every other day with F12/DMEM containing 5% FCS. One week after seeding, a confluent culture of mixed brain cells is observed under the phase-contrast microscope, with neuroblasts and oligodendroglia lying over a thin layer of astrocytes (Fig. 1A).

The cells are now ready for secondary culture, which expands the astrocytic population and also eliminates the neuronal and oligodendroglial contamination. This is accomplished by trypsinization (0.25%) and subculturing the cells onto uncoated plastic tissue culture trays at a 1:4 split in F12/DMEM supplemented with 5% FCS, and by changing the medium 24 hr later. During medium change, adhered neurons and oligodendrocytes are eliminated by gently shaking the flasks for up to 1 min. The time between seeding and medium change can be shortened if neuronal and oligodendroglial adhesion is excessive, as may occur with certain batches of serum or fetal brains. Three days later, the medium is changed once more, again with gentle shaking. Six days after seeding, a confluent monolayer of polygonal astrocytes, usually over 95% pure, is obtained (Fig. 1B). These cells are ideal for experimentation. Further passage or prolonged culture is not advisable, as this will age the astrocytes and also promote the overgrowth of fibroblasts and microglia.

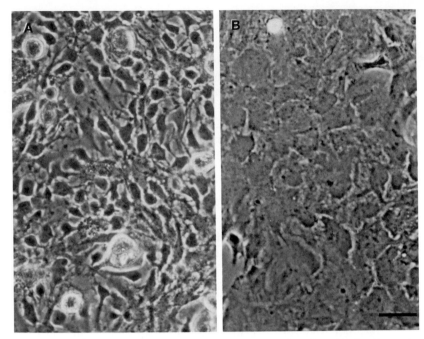

FIG. 1   Rat astrocyte cultures with various degrees of purity. (A) During primary culture, showing a mixed cell population. (B) During secondary culture, showing a homogeneous population of flat, polygonal astrocytes. Phase contrast. Bar in B, 40 μm.

Isolation of Schwann Cells from Peripheral Nerves

Principle

Schwann cells are more difficult to obtain than astrocytes because of their slow growth rate. The best source of Schwann cells is the peripheral sciatic nerve of newborn rats, where the cells are present in large quantities (85% of cell population). Here the main contaminants are fibroblasts which rapidly outgrow Schwann cells in culture. Hence the success in the isolation and culture of Schwann cells depends on the completeness of eliminating fibroblast contamination. The following approaches are frequently used in combination. First, compared to fibroblasts, Schwann cells adhere to the culture surface much slower and are detached from it much faster. By utilizing either differential attachment or differential detachment, some separation of the two cell types can be achieved. Second, rapidly dividing fibroblasts can be preferentially killed by antimitotic agents, leaving the quiescent Schwann cells relatively unharmed. Third, making use of surface markers specific to fibroblasts (such as the antigen Thy 1.1), the cells can be killed by complement-mediated lysis or removed by selective immunoadsorption ("panning" technique). Usually, the first two approaches are used for preliminary separation (90% pure). The residual fibroblasts are then eliminated by the third approach to obtain Schwann cells at a high degree of purity (95–99%). Complement-mediated lysis is fast but may yield fewer viable Schwann cells. Immunoadsorption is time-consuming but has the advantage of recovering most of the Schwann cells intact. In experienced hands both methods work equally well. The purity of the isolated Schwann cells can be verified by their spindle-shaped morphology, and by their capacity to bind antibodies to surface laminin and rat-specific nerve growth factor (NGF) receptor. Fibroblast contamination can be estimated by immunostaining for Thy 1.1 or fibronectin. Since isolated Schwann cells divide very slowly in serum alone (doubling time of 8 to 14 days), it is convenient to expand Schwann cell populations by using a combination of a growth factor (glial growth factor from pituitary extract) and a cyclic AMP-inducing agent (cholera toxin or forskolin).

Dissociation of Schwann cells from adult nerves, including human, is more difficult because of abundant connective tissue and myelin. Hence, more drastic enzyme treatment is necessary. Human Schwann cells can be identified by their surface markers such as laminin, human-specific NGF receptor, and the HNK-1 epitope (3).

Establishment of Schwann Cell Cultures from Neonatal Nerves

Reagents

Hanks' balance salt solution (HBSS)
Collagenase
Trypsin [0.25% (w/v)] in HBSS
Trypsin [0.25% (w/v)] with EDTA [0.1% (w/v)] in HBSS
F12/DMEM: Ham's F12 nutrient mixed with Dulbecco's modified Eagle's medium (DMEM) at 1 : 1 ratio (v/v) with antibiotics (penicillin 100 U/ml and streptomycin 100 μg/ml)
Fetal calf serum (FCS)
Laminin
Cytosine β-D-*arabino*-furanoside
Bovine pituitary extract
Cholera toxin
Forskolin

Procedure

Sciatic nerves form 2- to 5-day-old rats are aseptically removed and placed in chilled HBSS (4). Individual nerve fascicles are cleaned of epineurial connective tissue under a dissecting microscope and minced into small 1-mm³ fragments. The nerve fragments are incubated in HBSS containing 0.25% trypsin and 0.03% (w/v) collagenase for 45 min at 37°C (swirled gently every 15 min). The enzyme solution is carefully withdrawn with a pipette. After the addition of DMEM plus 10% FCS, the tissue is dissociated by trituration through a 22-gauge needle. The cell suspension is placed in a 10-ml centrifugation tube, washed with medium, and centrifuged for 5 min at 1000 rpm. The supernatant is decanted and the pellet is resuspended in F12/DMEM containing 10% FCS plus antibiotics and plated onto 25-cm² tissue culture flasks precoated with laminin (5 μg/ml in distilled water). The

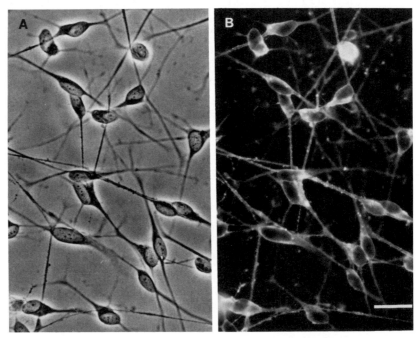

Fig. 2   Rat Schwann cells maintained in secondary culture for 4 weeks. These cells were purified by treatment with cytosine arabinoside after dissociation from sciatic nerves and by rapid trypsinization at first passage. (A) Phase-contrast micrograph. (B) Immunofluorescence (FITC) micrograph of the same cells showing rat-specific nerve growth factor receptors on cell surface. Note homogeneity of cell population. Bar in B, 20 μm.

cell suspension derived from about 14–20 nerves is seeded into one flask and incubated at 37°C in 5% CO_2 in air and saturated humidity. Two days later, the culture is exposed for 24–48 hr to an antimitotic medium consisting of F12/DMEM–10% FCS plus 10^{-5} M cytosine arabinoside. Subsequently, the cells are maintained in F12/DMEM–10% FCS containing crude bovine pituitary extract (5) (500 μg protein/ml; or better, CM-cellulose-Sephadex fraction at 10 μg protein/ml) and cholera toxin (0.5 μg/ml) to stimulate Schwann cell growth. Alternatively, forskolin (6) (2 μg/ml) may be used instead of cholera toxin. The medium is renewed every third day. When the cells become confluent, they are detached by 0.25% trypsin with 0.1% EDTA in HBSS and subcultured. At confluence, Schwann cells are admixed with about 7–15% fibroblasts. Schwann cells can be *preferentially* removed by *rapid trypsinization* (5 min) and gentle tapping of the flask and seeded on either laminin (5 μg/ml) or poly(L-lysine) (10 μg/ml)-coated coverslips. This method produces Schwann cell-enriched cultures which are over 90% pure and are adequate for most short-term experiments (Fig. 2). The cells are maintained in F12/DMEM with 5% (v/v) FCS or in defined N2 medium (7). In our hands, a modification of N2 containing insulin (5 μg/ml), transferrin (50 μg/ml), hydrocortisone (10 nM), biotin (10 ng/ml), sodium selenite (30 nM), and ascorbic acid (50 μg/ml) has proved to be optimal for Schwann cell survival while minimizing fibroblast growth (8). In order to achieve basal lamina assembly and myelin formation in Schwann cell–neuron cultures, the F12/DMEM nutrient requires the addition of both serum [15% (v/v) FCS] and ascorbic acid (50 μg/ml) (9).

Immunoadsorption of Fibroblasts

Reagents

    Phosphate-buffered saline (PBS)
    Goat anti-mouse IgG (Pel Freez)
    Mouse monoclonal IgG anti-Thy 1.1 (Pel Freez)
    FCS
    DMEM

Procedure

First, 75-cm² tissue culture flasks are coated aseptically with goat anti-mouse IgG antibody by pipetting 9 ml of the antibody diluted in PBS (2 mg/ml) into each flask (4). The flasks are incubated for 1 hr at room temperature, then for 18 hr at 4°C. The spent antibody solution is transferred to a sterile flask for future use, and the antibody-coated flasks may be stored at 4°C for up to 1 year. Before use the flasks are washed three times with PBS.

A partially pure Schwann cell culture is trypsinized, washed with DMEM–10% FCS, and incubated with mouse monoclonal IgG anti-Thy 1.1 (diluted 1 : 500; 250 μl/10^6 cells) at 37°C for 30 min. The cells are recovered by centrifugation and washed in DMEM. The cells are resuspended in 9 ml DMEM–5% FCS, poured into the flasks coated with goat antibody against murine IgG (see above), and incubated at 4°C for 60 min. Then the flask is gently swirled to resuspend the nonadherent Thy 1.1-negative Schwann cells which are carefully withdrawn with a pipette. The Schwann cells are recovered by centrifugation, washed in medium, and plated on tissue culture flasks for cell propagation. In our experience, each panning procedure reduces the fibroblast population by 8–15%.

Antibody-Mediated Lysis of Fibroblasts

Reagents
Mouse monoclonal IgM anti-Thy 1.1 (New England Nuclear)
Rabbit complement
DMEM
FCS

Procedure
A partially purified Schwann cell culture is trypsinized, washed with DMEM–10% (v/v) FCS, and resuspended in 0.5 ml of mouse IgM anti-Thy 1.1 (diluted 1 : 500) (10). After incubation for 30 min at 37°C, 2 ml of medium is added and the cells are recovered by centrifugation. The pellet is resuspended in 0.5 ml of freshly thawed rabbit complement (diluted 1 : 8) and incubated for 30 min at 37°C. Then the cells are washed once with DMEM–10% FCS and plated on tissue culture flasks for cell propagation. This procedure yields highly purified (about 99%) Schwann cells of which 60 to 70% are viable (10).

Establishment of Schwann Cell Cultures from Adult Nerves

Reagents
RPMI-1640 medium
FCS
HEPES
Dispase

    Collagenase
    Hyaluronidase
    Poly(L-lysine)

Procedure

Adult rat sciatic nerves or human sural nerve biopsy samples are meticulously cleaned of epineurial connective tissue and minced into small fragments as above (11). The nerve fragments are transferred to RPMI containing 15% FCS, 25 mM HEPES, and an enzyme mixture consisting of 1.25 U/ml Dispase, 0.05% (w/v) collagenase, and 0.1% (w/v) hyaluronidase, and incubated overnight at 37°C in 5% CO_2/95% air. The next day, the tissue is vigorously pipetted and triturated through a 20-gauge needle. The cell suspension is centrifuged at room temperature for 5 min at 1000 rpm and the supernatant is decanted and replaced with RPMI–15% FCS. The cells are plated on poly(L-lysine) (10 μg/ml water)-coated glass coverslips, or poly(L-lysine)-coated multiwell plates, and incubated at 37°C. After 24 hr the medium is changed, removing unattached tissue debris but leaving behind adherent cells. For 24–48 hr, the cultures are exposed to an antimitotic medium consisting of RPMI–10% FCS containing 10^{-5} M cytosine arabinoside which is subsequently replaced with RPMI–10% FCS. At 4 days in culture, about 80% of the isolated cells are Schwann cells by morphological and immunological criteria (11).

Acknowledgments

We thank Dr. Asgar Zaheer, Dr. Weixiong Zhong, and Mr. Louis Facto for preparation of the photographs. Financial support was provided by the Veterans Administration (Merit Review Award), the National Science Foundation (BNS-8607283), and the Diabetes-Endocrinology Research Center (DK-25295).

References

1. D. L. Thiele, M. Kurosaka, and P. E. Lipsky, *J. Immunol.* **131,** 2282 (1983).
2. R. Lim and J. F. Miller, *J. Cell. Physiol.* **119,** 255 (1984).
3. S. Schuller-Petrovic, W. Gebhart, H. Lassman, H. Rumpold, and D. Kraft, *Nature (London)* **306,** 1979 (1983).
4. J. G. Assouline, E. P. Bosch, and R. Lim, *Brain Res.* **277,** 389 (1983).
5. J. P. Brockes, G. E. Lemke, and D. R. Balzer, *J. Biol. Chem.* **225,** 8374 (1980).
6. S. Porter, M. B. Clark, L. Glaser, and R. P. Bunge, *J. Neurosci.* **6,** 3070 (1986).
7. J. E. Bottenstein and G. H. Sato, *Proc. Natl. Acad. Sci. U.S.A.* **76,** 514 (1979).

8. J. G. Assouline, Ph.D. thesis. Graduate College, The University of Iowa, Iowa City, 1988.
9. C. F. Eldridge, M. B. Bunge, R. P. Bunge, and P. Wood, *J. Cell Biol.* **105,** 1023 (1987).
10. J. P. Brockes, K. L. Fields, and M. Raff, *Brain Res.* **165,** 105 (1979).
11. E. Scarpini, B. Q. Kreider, R. P. Lisak, G. Meola, M. E. Velicogna, P. Baron, S. Beretta, M. Buscaglia, A. H. Ross, and G. Scarlato, *Brain Res.* **440,** 261 (1988).

[5]   Culture Methods for Oligodendrocyte Cell Lines and Oligodendrocyte–Type 2 Astrocyte Lineage Cells

Jane E. Bottenstein and Samuel F. Hunter

Cultured cells expressing an oligodendrocyte phenotype are useful models for understanding many aspects of normal central nervous system (CNS) development and myelination. Moreover, they can provide insights into a number of neurological disorders involving demyelination, e.g., multiple sclerosis. As a general strategy, we have used neural cell lines with the phenotype of interest to determine growth requirements shared with their normal cell counterparts (1). Only recently have clonal cell lines expressing substantial levels of oligodendrocyte differentiated properties become available: CO-13-7 (2) and ROC-1 to 6 series (3). The CO-13-7 cell line is a hybrid of a calf brain oligodendrocyte and a C6 glioma cell, and the ROC series of cell lines are the fusion products of rat brain oligodendrocytes and C6 glioma cells. All of these somatic cell hybrid lines express significant levels of oligodendrocyte-specific properties, including 2′,3′-cyclic nucleotide 3′-phosphodiesterase, galactocerebroside, and myelin basic protein.

We described earlier the soluble growth-promoting and substratum requirements for (1) selective proliferation of CO-13-7 and ROC-1 oligodendrocyte cell lines and (2) long-term maintenance of neonatal rat brain oligodendrocytes with significant reduction in astrocyte proliferation (4). Our recent studies report the *in vitro* effect of CNS neuronal cell line-derived growth factors on neonatal CNS gliogenesis (5) and bipotential oligodendrocyte–type 2 astrocyte (O–2A) progenitor cells from neonatal and mature rats (6, 7). O–2A progenitor cells, oligodendrocytes, and type 2 astrocytes constitute the O–2A cell lineage (8).

This chapter gives detailed methods for culturing oligodendrocyte cell lines and dissociated rat brain cells of the O–2A lineage. Neonatal and older brain tissue sources result in neuron-free cultures after a few days. The use of serum-free chemically defined medium significantly depletes the cultures of contaminating fibroblast and meningeal cells, and it favors the development of oligodendrocytes. To increase yields of O–2A lineage cells, neonatal O–2A progenitor cells can be initially expanded with neuronal cell line-derived growth factors. Removal of the growth factors results in enhanced differentiation into oligodendrocytes in serum-free conditions or, alternatively, induces differentiation into type 2 astrocytes in serum-containing conditions. The type 2 astrocyte-inducing factor present in serum has not yet been isolated and characterized, although ciliary neuronotropic factor has been shown to act similarly (9). We also include methods for preparing enriched cultures of O–2A lineage cells or mature oligodendrocytes.

General Procedures

Materials and Sources

Materials were obtained from the following vendors.

> High-glucose Dulbecco's modified Eagle's medium (DME; 430-2100), Ham's F12 medium (F12; 430-1700), penicillin–streptomycin–neomycin (600-5640), and gentamicin (600-5710) from GIBCO (Grand Island, NY)
>
> Hanks' balanced salt solution with (HBSS$^+$; 9222) and without (HBSS$^-$; 9230) calcium and magnesium salts, trypsin (9336), ethylenediaminetetraacetic acid (EDTA; 9314), and fetal bovine serum and calf serum (FBS) from Irvine Scientific (Santa Ana, CA)
>
> N-2-Hydroxyethylpiperazine-N'-2-ethanesulfonic acid (HEPES; H-3375), soybean trypsin inhibitor (T-9003 Type 1S), poly(D-lysine hydrobromide) (M_r 30,000–70,000; P-7886), human transferrin (T-2252), bovine insulin (I-5500), progesterone (P-0130), putrescine dihydrochloride (P-7505), phenylmethylsulfonyl fluoride (PMSF; P-7626), deoxyribonuclease I (D-4513), sucrose (S-9378 Grade 1), and Percoll (P-1644) from Sigma (St. Louis, MO)

Sodium selenite (spectrographically pure) from Johnson Matthey Chemical (London, England)

Biotin (2031) from Calbiochem-Behring (San Diego, CA)

Sodium citrate (SX0445-1) from MCB (Cincinatti, OH)

Ultrapure urea (821527) from ICN (Cleveland, OH)

Falcon sterile 100-ml plastic cups, polypropylene centrifuge tubes, and tissue culture plasticware from Becton Dickinson (Oxnard, CA)

Lab-Tek tissue culture chamber slides from Miles Laboratories (Naperville, IL)

Scissors (5.5 in.; 6812), dissecting scissors (4 in.; 5882), curved forceps (4 in.; 5135), and dissecting forceps (4 in.; 5095) from Roboz Surgical (Washington, DC)

Glass pestle (1985-11516), metal tissue sieve (1985-85000), metal mesh (380 μm; #40), and metal mesh (140 μm; #100) from Bellco (Vineland, NJ)

Glass microanalysis filter holders [(25 mm; XX1002530) and (47 mm; XX1004730)] from Millipore (Bedford, MA)

Nylon mesh [(20 μm; #460), (60 μm; #250), and (210 μm; #70)] from Tetko (Elmsford, NY)

Oak Ridge-style polycarbonate tubes (10 ml; 2611-B18) from Thomas Scientific (Swedesboro, NJ)

All other reagents were from Sigma

Water

High-quality water is essential for culture medium and other reagents when serum-free methods are used. The following low-maintenance water purification system is recommended: deionized water input, prefilter, carbon cartridge, two ion-exchange cartridges, pyrogen removal cartridge, and a final 0.22-μm filter unit in series. Purified water should have a resistance of 10–18 MΩ-cm. Alternatively, triple-distilled water is suitable.

Basal Medium

DME is used alone or mixed 1 : 1 with F12 medium. HEPES buffering agent is added to give a final concentration of 15 mM, and after mixing the pH is adjusted to 7.3. Finally, 1.2 g/liters sodium bicarbonate is added, medium is sterile filtered (0.22 μm), and stored 6 weeks or less in the dark at 4°C in aliquots.

Serum-Free Media

All medium supplements are sterile-filtered and stored at $-20°C$ unless otherwise noted. Stock solutions: 10 mg/ml transferrin in HBSS$^+$; 2.5 mg/ml insulin in 0.01 N HCl stored at 4°C only for 6 weeks or less; 0.5 mM primary selenite stock in water and 15 μM secondary stock in HBSS$^+$; 1 mM primary progesterone stock in ethanol stored at 4°C and 10 μM secondary stock in HBSS$^+$; 50 mM putrescine in HBSS$^+$; and 10 μg/ml biotin in HBSS$^+$.

When preparing and handling the following serum-free media, plastic pipettes and containers are always used to minimize protein adsorption. O1 Medium: 5 μg/ml insulin [or 100 ng/ml insulin-like growth factor I (IGF I)], 50 μg/ml transferrin, 30 nM selenite, and 10 ng/ml biotin in DME. O3 medium: 15 μg/ml insulin, 1 μg/ml transferrin, 30 nM selenite, and 10 ng/ml biotin in DME or a 1:1 mixture of DME and F12. N4 medium: 1 μg/ml transferrin, 5 μg/ml insulin, 100 μM putrescine, 20 nM progesterone, and 30 nM selenite in a 1:1 mixture of DME and F12. O1, O3, and N4 media are prepared fresh before use, as some loss of growth promotion is observed when medium is stored at 4°C for 1 week. Culture medium pH should always be 7.3 on initial contact with cells. It is advisable to equilibrate culture vessels containing medium in the CO$_2$ incubator before adding cells. Culture medium rapidly becomes alkalinized from exposure to air, especially in the laminar flow hood. For best results, cultured cells should spend minimal time in the sterile hood or in microscope observation.

Substratum Modifications

When using serum-free medium, all culture surfaces are modified by precoating with at least 2 μg/cm^2 poly(D-lysine), followed by the addition of 1 μg/cm^2 affinity-purified human fibronectin (see below). This is necessary for an optimal response to the soluble growth-promoting factors. Surfaces are completely covered for 5 min with a 0.05 mg/ml sterile solution of polylysine in water, followed by a sterile water wash; precoated vessels may be stored before use for several hours in a hydrated form (10). The water wash is aspirated, serum-free medium is added, fibronectin is added individually to vessels with swirling to ensure even distribution of this highly adhesive glycoprotein, and, finally, cells are added.

Purification of Fibronectin

Human fibronectin is purified [>98% by sodium dodecyl sulfate (SDS) gel electrophoresis] from plasma at room temperature by gelatin-Sepharose chromatography (11). Briefly, 0.45-μm-filtered plasma is applied to the column, after washing out unbound material with phosphate-buffered saline (PBS) containing 0.01 M sodium citrate (PBS–citrate; pH 7.2), then fibronectin is eluted with 0.05 M Tris-HCl buffer (pH 7.4) containing 4 M urea, fractions are collected in polypropylene tubes, and protein content is determined. Peak fractions are combined to obtain 0.25–1 mg/ml and are dialyzed at 4°C against PBS–citrate containing 1 M urea. About 10–30 mg of fibronectin can be isolated from 250 ml of human plasma. The protein concentration of the dialyzed solution is determined, and aliquots are made and stored at 4°C; activity has been retained for as long as 6 months. Division of a neuronal cell line is used to bioassay the fibronectin (10); usually 0.25–1.5 μg/cm^2 is optimal depending on the batch used. Commercial sources (Sigma, Bethesda Research Labs, and others) of fibronectin may require higher amounts for optimal activity.

Preparation of B104 Cell Conditioned Medium

A potent source of O–2A progenitor cell growth factors (5, 7) is found in conditioned medium produced by clonal B104 CNS neuroblastoma cells (12). Stock cultures of B104 cells are maintained in logarithmic phase in a 1 : 1 mixture of DME and F12 supplemented with 5% (v/v) horse serum and 5% (v/v) FBS. After a wash with HBSS$^-$, cells are detached with 0.05% (w/v) trypsin/0.5 mM EDTA in PBS (pH 7.0), 0.1% (w/v) soybean trypsin inhibitor in HBSS$^+$ is added, cells are centrifuged for 2 min in a tabletop centrifuge at lowest speed, the cell pellet is resuspended in N4 medium, and 10^4 cells/cm^2 are plated into 75-cm^2 tissue culture flasks with polylysine and fibronectin-modified surfaces. Four to five days later the conditioned medium is removed sterilely, 1 μg/ml of the protease inhibitor PMSF in ethanol is added, centrifuged at 3500 rpm for 15 min at 4°C to remove nonadherent cells, and aliquots are stored at −70°C. A method for producing larger volumes of this conditioned medium using Cytodex 2 microcarrier beads has been described (7). Protein concentration is determined and should be about 24–36 μg/ml. Activity is retained through 2–3 freeze–thaw cycles but not beyond that.

Oligodendrocyte Cell Lines

Maintenance of Cell Lines

Stock cultures are grown in 25- or 75-cm^2 tissue culture flasks in DME supplemented with 5% FBS and 5% calf serum. The surface area-to-culture volume ratio is kept at 6.2–8.3 cm^2/ml. Cells are maintained in an incubator with a humidified atmosphere of 95% air/5% CO_2 at 37°C. Medium is changed three times a week. For optimal results, cultures should never become confluent and crowded. Just prior to confluence, cells are briefly washed with HBSS$^-$, detached with 0.05% trypsin/0.5 mM EDTA in PBS, an equivalent volume of serum-containing medium is added to inactivate the trypsin, cells are centrifuged at low speed in a tabletop centrifuge at room temperature for 2 min, and the cell pellet is resuspended in culture medium. Cells are split 1:5 or 1:10 into new vessels. CO-13-7 population doubling time is about 21 hr in serum-containing medium.

Growth in Serum-Free Medium

Cells are detached from stock cultures as above, an equivalent volume of 0.1% soybean trypsin inhibitor in HBSS$^+$ is added, cells are centrifuged as above, the cell pellet is resuspended in O1 medium, cells are counted in a hemocytometer, and 1.2–4.0 × 10^4 cells/cm^2 are plated. The growth rate of CO-13-7 and ROC-1 cells in O1 medium is about 70% of that in serum-supplemented cultures, and cells can be subcultured several times and maintained for several months in O1 medium. CO-13-7 cells continue to express immunoreactive galactocerebroside, an oligodendrocyte-specific antigen, and have 2-fold increased levels of myelin-specific 2′,3′-cyclic nucleotide 3′-phosphodiesterase activity after 4 days in O1 medium. Figure 1 shows the morphology of CO-13-7 cells in serum-supplemented, basal, and O1 media. Process-bearing cells are observed in all conditions; however, in unsupplemented basal medium, the cells are significantly less numerous.

Dissociated Neonatal Rat Brain Cells

Standard Dissociation Method

Sprague–Dawley newborn rat pups (1–3 days postnatal) are used. A maximum of about 6 pups/person are processed to maximize the yield of cells/pup. All dissecting instruments and equipment are autoclaved prior to the

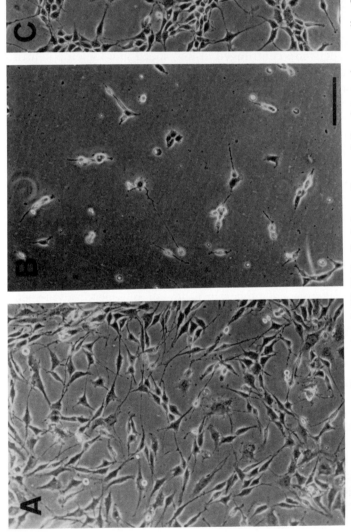

FIG. 1   Phase-contrast micrographs of CO-13-7 cells 3 days after replating into various media. Culture medium is DME supplemented with (A) 5% FBS and 5% calf serum (B) no addition, or (C) O1 components. Culture surfaces in C were polylysine- and fibronectin-modified. Cell inoculum was 10^5 cells/8 cm^2. Bar in B, 100 μm. [Reproduced from Bottenstein (4) with permission.]

dissociation procedure, which is performed sterilely in a laminar flow hood at room temperature. Sterile 100-ml plastic cups with metal sieves (380 and 140 μm) to collect the first two filtrates are set up in the hood. A glass filter apparatus with a 20-μm nylon mesh installed is clamped onto a stand, and a 50-ml polypropylene centrifuge tube is placed underneath to catch the final filtrate. Dissociation medium is prepared: DME supplemented with 10% calf serum, 50 μg/ml penicillin, 50 μg/ml streptomycin, 10 μg/ml neomycin, and 50 μg/ml gentamicin; 100 ml is sufficient for one litter of pups (two simultaneous dissociations).

Each pup is held by its muzzle and rinsed with 70% (v/v) ethanol from a spray bottle and then quickly decapitated using large scissors. The severed head is placed on a gauze square and held firmly at the jaws. The scalp is cut with small scissors along the midline from the neck as far anteriorly as possible. The scalp is retracted with the fingers, being careful not to contaminate underlying tissue. The cartilaginous skull is similarly incised starting at the foramen magnum. The meninges between the skull and the dorsal brain surface are separated by insertion of the point of the blunt forceps and a gentle back and forth movement. Each side of the skull is pulled away laterally with forceps to expose the brain surface. A spatula is used to sever the olfactory tract and cranial nerves, and the whole brain is lifted from the base of the skull and placed in a small petri dish with enough dissociation medium to cover the brain. After each use of a dissecting instrument, it is dipped in ethanol and allowed to dry while resting tip up on a petri dish.

After all the brains are collected, they are trimmed of residual meningeal tissue. Each brain is held with fine forceps and the sheets of fibrous tissue, which are closely adherent to the brain surface and contain prominent blood vessels, are pulled free with blunt forceps. If a specific part of the brain is to be used, c.g., cerebellum or cerebral cortex, it can be dissected free at this time. After the meninges are removed, the brains are transferred to a 60-mm petri dish containing 7 ml of dissociation medium. The brain is then minced with fine scissors for 4 min to produce 1- to 3-mm fragments. The 380-μm metal mesh is wetted with 1 ml of dissociation medium and is spread evenly with a glass pestle. The brain fragments are swirled to suspend them, poured into the center of the mesh, and pressed through with gentle vertical motions of the glass pestle for 2 min. The fragments are wetted every 30 sec with 0.5 ml of dissociation medium. The mesh is rinsed from above with 2 ml of dissociation medium and from the bottom by pipetting several milliliters of the filtered cell suspension onto the underside of the mesh. The finer 140-μm mesh is wetted with 1 ml of dissociation medium and is spread evenly with the plunger of a 5-ml disposable syringe. The first filtrate is added to the second mesh and stirred with the plunger. In addition, gentle vertical motion of the plunger for 2 min pushes the cells through the mesh. Small volumes of dissociation medium are frequently applied to keep the cells hydrated. The second mesh is washed as described above. The 20-μm nylon mesh in the filter apparatus is wetted with 1 ml of dissociation medium and checked for leaks. The cell suspension is then poured into the filter apparatus and stirred gently and continuously with a glass rod. The single-cell filtrate is collected for up to 15 min; flow rate averages about 1 ml/min for 15 min if continuously stirred. Gentle, brief agitation of the filter apparatus increases the flow rate slightly. The last few milliliters usually do not pass through because the flow rate slows markedly at the end.

The final filtrate is centrifuged at low speed (100 g) in a tabletop centrifuge for 3 min, and the supernatant is discarded by aspiration. The cell pellet is resuspended in O3 medium (0.5 ml/brain) with penicillin–streptomycin–neomycin (concentrations as above) but no gentamicin. A 1 : 10 dilution of the cell suspension is counted in a hemocytometer. The typical yield is 25–30 $\times$ 10^6 cells/brain. Optimal plating density with this method is 5 $\times$ 10^5 cells/cm^2; each culture vessel is rocked back and forth several times (avoiding vortexing) to evenly distribute the cells. Cultures are kept in the sterile hood a minimal time to avoid alkaline shifts in pH. If many culture vessels are to be inoculated, it is important to agitate the concentrated cell suspension gently but frequently to maintain the cells in suspension and inhibit aggregation. Attachment of cells occurs rapidly in serum-free medium, but it is best not to disturb the cultures for at least 24 hr. A plating efficiency of about 5–10% can be expected. Media are first changed after 4 days and at 3- to 5-day intervals thereafter depending on the pH (more often if the medium becomes acidic). Antibiotics are only present in the initial plating medium.

Characterization of Neonatal Cultures in Serum-Free Medium

It is important to include a control condition for comparison to experimental treatments. Immunostaining for cell type-specific antigens is the best method for identifying the cells (7). After 4 days in serum-free O3 medium, the cultures contain about 70% type 1 astrocytes, 15% oligodendrocytes, 2% O–2A progenitor cells, 2% type 2 astrocytes, and 7% microglia by immunostaining criteria. Less than 1% of cells are neurofilament-positive, <2% are Thy-1 antigen-positive, and total cell density is typically 300 cells/mm^2. After 1 week or longer, most cellular debris disappears due to the action of phagocytic cells. Since most bipotential glial progenitors differentiate rapidly into oligodendrocytes in serum-free medium, this system is useful for studying growth factors for glial progenitors and immature oligodendrocytes, as well as for analysis of differentiated oligodendrocytes. These cultures can be maintained for several months in O1 or O3 medium.

Treatment with B104 Conditioned Medium

To enhance the yield of O–2A lineage cells, neonatal rat brain cultures are treated with conditioned medium (CM) derived from B104 CNS neuroblastoma cells. The combined use of O3 medium and B104 CM is both simple and reliable. It greatly expands the numbers of O–2A progenitors and oligodendrocytes without the use of serum, expensive growth factors, such as platelet-derived growth factor (13), or complicated separation methods. Optimal results are obtained with 8–12 μg CM protein/ml, which represents about 33% conditioned medium/67% O3 medium (v/v). Control cultures contain an equivalent dilution with unconditioned N4 medium. It is important for the CM to be present from the time of plating, since progenitor cell differentiation will rapidly occur otherwise. After 4 days *in vitro*, 51% type 1 astrocytes, 23% O–2A progenitors, 15% oligodendrocytes, 6% microglia, and 3% type 2 astrocytes are present; total cell density is about 400 cells/mm^2. By 8 days *in vitro*, 53% type 1 astrocytes, 22% oligodendrocytes, 15% O–2A progenitors, 6% microglia, and 3% type 2 astrocytes are present; total cell density is about 500–600 cells/mm^2. The increase in O–2A progenitors is 12- to 15-fold over control at both times, and oligodendrocytes are increased about 4-fold over control at 8 days *in vitro*. Figure 2 shows the multipolar process-bearing morphology and expression of the oligodendrocyte-specific galactocerebroside antigen in these cultures at 9 days *in vitro*. Note the extensive network of oligodendrocyte processes. After 3 weeks in culture, the activity of the myelin-specific enzyme 2',3'-cyclic nucleotide 3'-phosphodiesterase is increased 12-fold over the O3 medium control (5).

Enhanced Differentiation into Oligodendrocytes or Induction of Type 2 Astrocytes

To enhance differentiation of O–2A progenitor cells into oligodendrocytes further, B104 CM is removed at 4 days *in vitro* and replaced with serum-free O3 medium. Three days later, oligodendrocytes are increased 3-fold, representing a 5-fold increase compared to cells in O3 medium for 7 days, a condition which already favors oligodendrocyte development. The resulting cultures are about 33% oligodendrocytes. Alternatively, to induce differentiation into type 2 astrocytes, B104 CM is removed at 4 days *in vitro* and replaced by O3 medium with 10% (v/v) FBS. Three days later, type 2 astrocytes are increased 12-fold, representing a 32-fold increase compared to cells in O3 medium for 7 days. Type 1 astrocytes also proliferate vigorously in serum-containing medium. These cultures contain about 18% type 2 astrocytes.

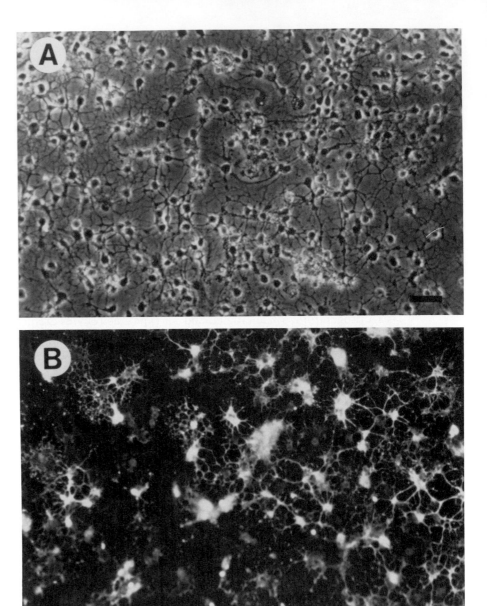

FIG. 2 Morphology and galactocerebroside expression of neonatal rat brain cells after 9 days *in vitro*. Cells were plated at a density of $5 \times 10^5/cm^2$ in O3 medium with 33% B104 CM on polylysine- and fibronectin-modified culture surfaces. (A) Phase-contrast and (B) fluorescence micrographs of cells immunostained for galactocerebroside. Bar in A, 50 μm. [Reproduced from Bottenstein *et al.* (5) with permission.]

Percoll Density Gradient Procedure

Most of the cellular debris and erythrocytes present in the cell suspension at the time of initial plating can be removed by centrifugation in a Percoll gradient before plating. This is recommended when cultures are to be analyzed within the first week *in vitro*. A 10-ml Oak Ridge-style polycarbonate tube is rinsed with 70% ethanol and allowed to dry in the sterile hood. A 1.25 M sucrose stock solution in water is made and filter-sterilized. An 80% (v/v) Percoll stock solution is made by adding 2 ml of sucrose stock to 8 ml of sterile Percoll. First, 10^8 dissociated neonatal rat brain cells are added to the polycarbonate tube, followed by 2.8 ml of 80% Percoll, and, finally, additional dissociation medium to give an evenly dispersed mixture of cells in a final volume of 9.5 ml [24% (v/v) Percoll/74 mM sucrose]. Another tube is made with the same components but no cells. The tubes are balanced and spun at 21,600 rpm (30,000 g) for 45 min in a Ti50 rotor in a Beckman L8M ultracentrifuge at 4°C. Several layers result: a thin layer of debris on top; a thick, opaque layer of debris; a cloudy layer of debris; a clear, cell-containing layer; a thin, erythrocyte-containing layer; and an amber bottom layer of Percoll. The upper layers of debris are discarded by aspiration. The clear, intermediate cell layer (2–3 ml) above the erythrocyte layer is carefully transferred to a 15-ml centrifuge tube using a sterile Pasteur pipette. The cells are washed first by adding 12 ml of dissociation medium and spinning at 190 g in a tabletop centrifuge for 10 min, then washed again with 5 ml HBSS$^+$, and resuspended in 1 ml of O3 medium. An aliquot is counted after a 1 : 10 dilution, and cells are plated at 1.3–2.5 × 10^5/cm^2. Only about 10% of the cells applied to the gradients is recovered. However, since the plating efficiency is about 25% compared to 5–10% in the standard dissociation method, 2- to 4-fold less Percoll gradient-processed cells are plated.

A typical field of mainly bipolar O–2A progenitors is shown in Fig. 3 after 3 days *in vitro*. Cells were plated into 33% B104 CM/67% O3 medium. This method produces cultures that are significantly cleaned up and have less background in subsequent immunostaining procedures.

Enrichment of O–2A Lineage Cells

A method was developed to decrease the percentage of non-O–2A lineage cells in the cultures. Enriched secondary cultures are derived from primary cultures of dissociated neonatal rat brain cells in serum-containing medium by separating the superficial, process-bearing cells from the underlying bed layer of primarily type 1 astrocytes and microglia (14). Using the standard dissociation procedure above, 5 × 10^5 cells/cm^2 are plated in 75-cm^2 tissue

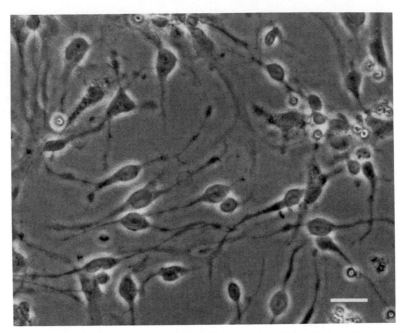

Fig. 3   Percoll gradient-processed neonatal rat brain cells at 3 days *in vitro*. Cells were plated in O3 medium with 33% B104 CM on polylysine- and fibronectin-modified culture surfaces. Bar, 20 μm.

culture flasks in DME supplemented with 15% calf serum on polylysine-coated surfaces. At 7–13 days *in vitro*, the cultures are washed once with HBSS$^-$, incubated in the same solution for 4 min, and vigorously shaken for 5 sec at the end of every minute. The cell-laden supernatants are replated at 2×10^4 cells/cm^2 in serum-containing medium or onto polylysine- and fibronectin-modified surfaces in O3 medium. A plating efficiency of 80–100% can be expected.

Figure 4A shows cells prior to the isolation procedure. Excellent separation of the process-bearing cells (Fig. 4B) from the bed layer (Fig. 4C) is evident in these serum-containing cultures. If serum-free culture is used after the isolation, secondary cultures after 1 day in O3 medium contain 24–30% GFAP-positive cells (mostly type 1 astrocytes), which is a 2- to 3-fold decrease in percentage compared to primary cultures after 4 days *in vitro*; 26% galactocerebroside-positive oligodendrocytes, a 2-fold increase compared to primary cultures after 4 days *in vitro*; and 54% A2B5-positive cells (immature oligodendrocytes and O–2A progenitors), a 4-fold increase com-

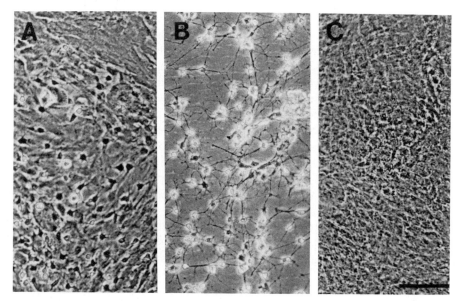

FIG. 4   Phase-contrast micrographs of cells maintained in DME supplemented with 10% calf serum. (A) Mixed culture after 13 days *in vitro,* (B) isolated process-bearing cells obtained from A and shown 2 days later, (C) remaining bed layer of primarily type 1 astrocytes obtained from A and shown 2 days later. Bar in C, 100 μm.

pared to primary cultures after 4 days *in vitro.* The ratio of GFAP-positive to A2B5-positive cells is decreased 8- to 12-fold, indicating substantially fewer contaminating cells. The O–2A progenitors in this enriched preparation are equally responsive to the growth factors in B104 CM as are the original cultures. Thus, the contaminating type 1 astrocytes probably play no role in the growth factor action (7).

Dissociated Mature Rat Brain Cells

Isolation and Culture of Mature Oligodendrocytes

While neonatal rat brain is an ideal source of bipotential glial progenitors, the mature brain is used as a source of differentiated oligodendrocytes. The procedure described here is a modification of the method of Snyder *et al.* (15). Changes in the method have increased the cell yield but decreased the percentage of oligodendrocytes somewhat (W. Norton and M. Farooq, personal communication). In addition, we have made other changes: mesh sizes, direct plating of cells into serum-free O3 medium, and isolation of oligodendrocytes from whole brain rather than white matter only. A combination of enzymatic and mechanical dissociation is employed, followed by sucrose density gradient centrifugation to remove myelin and other debris. Most astrocytes and neurons lyse during the procedure, so the major contaminating elements are erythrocytes and free nuclei. Either 30- or 60-day-old rats can be used, and three to six animals can be processed by one person in 20 min. The procedure described can accommodate up to ten brains.

The following equipment is prepared before the isolation of oligodendrocytes. A 12 × 12 cm piece of 210-μm nylon mesh is fastened securely over the mouth of a 9-cm diameter polypropylene funnel with autoclave tape. A 47-mm filter apparatus is fitted with a 60-μm nylon mesh, and a large rubber stopper is pushed onto the stem. This stopper should be larger in diameter than the mouth of a 125-ml vacuum filtration Erlenmeyer flask. These articles, as well as a 50-ml Erlenmeyer flask; new single-edged razor blade; 10-ml beaker; large scissors; fine scissors; blunt, curved forceps; fine-pointed forceps; spatula; and hemostat clamp, are autoclaved. The sterile funnel is placed over a 100-ml polypropylene cup, and the filter apparatus is clamped to a ring stand with the vacuum filtration flask positioned underneath to catch the filtrate.

Gradients and enzyme solutions are also prepared beforehand. HBSS$^+$ (250 ml with 25 mM HEPES, pH 7.35) and 70% (w/v) sucrose in HBSS$^+$ (200 ml) with 50 μg/ml penicillin, 50 μg/ml streptomycin, 10 μg/ml neomycin added are made up. Sucrose is dissolved by warming to 50°C and is then cooled to room temperature. A 2-ml aliquot of 70% sucrose is weighed in a tared dish to verify that specific gravity is 1.24 g/ml to within 1%. Further dilutions of the 70% sucrose solution with HBSS$^+$ are made to 48% (100 ml) and 44% (35 ml). The remaining 70% sucrose solution is stored at 4°C until needed later in the procedure. Eight gradients are prepared using sterile, polypropylene 50-ml centrifuge tubes with milliliter markings. Twelve milliliters of 48% sucrose is added to each tube, caps are replaced, put in a metal rack, and frozen at −70°C for 45 min. The tubes are then quickly removed, uncapped, 4 ml of 44% sucrose solution is quickly and carefully added, and stored up to several weeks at −20°C until needed. Trypsin stock (2.5% in 0.9% saline in 1-ml aliquots stored at −20°C) is thawed just prior to the procedure and kept on ice. A fresh 1 mg/ml solution of deoxyribonuclease I (DNase) in sterile water is prepared, sterile-filtered, and kept at 4°C or on ice until use. A 5-ml aliquot of calf serum is also kept on ice.

Rats are sacrificed by decapitation, and the brains are quickly removed as follows. The scalp is rinsed with 70% ethanol and resected using large scissors, and two oblique cuts are made with scissors from the foramen magnum toward the outer canthus of each eye, carefully avoiding the brain tissue with the point of the scissors. The cuts are extended anteriorly to a position midline between the orbits. To free the top part of the skull, the free edge of the occipital bone is clamped with a hemostat and is pulled away in a dorsal direction. Any bone or dura mater remaining over the brain is removed carefully with forceps. The frontal poles are lifted with the forceps, and the olfactory tracts are severed. Brains are gently pulled free from the skull, severing the cranial nerves and adherent connective tissue, placed in a tared petri dish with 3 ml of HBSS$^+$/brain, weighed, and HBSS$^+$ added to bring the total to 3 ml/g tissue. Any remaining meningeal tissue is removed after weighing.

Trypsin is added (0.12 ml/g tissue) to a final concentration of 0.1%. The tissue is rapidly minced with a razor blade for 3 min using a rapid vertical motion. DNase is added (10 μl/ml HBSS$^+$) to give a final concentration of 10 μg/ml. Mincing with fine scissors is continued for an additional 2 min. Minced tissue and medium are transferred to a 50-ml Erlenmeyer flask, which is sealed with Parafilm that has been rinsed briefly with 70% ethanol. The flask is placed in a shaking water bath at 37°C for 30 min, and the contents of the flask are resuspended with a swirling motion every 10 min. At the beginning of this incubation, the gradients (four gradients/three brains) are removed from the freezer and placed at room temperature to thaw. After the tissue has incubated for 30 min, the flask is transferred to ice for 5 min, 1 ml/g tissue of cold calf serum is added, and the tissue and medium are transferred to a sterile 50-ml centrifuge tube. The tube is capped, spun at 190 g in a tabletop centrifuge for 5 min, and the supernatant is discarded by aspiration.

A 10 μg/ml DNase solution in HBSS$^+$ (10 ml/g tissue) is prepared. The funnel with a 210-μm nylon mesh installed is wet with 1 ml of DNase solution, and the solution is evenly spread with the bottom of a 10-ml beaker. The cell pellet is transferred to the surface of the mesh with a spatula. Then cells are spread and gently pressed through using the bottom of a 10-ml beaker and a vertical motion. Cells are kept wet at all times with the DNase solution. All of the DNase solution is used in this process, and the cells on the underside of the mesh are rinsed free with it. A small amount of reddish, stringy residue will remain on the mesh.

The filtrate from this step is further processed to remove large cellular aggregates and capillaries. The cell suspension is poured into the filter apparatus and a slight vacuum is created by sealing the mouth of the vacuum flask against the rubber stopper on the stem of the filter, drawing the suspension into the flask. The filtrate is transferred back to the cup, and the procedure is repeated two more times. Finally, the contents of the filtration flask are poured into a fresh cup. Cold 70% sucrose solution is added in a 1 : 1 proportion to the cell suspension and mixed well by stirring and triturating with a

25-ml plastic pipette. About 15–20 ml of the 35% sucrose/cell suspension is added to each of the thawed gradients. They are layered slowly (0.2–0.5 ml/sec) onto the surface of the gradients, with minimal perturbation of the lower layers. Gradients are then centrifuged in an IEC DPR-6000 centrifuge at 3500 rpm (3000 g) at 4°C for 15 min. The resulting gradient shows a thick upper layer of myelin and debris and a loose pellet of cells overlapping with a diffuse layer of erythrocytes at the bottom. The upper layers from four gradients are carefully discarded by aspiration down to the 7.5-ml mark on the tubes. The remaining gradient volume is collected and added to two new 50-ml tubes (15 ml/tube). The gradient tubes are then washed with 7.5 ml of HBSS$^+$ to free cells which are adherent to the walls of the tube, the wash solution is added to the new 50-ml tubes (15 ml/tube), and the tubes are spun at room temperature for 10 min at 1200 rpm (250 g) in a tabletop centrifuge. The supernatant is discarded by aspiration down to 4.5-ml, 10 ml of HBSS$^+$/DME (1 : 1) with 10 μg DNase/ml is added to each tube, and the pellet is resuspended by trituration with a 5-ml plastic pipette. The entire volume of each tube is then transferred to a 15-ml centrifuge tube and is spun at room temperature for 8 min in a tabletop centrifuge at 1200 rpm. The supernatants are aspirated down to 0.3–0.5 ml, and the pellets are gently resuspended in 2 ml of DME with 15% calf serum. Cell suspensions from both tubes are combined, and an aliquot diluted 1 : 10 is counted in a hemocytometer. Yield is about 6×10^6 cells/g tissue or 9×10^6 cells/brain.

If serum-containing cultures are desired, cells can be further diluted at this point and plated. When serum-free cultures are desired, DNase (10 μg/ml) is added to facilitate resuspension of the cells, the tube is centrifuged for 5 min in a tabletop centrifuge at 1200 rpm, and the supernatant is aspirated to the top of the pellet. The cell pellet is resuspended in 2 ml of O3 medium and plated at 5×10^5 cells/cm^2 onto polylysine- and fibronectin-modified surfaces in serum-free O3 medium. The procedure takes about 3.5–4.0 hr from the time of sacrifice until plating. A plating efficiency of about 5–10% can be expected.

Characterization of Mature Brain Cultures

The cells attach rapidly but do not extend processes for several days. After 1 week *in vitro*, many multipolar, galactocerebroside-positive oligodendrocytes (see Fig. 5) with a dense network of fine processes are present. Cultures can be maintained in O3 medium for several months. A small number of type 1 astrocyte progenitors are present in the original predominantly (about 90%) oligodendrocyte suspension, resulting in the appearance of new type 1 astrocytes with time (16). After 8 days *in vitro* in serum-free O3

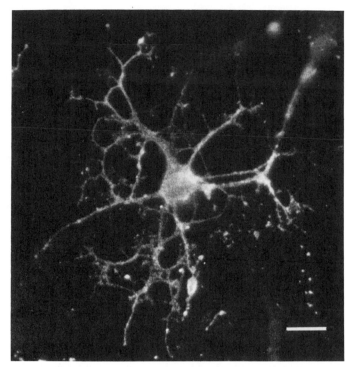

FIG. 5   Differentiated oligodendrocyte from mature rat brain after 8 days *in vitro*. The cell shown is from a culture in O3 medium on a polylysine- and fibronectin-modified culture surface. The cell has been immunostained for galactocerebroside. Bar, 10 μm.

medium there are about 70% oligodendrocytes, 20% type 1 astrocytes, 4% type 2 astrocytes, and 3% O–2A progenitors by immunostaining criteria; cell density is about 250 cells/mm². Similar percentages of oligodendrocytes are obtained after 7 days *in vitro* by using rat corpus callosum, a Percoll gradient method, and cultures containing 2.5% FBS (17). If serum-containing medium is used instead of O3 or O1 medium, type 1 astrocytes and fibroblastic cells will inevitably overgrow the cultures. Cytosine arabinoside (ara-C) administered at 3 days *in vitro* and continuously thereafter inhibits proliferation of type 1 astrocytes and other dividing cells in serum-containing medium (17). While a concentration of 2.5 μM ara-C is effective in serum-containing cultures, this concentration may need to be lowered in serum-free conditions to avoid toxicity. This reagent may be useful in maintaining high percentages of oligodendrocytes over a period of several weeks.

Summary

We have described methods for serum-free culturing of continuous oligodendrocyte cell lines and cells of the oligodendrocyte–type 2 astrocyte (O–2A) lineage. Serum-free O1 medium sustains proliferation of the oligodendrocyte cell lines, but not those of other phenotypes, and is suitable for maintaining both neonatal and mature oligodendrocytes for extended periods of time *in vitro*. Serum-free cultures of mechanically dissociated neonatal rat brain cells in O1 or O3 medium consist principally of oligodendrocytes and type 1 astrocytes. However, exposure to neuronal cell line-derived growth factors results in amplification of the small numbers of O–2A progenitors that are present. Removal of these growth factors and substitution with O3 medium or FBS produces even greater numbers of oligodendrocytes or type 2 astrocytes, respectively, by promoting the differentiation of the O–2A progenitors. To reduce the background of debris and erythrocytes, the initial dissociated cell suspensions can be processed by Percoll density gradient centrifugation. In addition, highly enriched cultures of (1) O–2A lineage cells can be prepared using primary neonatal rat brain cultures and a simple mechanical method or (2) oligodendrocytes by using mature rat brains and sucrose density gradient centrifugation. Finally, for all methods described for culturing brain cells, the use of serum-free medium for direct plating and maintenance greatly reduces the type 1 astrocyte and fibroblast-like cell contamination which inevitably occurs with serum-containing medium.

References

1. J. E. Bottenstein, *in* "Cell Culture in the Neurosciences" (J. E. Bottenstein and G. Sato, eds.), p. 3. Plenum, New York, 1985.
2. F. A. McMorris, S. Miller, D. Pleasure, and O. Abramsky, *Exp. Cell Res.* **133**, 395 (1981).
3. F. A. McMorris, D. Fu, D. Raible, R. Mozell, S. L. Preston, B. O. Kreider, and D. S. Snyder, *J. Neurochem.* **48**, s133 (1987).
4. J. E. Bottenstein, *Proc. Natl. Acad. Sci. U.S.A.* **83**, 1955 (1986).
5. J. E. Bottenstein, S. F. Hunter, and M. F. Seidel, *J. Neurosci. Res.* **20**, 291 (1988).
6. S. F. Hunter and J. E. Bottenstein, *Soc. Neurosci. Abstr.* **14** (Part 1), 321 (1988).
7. S. F. Hunter and J. E. Bottenstein, *Dev. Brain Res.* **49**, 33 (1989).
8. M. C. Raff, R. H. Miller, and M. D. Noble, *Nature* (*London*) **303**, 390 (1983).
9. S. M. Hughes, L. E. Lillien, M. C. Raff, H. Rohrer, and M. Sendtner, *Nature* (*London*) **335**, 70 (1988).
10. J. E. Bottenstein and G. Sato, *Exp. Cell Res.* **129**, 361 (1980).
11. J. E. Bottenstein, *in* "Cell Culture Methods for Molecular and Cell Biology: Vol.

4. Methods for Serum-Free Culture of Neuronal and Lymphoid Cells'' (D. W. Barnes, D. A. Sirbasku, and G. H. Sato, eds.), p. 3. Liss, New York, 1984.

12. D. Schubert, S. Heinemann, W. Carlisle, H. Tarikas, B. Kimes, J. Patrick, J. H. Steinbach, W. Culp, and B. Brandt, *Nature (London)* **249**, 224 (1974).

13. M. Noble, K. Murray, P. Stroobant, M. D. Watterfield, and P. Riddle, *Nature (London)* **333**, 560 (1988).

14. J. E. Bottenstein, *Adv. Biosci.* **61**, 3 (1986).

15. D. S. Snyder, C. S. Raine, M. Farooq, and W. T. Norton, *J. Neurochem.* **34**, 1614 (1980).

16. W. T. Norton, M. Farooq, F.-C. Chiu, and J. E. Bottenstein, *Glia* **1**, 403 (1988).

17. M. Hirayama, D. H. Silberberg, R. P. Lisak, and D. P. Pleasure, *J. Neuropathol. Exp. Neurol.* **42**, 16 (1983).

[6] Neuropharmacological Analyses in Organotypic Cultures of Spinal Cord and Dorsal Root Ganglia

Stanley M. Crain

Physiological Properties of Spinal Cord–Ganglion Explants

Organotypic cultures of spinal cord explants provide valuable preparations for analyses of many basic problems in neurobiology, both during critical stages of development *in vitro* as well as after maturation of complex neuronal network functions characteristic of these cells. Electrophysiological analyses of spinal cord tissues explanted from rat, as well as human, embryos provided the first demonstration that central nervous system (CNS) neurons could form functional synaptic networks manifested by the generation of complex bioelectric discharges during months of isolation *in vitro* (1) (see reviews in Refs. 2 and 3). When cord tissues are explanted together with sensory dorsal root ganglion (DRG) neurons (e.g., Fig. 1A and B), DRG neurites have been shown to project preferentially into dorsal, rather than

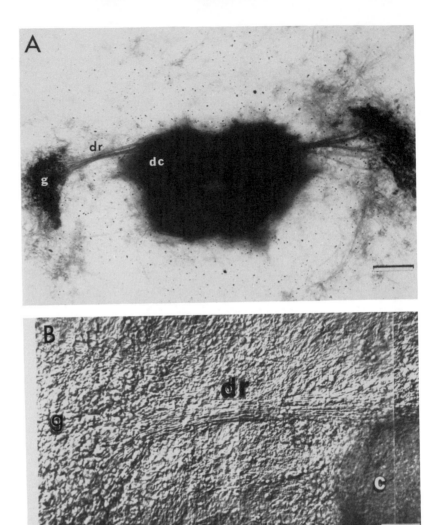

Fig. 1 Explants of 13-day-old fetal mouse spinal cord transverse sections with attached DRGs. (A) Overall view of a cord–DRG explant [Holmes' silver stain, whole mount, 35 days *in vitro*, and exposed to 10 BÚ/ml nerve growth factor (NGF) during the first week after explantation]. Note the orderly dorsal root fascicles (dr) from the DRGs (g) converging toward and entering the dorsal region of the cord explant (dc). Bar, 300 µm. (B) Higher power view of the left side of the same cord–DRG explant photographed during bioelectric tests (Nomarski interference optics). Note the contours of the DRG perikarya within the ganglion (g), their prominent nuclei and nucleoli, as well as the fascicle of DRG central axons constituting the dorsal root (dr) which enters the dorsal region of the dense cord tissue (c). The ganglion, dorsal root, and cord are lying on top of a layer of nonneuronal cells that have grown out onto the collagen substratum. Bar, 100 µm. (C) Preferential projections of another cord–DRG explant. Horseradish peroxidase (HRP) labeling of DRG

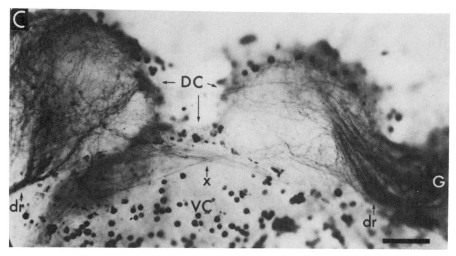

Fig. 1

into equally available ventral, regions of the cord (Fig. 1C) and to establish specialized dorsal horn synaptic networks (4–7a).

The dorsal horn network discharges evoked in these cord explants by application of electric stimuli to the DRG inputs show a remarkable degree of pharmacological specificity (4, 8) (Fig. 2). Recordings of DRG-evoked dorsal horn field potentials with extracellular microelectrodes provide a use-

---

neurites was carried out at 6 days *in vitro*. Closure of the dorsal cord (DC) was incomplete at explantation, so that most of the DC tissue was still separated in two halves. Note abundant DRG neurites in dorsal roots (dr) arising from DRGs [(G) left DRG is beyond field of view] that ramify and arborize throughout the dorsal cord regions, whereas almost none invade the equally available ventral region of the cord (VC). Note the decussation of two orderly fascicles of DRG neurites (x), each projecting to the contralateral DC. (Many DRG neurites also formed bridges on the collagen substrate across the gap between the DC halves, but these fascicles are not clearly visible in this focal plane.) DRG neurites were selectively labeled by extracellular microiontophoretic injections of HRP into the attached DRGs: cultures were processed as whole mounts; all labeled perikarya in these photomicrographs are nonneuronal cells, primarily macrophages, that have taken up HRP from the bathing fluid; no back-filling of cord neurons occurred. Bar, 100 μm. [(A and B) From Ref. 15. Reprinted with permission from *Neuroscience (Oxford)*, **17**, A. Chalazonitis and S. M. Crain, Copyright 1986, Pergamon Press PLC. (C) From Ref. 7a. Reprinted with permission from S. M. Crain, *in* "Neuroscience Approached through Cell Culture" (S. E. Pfeiffer, ed.), Vol. 2, p. 1. CRC Press, Boca Raton, Florida, 1983. Copyright CRC Press, Inc., Boca Raton, Florida.]

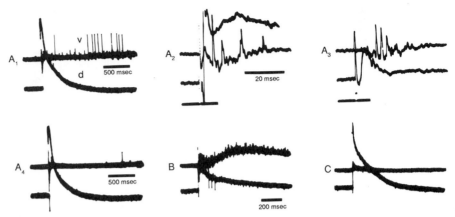

FIG. 2 Prominent sensory-evoked synaptic network responses restricted to dorsal regions of mouse cord–DRG explant (2 weeks *in vitro*) and differential sensitivity of these responses to γ-aminobutyric acid (GABA) and its antagonist. (A_1) Note large early-latency negative slow-wave potential evoked in dorsal cord (d) by single focal DRG stimulus in balanced salt solution (BSS). Ventral cord response (v) begins after longer latency and involves primarily a small positive slow-wave and variable-spike barrage. (A_2) At a faster sweep rate, the early latency, sharp rising phase, and the complexity of the dorsal horn network response are seen more clearly. (A_3) Reduction (10-fold) of DRG stimulus intensity evokes a smaller, but still prominent, dorsal cord response, and the ventral cord discharge now begins after a longer latency, during the falling phase of the dorsal cord response. (A_4) Larger DRG stimulus (as in A_1) again elicits characteristic large dorsal cord response just before drug application. (B) Introduction of the GABA antagonist, bicuculline (10 μM), leads to a marked decrease in amplitude of this response, concomitant with the onset of a convulsive negative slow-wave and repetitive-spike discharge in the ventral cord. (C) After transfer to 1 mM GABA, the large dorsal horn network response is restored (see A_4), in contrast to almost complete blockage of the ventral cord discharge. (Note that upward deflection indicates negativity at the recording electrode; onset of the stimulus is indicated by the first sharp pulse or break in the base line of each sweep.) All records show maximal responses evoked by large stimuli with standard placements of recording microelectrodes within the cord and stimulating electrodes within the DRG tissue. (Reproduced from Ref. 4 with permission.)

ful electrophysiological indicator of the efficacy of DRG presynaptic terminals in activating dorsal cord target neurons. γ-Aminobutyric acid (GABA) selectively enhances these responses at concentrations that block ventral cord discharges (Fig. 2C). Furthermore, the degree to which sensory-evoked dorsal horn responses are depressed by acute exposure of the explants to a large series of opioid agonists (e.g., Fig. 3A_1 and A_2) correlates well with

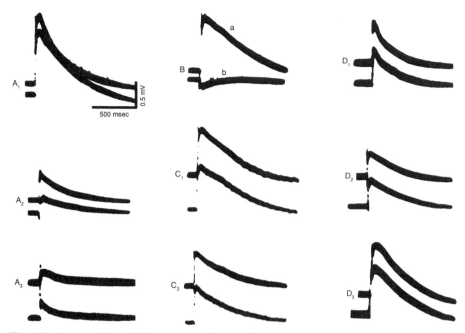

FIG. 3   Attenuation of depressant effects of morphine and serotonin on sensory-evoked dorsal horn network responses in mouse cord–DRG explants (2–3 weeks *in vitro*) by (1) chronic exposure to morphine or pertussis toxin (PTX) and (2) brief treatment with forskolin or cyclic AMP analogs. (A_1–A_3) Control explant. (A_1) Dorsal cord responses are evoked at two sites by a single DRG stimulus in BSS. (A_2) Responses are markedly attenuated within a few minutes after exposure to 0.1 μM morphine. (A_3) Similar depressant effects occur in 0.01 μM serotonin (5-HT) after initial restoration in BSS. (B) Large dorsal cord network response is evoked in another cord–DRG explant after chronic exposure to 1 μM morphine for 2 days at 35°C. The dorsal cord response (a) remains large even after increasing morphine concentration to 100 μM (not shown). (b) The typical ventral cord response in these explants is shown (in this record only). (C_1 and C_2) Explant treated with PTX (10 μg/ml) for 2 days. (C_1) Characteristic dorsal cord responses are still evoked after introduction of 10 μM morphine, and only a slight depression of cord responses occurs even in 100 μM morphine (not shown). (C_2) Exposure to 20 μM 5-HT is also ineffective [whereas dorsal horn responses in control explants are severely attenuated at 0.01–0.1 μM levels (e.g., A_3)]. (D_1) Addition of 1 μM morphine fails to depress dorsal cord responses in a cord–DRG explant pretreated for 30 min with 50 μM forskolin. (D_2 and D_3) Pretreatment with cAMP analogs also attenuates the usual depressant effects of morphine on dorsal cord responses. Dioctanoyl-cAMP was effective at a relatively low concentration (0.1 mM) against 1 μM morphine (D_2), whereas 10 mM dibutyryl cAMP was required to antagonize the effect of 0.1 μM morphine (D_3). (Note that all recordings were made after 10-min test periods, unless otherwise indicated.) (Reproduced from Refs. 10–12.)

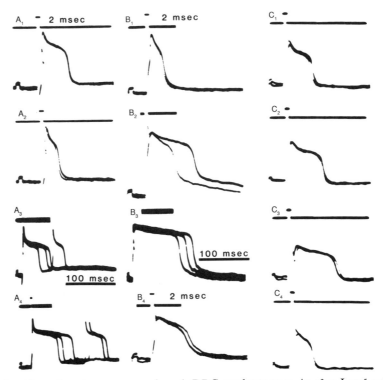

FIG. 4   After chronic exposure of cord–DRG explants to D-ALA²-D-LEU⁵-enkepha-lin (DADLE), characteristic opioid shortening of the Ca^{2+} component of the action potential duration (ADP) of many DRG neurons fails to occur. Instead, when higher concentrations of DADLE are acutely applied, the APD is prolonged, resembling effects produced in naive neurons by brief treatment with forskolin (FSK). (A_1–A_4) Control cord–DRG explant grown in regular culture medium. Sequential recordings from the same neuron. (A_1) Action potential (AP) generated by a DRG neuron in BSS containing 5 mM Ca^{2+} and 5 mM Ba^{2+} in response to a brief (2 msec) intracellular depolarizing current (similar 2-msec stimulus was used in all subsequent records). Addition of Ba^{2+} and high Ca^{2+} enhanced inward Ca^{2+} current, and Ba^{2+} suppressed delayed rectifying K^+ channels, thereby prolonging the APD and providing a promi-nent base line response for pharmacological tests (15–17). (A_2) The APD is signifi-cantly shortened by 1 min after addition of 1 μM DADLE. (A_3) After withdrawal of the opioid and restoration of initial APD, exposure to 50 μM FSK results in marked prolongation of the APD which is maintained during the 20-min test period (note the slower sweep rate in A_3 and A_4). Note also that an additional AP is generated following one of the initial APs (three superimposed sweeps). (A_4) During exposure to 10 μM DADLE (in the presence of FSK), the APD is still further *prolonged* and then stably maintained (20-min test periods), in contrast to the opioid-induced APD shortening observed in control BSS (cf. A_2). The durations of the long-latency sec-ondary APs are also increased (cf. A_3). (B_1–B_4 and C_1–C_4) Cord–DRG explants after chronic opioid exposure to 1 μM DADLE for 5–10 days. (B_1) AP generated in BSS

their analgesic potency *in situ* (8, 9). Chronic exposure of cord DRG explants to morphine or opioid peptides for several days results in a marked attenuation of the opioid-depressant effects on dorsal horn responses (9, 10) (Fig. 3B), resembling the development of opioid tolerance to spinal analgesia *in situ*. These opioid tolerance effects can be mimicked by chronic exposure of cord–DRG explants to pertussis toxin, which blocks inhibitory G-protein linkages between opioid receptors and ionic channels (11) (Fig. $3C_1$ and C_2), or by acute treatment with agents that elevate cyclic AMP levels (12) (Fig. $3D_1–D_3$). Together with correlative analyses of opioid alterations in the adenylate cyclase–cyclic AMP levels of these explants (13), our studies provide new insights into the possible role of this second messenger system in opioid tolerance mechanisms (12–14a).

Intracellular recordings from the perikarya of DRG neurons in these explants have provided significant data on the degree to which opioid analgesia and tolerance may be due to primary effects on presynaptic DRG components of dorsal horn networks (14–17). Analyses of opioid alterations of the calcium component of the action potential duration (APD) of DRG neurons have revealed not only opioid-induced APD shortening (Fig. $4A_1$ and A_2) as a causal factor in opioid inhibitory effects on dorsal horn functions (see review in Ref. 16a), but also opioid-induced APD *prolongation* as a possible opioid excitatory mechanism involved both in the development of tolerance (16) (Fig. $4A_4$, $B_1–B_4$, and $C_1–C_4$) and in dual concentration-dependent opioid modulation of nociceptive signal transmission in some types of sensory neurons (17–17b) (Fig. 5).

Cocultures of cord–DRG explants with peripheral target tissues, e.g., skeletal muscle (18, 19) (see review in Ref. 3) or sympathetic ganglia (20), have provided additional types of organotypic culture models for analyses of

---

containing 1 μM DADLE. (B_2) The APD is progressively prolonged (from 4 to 9 msec) during the first 2 min after increasing DADLE concentration to 10 μM. (B_3) After 10 min of exposure to 10 μM DADLE, the APD is further prolonged to 100 msec (note the slower sweep rate). (B_4) After reducing DADLE concentration back to 1 μM, the APD shortens to about 11 msec within 10 min. (C_1) AP of DRG neuron in another explant maintained in 1 μM DADLE. (C_2 and C_3) After increasing DADLE concentration to 10 μM, the APD is progressively prolonged from 9 to 14 msec by 3 min (C_2) and to 17 msec by 6 min (C_3). (C_4) After coperfusion of 10 μM naloxone with 10 μM DADLE, the APD is gradually shortened to 6 msec (by 15 min). (Note that in this figure, all records are from cord–DRG explants tested at 3–7 weeks *in vitro*.) Calibration pulse preceding each AP: 10 mV and 2 msec. A depolarizing stimulus current pulse (2 msec) is displayed on the upper (base line) trace of records A_1 and A_2; B_1, B_2, and B_4; and $C_1–C_4$. Recordings were photographed as three superimposed sweeps of the oscilloscope. (Reproduced from Ref. 16 with permission.)

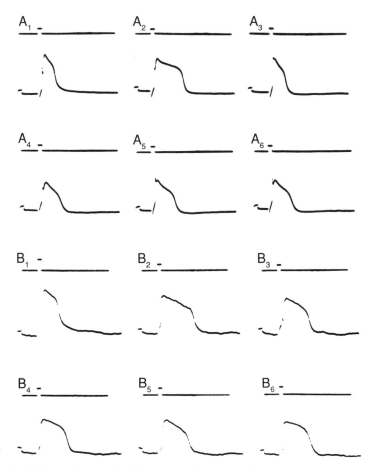

FIG. 5   DADLE prolongs the APD of DRG neurons in cord–DRG explants at low concentration and shortens the APD at higher concentration. Both effects are prevented by the opioid antagonists, diprenorphine (A_4–A_6) and naloxone (B_4–B_6). (A_1) AP generated by a DRG neuron in a naive cord–DRG explant in BSS containing 5 mM Ca^{2+} and 5 mM Ba^{2+}, in response to a brief (2 msec) intracellular depolarizing current (the same 2-msec stimulus was used in all subsequent records). (A_2) The APD is prolonged within 5 min after addition of 10 nM DADLE. (A_3) The APD is shortened within 5 min after increasing DADLE concentration to 1 μM. (A_4–A_6) Tests on the same neuron after BSS rinse and pretreatment with 10 nM diprenorphine. (A_4) The APD is not altered after 5 min in 10 nM diprenorphine. (A_5) The APD is only slightly prolonged after coperfusion of 10 nM DADLE and diprenorphine, in contrast to the marked opioid-induced prolongation elicited prior to introduction of the antagonist (cf. A_2). (A_6) The APD is also unaltered after addition of 1 μM DADLE, in contrast to the marked shortening elicited in the absence of diprenorphine (cf. A_3). (B_1) The AP generated by another DRG neuron in BSS containing 5 mM Ca^{2+} and 5

neuromuscular development and regeneration, as well as neurospecificity mechanisms.

Tissue Culture Techniques

The procedure that has produced the most highly differentiated CNS cultures involves explantation of small fragments ($\sim$1 mm^3) of embryonic tissue (e.g., fetal rodent spinal cord) (Fig. 1) onto collagen-coated coverglasses, with their subsequent incubation at 34–35°C in Maximow depression-slide chambers as "lying-drop" preparations (3, 21, 22). The explants are cut so that one dimension is well under 1 mm in order to facilitate diffusion of metabolites to and from the cells within the central region of the tissue. Spinal cord with meningeal covering and attached DRGs are generally dissected from fetal mice [e.g., Swiss, CD-1 (Charles River Labs., NY)] at 13–14 days *in vitro*. Transverse sections of the cord are cut the width of a ganglion ($\sim$0.5–0.7 mm thick). Dissection of embryonic CNS tissues and slicing to appropriate explant size require considerable skill to minimize surgical trauma to these extremely fragile structures (22). The culture medium is changed twice a week and generally contains mammalian serum in a balanced salt solution (BSS) with embryo extract or other special nutrients. A medium often used in our laboratory for culturing mammalian CNS explants consists of human placental serum (15–30%), Eagle's minimum essential medium (55–70%), chick embryo extract (10%), and Hanks' balanced salt solution (HBSS) supplemented with glucose (600 mg %) and glutamine (2 mM). In cord–DRG cultures, the medium is also supplemented for the first week with nerve growth factor (NGF-7S) at a concentration of 10–300 biological units (BU)/ml (approximately 0.1–3 μg/ml). This permits survival and maturation of representative populations of embryonic mouse DRG neurons and enhanced afferent innervation of the dorsal region of the cord explant (3, 4). The total volume of medium in the Maximow chamber is approximately 0.1 ml and the overlying air space about 2 ml. Care must be

---

mM tetraethylammonium (TEA) (see Ref. 17). (B$_2$) The APD is prolonged within 5 min after addition of 10 nM DADLE (as in the test made in A$_2$). (B$_3$) The APD is shortened within 2 min after perfusion with 1 μM DADLE (as in A$_3$). (B$_4$–B$_6$) Tests on the same neuron after BSS rinse and pretreatment with naloxone. (B$_4$) The APD is not altered after 5 min in 10 nM naloxone. (B$_5$) The APD is unaltered after addition of 10 nM DADLE, in contrast to the opioid-induced prolongation elicited prior to introduction of the antagonist (cf. B$_2$). (B$_6$) The APD is also unaltered after addition of 1 μM DADLE, in contrast to the shortening elicited in the absence of naloxone (cf. B$_3$). (Reproduced from Ref. 17 with permission.)

taken to ensure sterility during all of the experimental manipulations, especially since antibiotics are generally omitted to avoid possible noxious side effects of these agents on neural tissues. Meticulous procedures are also necessary to minimize chemical impurities in the culture chamber components and in the nutrient media, since CNS tissues are particularly sensitive to many chemical contaminants (21).

The relatively small volume of nutrient fluid used in the Maximow slide assembly appears to facilitate automatic "conditioning" of the culture medium. Cellular exudates favorable to neuronal maturation might thereby be maintained at significantly higher concentrations in the vicinity of the explant. This stratagem, however, involves the risk that noxious catabolites might not be adequately diluted away from the neurons. The small volume of culture medium requires frequent replenishment, depending on the rate of metabolic activity of the tissue (2–3 times per week).

Electrophysiological Techniques

Extracellular Recordings

The culture coverglass is transferred from the Maximow slide to a bioelectric recording chamber on an inverted microscope for electrophysiological studies. For extracellular recordings a closed chamber is often used in our laboratory, in which microelectrodes can be positioned with miniaturized magnetic micromanipulators, under direct visual control at high magnification, for focal recording and stimulation at several sites within an explant (3). Extracellular microelectrode recordings are made with chloridized silver electrodes via saline-filled pipettes with tip diameters of 1–5 μm, and electric stimuli (0.1–0.5 msec duration) are applied through pairs of similar pipettes with 5- to 10-μm tips. Bioelectric signals are recorded with high-input impedance preamplifiers and a four-channel oscilloscope (passband 0.2 c/sec–10 kc/sec). Recordings are made in 0.5–1 ml BSS (pH 7.2, 34°C). The fluid bathing the explants is changed via Teflon tubing which connects syringes to the culture dish.

Single focal DRG stimuli elicit complex negative slow-wave potentials restricted to dorsal regions of the spinal cord explants, arising abruptly after short latencies of 2–3 msec and often lasting more than 500 msec (e.g., Fig. 2). These extracellularly recorded field potentials resemble primary and secondary sensory-evoked synaptic-network responses in dorsal spinal cord *in situ* (3, 4). The amplitude of the dorsal horn responses can generally be graded by increasing the DRG stimulus intensity, but stimulus–response data are difficult to standardize due to the variability in DRG neurite projections and dorsal horn target zones from one explant to another. Therefore, maximal dorsal cord responses evoked by large DRG stimuli are often utilized in pharmacological tests (Fig. 3) to ensure excitation of a representative sample of the population of DRG neurons participating in the dorsal horn networks (9–12).

Intracellular Recordings

An open bioelectric recording chamber is used to permit entry and positioning of a micropipette mounted on a large rack-and-pinion-controlled (e.g., Leitz) or hydraulic (e.g., Narashige) micromanipulator. The recording chamber is attached to a micrometer-driven mechanical stage on an inverted microscope clamped to the same baseplate as the micromanipulator. The baseplate supporting the microscope and micromanipulator is mounted on an air-cushioned vibration-free platform (e.g., Micro G).

For intracellular recordings, micropipettes are prepared from omega-dot tubing using a Brown–Flaming pipette puller. The pipettes are filled with 3 M potassium chloride or 1 M potassium citrate and have resistances of about 60–100 MΩ. A chloridized silver wire inserted into the pipette is connected to a neutralized-input capacity preamplifier with a bridge circuit (e.g., WPI-M4A) for current injection through the recording microelectrode. The micropipette is clamped to the micromanipulator at an angle of about 35° from the vertical plane and advanced down to the neurons. A long-working-distance condenser is used to provide adequate clearance for the micropipette, and positioning is made during direct visual monitoring of the neurons at magnifications of 200–400×. Impalement of the neuron is often facilitated by applying a high-frequency "ringing" pulse to produce a brief mechanical oscillation of the electrode tip.

Intracellular depolarizing current pulses (<1 nA, 1–100 msec) are applied at 0.1 Hz through the bridge circuit. Impalements of DRG neurons are generally maintained for 0.5–3 hr in order to allow time for bath perfusion of a series of test solutions (Figs. 4 and 5). Perfusions are made with manually operated push–pull syringes (1–3 ml capacity), at rates of 0.5–2 ml/min. The bath fluid (~1 ml) is maintained at 34°C; pH is maintained at about 7.2–7.4. The usual bicarbonate and phosphate buffers in HBSS are often replaced by 10 mM HEPES (see further details in Refs. 15–17).

Acknowledgment

This work was supported by research grants DA-02031 and DA-05203 to S. M. Crain. The cultures were prepared by Edith R. Peterson and colleagues in facilities kindly provided by Dr. M. B. Bornstein.

References

1. S. M. Crain and E. R. Peterson, *Science* **141,** 427 (1963).
2. S. M. Crain, *Int. Rev. Neurobiol.* **9,** 1 (1966).
3. S. M. Crain, "Neurophysiologic Studies in Tissue Culture." Raven, New York, 1976.
4. S. M. Crain and E. R. Peterson, *Brain Res.* **79,** 145 (1974).
5. S. M. Crain and E. R. Peterson, *Dev. Brain Res.* **2,** 341 (1982).
6. E. R. Peterson and S. M. Crain, *Dev. Brain Res.* **2,** 363 (1982).
7. N. R. Smalheiser, E. R. Peterson, and S. M. Crain, *Dev. Brain Res.* **2,** 383 (1982).
7a. S. M. Crain, *in* "Neuroscience Approached through Cell Culture" (S. E. Pfeiffer, ed.), Vol. 2, p. 1. CRC Press, Boca Raton, Florida, 1983.
8. S. M. Crain, B. Crain, E. R. Peterson, and E. J. Simon, *Brain Res.* **157,** 196 (1978).
9. S. M. Crain, *in* "Mechanisms of Tolerance and Dependence" (C. Sharp, ed.), Natl. Inst. Drug Abuse Res. Monogr. ADM 84-1330, p. 260. U.S. Govt. Printing Office, Washington, D.C., 1984.
10. S. M. Crain, B. Crain, T. Finnigan, and E. J. Simon, *Life Sci.* **25,** 1797 (1979).
11. S. M. Crain, B. Crain, and M. H. Makman, *Brain Res.* **400,** 185 (1987).
12. S. M. Crain, B. Crain, and E. R. Peterson, *Brain Res.* **370,** 61 (1986).
13. M. H. Makman, B. Dvorkin, and S. M. Crain, *Brain Res.* **445,** 303 (1988).
14. S. M. Crain, *in* "Regulatory Role of Opioid Peptides" (P. Illes and C. Farsang, eds.), p. 186. VCH, Weinheim, 1988.
14a. G.-G. Chen, A. Chalazonitis, K.-F. Shen, and S. M. Crain, *Brain Res.* **462,** 372 (1988).
15. A. Chalazonitis and S. M. Crain, *Neuroscience (Oxford)* **17,** 1181 (1986).
16. S. M. Crain, K.-F. Shen, and A. Chalazonitis, *Brain Res.* **455,** 99 (1988).
16a. R. A. North, *Trends Neurosci.* **9,** 114 (1986).
17. K.-F. Shen and S. M. Crain, *Brain Res.* **491,** 227 (1989).
17a. K.-F. Shen and S. M. Crain, *Neuropharmacology,* in press (1990).
17b. S. M. Crain and K.-F. Shen, *Trends Pharmacol. Sci.* **11,** 77 (1990).
18. E. R. Peterson and S. M. Crain, *Exp. Neurol.* **36,** 136 (1972).
19. E. R. Peterson, E. B. Masurovsky, A. Spiro, and S. M. Crain, *Muscle Nerve* **9,** 787 (1986).
20. A. Chalazonitis, S. M. Crain, and J. Kessler, *Brain Res.* **458,** 231 (1988).
21. M. B. Bornstein, *in* "Tissue Culture: Methods and Applications" (P. F. Kruse and M. K. Patterson, eds.), p. 86. Academic Press, New York, 1973.
22. E. R. Peterson, *Tissue Cult. Assoc. Man.* **4,** 921 (1978).

[7] Isolation, Culture, and Use of Viable Central Nervous System Perikarya

Gary R. Dutton

The use of primary neuronal and glial cell cultures as tools for investigating neurobiological problems has gained widespread acceptance. Among the advantages of such systems is the ease with which the culture environment can be manipulated, allowing control over cell composition and exposure to drugs, growth factors, and substrate materials which may be used to perturb *in vitro* development, differentiation, and cellular interactions. It is clear that cells grown in culture retain some, but not all, of the physicochemical characteristics of their *in situ* counterparts, thus making them useful models for studying the influence of both intrinsic and extrinsic factors on form and function. On the other hand, disadvantages of using cultures include limitations on cell yield, culture viability, reproducibility, and accurate cellular representation *in vitro* of the original starting tissue. These problems may interfere with the interpretation of results and restrict the practical application of certain biochemical techniques in cases where substantial sample size and number are required. This chapter deals with the description of a simple and rapid cell isolation procedure, which, when applied to various brain regions of postnatal rodents, results in the production of viable neuronal and glial perikarya. Furthermore, these neural perikarya can be reproducibly isolated in large numbers and successfully maintained under varying culture conditions, allowing the application of experimental techniques requiring hundreds of millions of cells in a single experiment.

Isolation of Perikarya

Historically, the cell isolation described here evolved from the original work of Moscona (1) and Steinberg (2) and the later work, as applied to the postnatal mammalian cerebellum, of Barclay *et al.* (3), Lasher and Zagon (4), and Messer (5). This procedure involves mild trypsinization and trituration, and, while based on modifications of a method originally designed for the isolation of viable perikarya from postnatal rat cerebellum (6, 7), can be successfully applied to other regions of the postnatal central nervous system (CNS). As demonstrated here, the results are very reproducible, resulting in high yields of cells which can be maintained in culture with high plating

Methods in Neurosciences, Volume 2

efficiencies. Because of space limitations, only removal of the intact brain is described. Reference to details of regional dissections may be found throughout the literature (e.g., for hippocampus, see Ref. 8).

Materials and Reagents

Directions for assembling and preparing materials and reagents needed for the isolation of cells from 3 to 400 mg wet weight of starting tissue (one tube) are given below. However, as many as six tubes can be easily handled in a single experiment, in which case one would assemble an additional item of material and prepare a proportionately greater amount of reagent for each additional tube used.

Materials

Glassware should be siliconized prior to use (Prosil-28, PCR Research Chemicals, Inc.). All the following items may be sterilized by autoclave, or alternatively using dry heat or 70% (v/v) ethanol depending on the heat-resistant nature of the materials involved. The latter procedures are described for laboratories which do not have access to an autoclave.

Heat-sterilize the following (45–60 min at 200°C in a dry oven)
  One siliconized, cotton-plugged 9-in. Pasteur pipette
  One siliconized 50-ml graduated glass conical centrifuge tube (e.g., Fisher #05-525)
  One siliconized 50-ml screw-cap Erlenmeyer flask (trypsinization flask)
Alcohol-sterilize the following (immerse 15–30 min in 70% ethanol followed by air drying in a sterile hood)
  One 8-in. stainless steel spatula with one tapered end and one rounded end (e.g., Fisher #21-401-10)
  One 6-in., 18-gauge blunt-end needle
  One screw-cap for a 50-ml Erlenmeyer flask
  One cap for a conical tube (Kimbal)
  One 3-in. frosted-glass plate (for removing tissue meninges)
  One pair of dissecting scissors (e.g., Braun delicate, 4.5-in. curved)
  One plastic tissue-chopping disk for McIlwain Tissue Chopper
  The assembled razor blade, chopping head, and stage of the McIlwain Tissue Chopper (Mickle Laboratory Engineering Co., Gromshall, Surrey, England) should also be alcohol-sterilized and covered until use

Reagents

All solutions are based on a Ca^{2+},Mg^{2+}-free Earle's balanced salt solution with partial substitution of N-(2-hydroxyethyl)piperazine-N'-(2-ethane-sulfonic acid) (HEPES) for $NaHCO_3$ and is referred to here as H-EBSS. Glucose is not added to the H-EBSS stock solution in order to reduce the probability of bacterial and fungal growth during storage. Reagents may be made up under nonsterile conditions. Solutions A–E (below) should be prepared no more than 2 hr prior to beginning the experiment.

H-EBSS stock solution
    Make up to 1 liter with components below using Milli-Q water, adjust to pH 7.4, and store at 4°C

Chemical	Grams per liter	Final concentration (mM)
NaCl	8.08	13.8
KCl	0.40	5.0
HEPES (hemisodium salt)	6.23	25.0
$NaHCO_3$	0.35	4.2
$NaH_2PO_4 \cdot H_2O$	0.14	1.0
Phenol red	0.01	(0.01%)

Solution 1H
    To 50 ml of H-EBSS, add 0.125 g of glucose, 0.150 g of bovine serum albumin (BSA, fraction V; Sigma, St. Louis, MO, Cat. #A-2153), and 0.5 ml of an aqueous 3.82% (w/v) $MgSO_4$ solution
4% BSA solution
    To 25 ml of H-EBSS, add 1 g of BSA and 0.2 ml of 3.82% $MgSO_4$ solution
Trypsin solution
    Add 2.5 mg of trypsin (bovine pancreas, Sigma, Cat. #T-8253) to 10 ml of solution 1H
Concentrated deoxyribonuclease (DNase)/trypsin inhibitor solution
    Dissolve the following components in 10 ml of solution 1H
        One-tenth milliliter (0.1 ml) of 3.82% $MgSO_4$ solution. The amounts of both DNase and trypsin inhibitor should be adjusted depend-ing on the enzyme activity listed on the labels
        For DNase I (bovine pancreas, Sigma, Cat. #D-5025), activity is expressed as Kunitz units per milligram. Use 1300 Kunitz units per 10 ml of solution
        For trypsin inhibitor (soybean, Sigma, Cat. #T-9003), activity is

expressed as the number of milligrams of trypsin inhibited by 1 mg of inhibitor. Use enough trypsin inhibitor per milliliter of solution to inhibit about 1.35 mg of trypsin

Dilute DNase/trypsin inhibitor solution

Approximately 10 ml of solution is prepared by combining 1.6 ml of the concentrated DNase/trypsin inhibitor solution (above) with 10 ml of solution 1H

Procedures

Except for the centrifugation and incubation steps, all manipulations should be performed in a sterile hood or cabinet. Solutions are sterilized by passing through a 0.22-μm membrane filter. For small volumes ($\leq$50 ml) disposable filter units (Millex-GV, Millipore, Bedford, MA) attached to a 20-ml syringe are used. For larger volumes (e.g., culture media) sterile 250- or 500-ml Nalgene filter units are used. Excluding set up and dissection time, the average preparation takes about 1–1.5 hr. With the exception of the 37°C incubation, all steps are carried out at room temperature.

Tissue Preparation

1. Rapidly decapitate animals (usually 1–10 days of age) and spray heads with 70% ethanol solution.
2. Remove brain by inserting one blade of dissecting scissors into the foramen magnum. Run blade along the inside of the skull, cutting from the foramen magnum to almost the eye socket. Repeat the process on the other side of the head.
3. Place the tip of the scissors at the foramen magnum, just under the skull flap created. Gently hold the head by placing your thumb and index finger at the angles of the jaw. Your middle finger should rest at the nose and serve as a fulcrum. Lift the skull flap and pull it forward to expose the brain. Care must be taken not to squeeze the skull.
4. Remove whole brain from back to front, placing the thin spatula blade under the brain at the foramen magnum and lifting carefully. Perform desired dissection(s), place tissue on frosted-glass plate (to prevent slippage) and remove meninges. Transfer cleaned tissue to plastic cutting disk and cover with a small volume of solution 1H to prevent drying.
5. Drain solution from tissue just prior to chopping.
6. Chop tissue using McIlwain Chopper with micrometer set for 400-μm spacing.
7. Turn disk 90° and repeat chopping to produce 400-μm tissue blocks.

Trypsinization

1. Transfer chopped tissue with tapered end of spatula to a 50-ml glass conical tube using 10 ml of trypsin solution and stir thoroughly to separate and suspend tissue blocks.
2. Decant entire contents into a trypsinization flask.
3. Cap securely and place in 37°C shaking water bath for 15 min.

Trypsin Inhibition

1. Decant trypsinized cells into original 50-ml glass conical tube.
2. Rinse trypsinization flask with an equal amount (10 ml) of dilute DNase/trypsin inhibitor solution and decant into the 50-ml conical tube containing the trypsinized cells. Swirl gently to mix and inhibit trypsinization.
3. Sediment tissue blocks by rapid and brief (5 sec) centrifugation at 100 g.

Preparation of Cell Suspension

1. Remove supernatant from sedimented tissue blocks.
2. Add 4–5 ml of concentrated DNase/trypsin inhibition solution to the pelleted tissue.
3. Dissociate tissue by trituration (10–15 times) through a 9-in. Pasteur pipette. Trituration consists of taking tissue fragments up into the pipette and squirting them out against the side or bottom of the conical tube. Avoid foaming caused by aspiration of air.
4. Allow suspension to settle (2–5 min).
5. Carefully remove cloudy cell-containing supernatant using a Pasteur pipette and transfer to a graduated 15-ml conical polystyrene centrifuge tube (Corning, #25310).
6. Repeat steps 1 through 5 once again, combining cell suspensions.
7. After 5 min, remove any settled tissue clumps from the combined cell suspensions with a Pasteur pipette.
8. Carefully underlay cell suspension with 4% BSA solution using a 6-in., 18-gauge steel needle. There should be a distinct interface between the heavier/clear 4% BSA and the lighter/cloudy cell suspension. Use 1 ml of 4% BSA for each 1–2 ml of cell suspension.
9. Centrifuge at 50–100 g for 3–5 min. Adjust force and time within these ranges to minimize debris without appreciably reducing cell yield.
10. Completely remove supernatant from pelleted cells.

Note: Steps 8 and 9 (above) involving centrifugation of the cell suspension through a 4% BSA solution appear to be critical in preserving neuronal viability (see Ref. 8).

Counting and Sizing Perikarya

1. To each 100–200 μl of pelleted cells add 5 ml of culture medium (see below) and carefully resuspend using a 1-ml Eppendorf pipette by gentle trituration 2–5 times.
2. Make a 1 : 2000 dilution of the cell suspension by adding 10 μl to 20 ml of Isoton II (Curtin Matheson #375-212) in a glass scintillation vial, and mix gently by inverting.
3. Count and size cells using a Coulter Counter Model ZBI with a 140-μm orifice tube with the instrument settings shown in Table I.
4. Make all Coulter counter readings in triplicate and determine mean values. Cell size range and equivalent volumes are given in Table II. Where cell sizing is not important, one may quickly determine total cell number by calculating only T − A. In general, 1/dilution × 2 × T − A = total cells/ml suspension. The inverse of the dilution is multiplied by 2, since the instrument counts only 0.5 ml of solution. If an electronic cell counting device is not available, a hemocytometer may be used.

Preparation of Cell Cultures

Media

Highly enriched neuronal and glial cultures may be obtained from the same starting cell suspension simply by altering culture conditions as set out below. The conditions necessary for preparation and storage of stock solutions that are used in preparing both types of cell cultures are given in Table III.

TABLE I   Coulter Counter Instrument Setting[a]

Fraction designation	Threshold settings[b]		Amplification	Aperture current
	Lower	Upper		
T − A[c]	16	Infinity	1	$\frac{1}{8}$
A[d]	10	16	1	$\frac{1}{8}$
B	16	31	1	$\frac{1}{8}$
C	31	61	1	$\frac{1}{8}$
D	15	50	2	$\frac{1}{4}$
E	50	Infinity	2	$\frac{1}{4}$

[a] Model ZBI, 140-μm orifice tube.
[b] See Table II for equivalent cell diameters and volumes with these settings.
[c] Total cell number.
[d] Debris.

TABLE II   Cell Size Analysis of Coulter Counter
Settings for Isolated Perikarya

Fraction	Cell size range (diameter, μm)[a]	Equivalent volume (μm^3)
A (debris)	5.5– 6.5	80–130
B	6.5– 8.0	130–250
C	8.0–10.0	250–500
D	10.0–14.5	500–1600
E	≥14.5	≥1600

[a] Equivalent spherical diameter.

Neuronal Medium

The medium (100 ml final volume) for neuronal cultures is prepared by combining and sterile filtering (0.22-μm filter) stock solutions in the amounts shown in Table IV (9).

TABLE III   Cell Culture Media Stock Components

Stock solutions[a]	Aliquot size (ml)	Storage temperature (°C)
KCl[b] (2 M, 7.2 g/50 ml H$_2$O)	10	−20
Glutamine[b] (0.2 M, 2.92 g/100 ml H$_2$O)	10	−20
Glucose[b] (1.33 M, 12 g/50 ml H$_2$O)	10	−20
Gentamicin sulfate (Sigma Cat. #G-7507)	10	4
5-Fluorodeoxy-2′-uridine (FdU) (3.2 mM, 8 mg/10 ml H$_2$O; Sigma Cat. #F-0503)	10	−20
Chick embryo extract (CEE) (ultrafiltrate; Gibco Cat. #620-6460)	20	4
Fetal bovine serum (FCS) (heat inactivated at 56°C for 30 min and sterile filtered using 0.45-μm filter)	50	−20
Eagle's minimal essential medium (MEM) with Earle's basic salt solution	500	4
Poly(D-lysine) (PDL) (50 μg/ml H$_2$O; Sigma Cat. #P-1149)	50	4

[a] All aqueous solutions are prepared with Milli-Q water.
[b] May be stored until use without first sterilizing.

TABLE IV   Neuronal Culture Medium

Stock solution[a]	Amount (ml)	Final concentration
KCl[b]	1.00	20 mM (25 mM total)
Glutamine	1.00	1 mM
Glucose	2.50	33 mM
Gentamicin	0.12	180 μM
FdU[c]	0.025/ml medium	80 μM
CEE	2.50	2.5%
FCS	10.00	10.0%
MEM	83.00	83.0%

[a] For definition of abbreviations see Table III.
[b] Elevated K^+ is essential for optimal neuronal survival (9).
[c] FdU is added 16–24 hr after plating to inhibit mitosis of nonneuronal cells.

Glial Medium

The medium (100 ml final volume) for glial cultures is prepared by combining and sterile filtering (0.22-μm filter) stock components in the amounts shown in Table V.

Plating Cells for Culture

For both neuronal and glial cultures, poly(D-lysine)-coated substrates (glass coverslips or plastic culture wells) are prepared by pretreating for 30 min with PDL solution, removing excess, and air drying in a sterile hood. This treatment reduces cell aggregation during the culture period. The size and shape of the coverslips and/or culture wells may vary, depending on the nature of the experiment planned.

The density at which the cells are plated should be both a function of the type of cultured cells desired (neurons or glia) and their subsequent use. For most experiments, primary glial cultures are seeded at 1×10^5 cells/cm^2 and

TABLE V   Glial Culture Medium

Stock solution[a]	Amount (ml)	Final concentration
Glutamine	1.00	2 mM
Glucose	2.50	33 mM
Gentamicin	0.12	180 μM
FCS	10.00	10.0%
MEM	87.00	87.0%

[a] For definition of abbreviations see Table III.

used 17–20 days later, at which time the cells are confluent and devoid of neurons (10). Neuronal cultures can be plated at any dilution, but cell survival may be a limiting factor at densities of less than 10^4 cells/cm^2 (11). Maximal densities for neuronal cultures are approached above 1.5×10^6 cells/cm^2 (unpublished observation).

Regardless of the initial plating density, cells destined for PDL-coated glass coverslips are first resuspended in the appropriate culture medium at the desired final concentration. This suspension is then applied to only the coverslip surface, allowing the medium to "bead-up," thus preventing the cells from spreading and attaching to the surrounding culture well in which they will be housed. Cultures are placed in a CO_2 incubator (6% CO_2/94% air) at 37°C for 30–60 min to allow cell attachment. The cultures are then removed, additional medium is added to an appropriate final volume, and they are returned to the incubator. Normally, medium is changed every 3–4 days, except in cases where neuronal cultures are used within 10 DIV. In this latter case, excess medium is added initially so that subsequent changes over the 10-day period are unnecessary. This results in greater neuronal survival. In longer-term neuronal cultures, medium changes may be made every 4–6 days by replacing only one-third to one-half of the original medium. This is less traumatic to the cells than changing the entire medium volume, which can, on occasion, result in almost total neuronal cell death. This phenomenon, at least in part, is probably a function of the toxicity of the serum used. Thus, careful selection of a serum batch which maximally supports neuronal viability must be undertaken.

Although their use is not discussed here, many alternative substrates and growth media may be employed for the maintenance of neural cultures. In addition, even though the cell isolation procedure described here works as well for mice as it does rats, cultured mouse neurons appears to require horse serum-containing medium for best results (5).

Cultures of Brain Regions of Postnatal Rat

The versatility of the method described above is demonstrated here using 5-day-old rats. Cells were isolated and cultured from five regions of the brain (cerebellum, CB; olfactory bulb, OF; cerebral cortex, CCX; hippocampus, HC; hypothalamus, HY). Cultures were plated at 0.2×10^6 cells/cm^2 in PDL-coated 35-mm plastic culture dishes, and one medium change was made at 4 DIV.

Table VI shows that, while the whole tissue DNA content of each region varied from approximately 4.5 to 1.5 mg/g wet weight, the highest values

TABLE VI   Yield of Perikarya from Dissociated Brain Regions of 5-Day-Old Rats[a]

Region	Tissue DNA (mg/g wet wt)	Total cell yield ($\times 10^{-6}$)/g wet wt	Percentage of tissue DNA recovered in cell suspension
CB	4.55 ± 0.10 (10)	254.00 ± 13.11 (6)	38.61 ± 1.04
OF	4.54 ± 0.12 (9)	162.00 ± 15.00 (6)	26.10 ± 2.37
CCX	2.31 ± 0.10 (8)	73.60 ± 4.27 (4)	22.50 ± 1.18
HC	1.78 ± 0.07 (9)	53.40 ± 0.45 (5)	21.41 ± 3.04
HP	1.55 ± 0.07 (6)	7.08 ± 0.36 (6)	31.10 ± 3.34

[a] DNA content was determined by the method of Zamenhof *et al.* (15). Results expressed as mean ± SEM; values in parentheses represent the number of experiments performed. CB, Cerebellum; OF, olfactory bulb; CCX, cerebral cortex; HC, hippocampus; HP, hypothalamus.

were seen in the cerebellum and olfactory bulb, probably reflecting the higher cell packing densities known to occur in these areas. Cell yields varied according to region over an almost 100-fold range (e.g., cerebellum versus hypothalamus). However, DNA yields for each region did not differ by more than 2-fold, demonstrating that a large percentage of the total cellular material was recovered in the final cell suspension. This suggests that the cells isolated may be representative (as to proportion and type of cell) of the parent tissue, an observation which has been substantiated for the cerebellum (12, 13).

Figure 1 shows a Coulter Counter analysis of perikaryal sizes and amount of subcellular debris found in the cell preparations of each region. Note that the amount of debris (fraction A) varied with the region considered and ranged from a minimum value of 5% for cerebellum to a maximum of about 40% for cerebral cortex, hippocampus, and hypothalamus. Since the debris are subcellular, they do not interfere with culturing, but could potentially cause problems in studies of freshly prepared perikarya unless first removed. Thus, it is recommended that the centrifugation step involving sedimenting the cell suspension through 4% BSA be altered to minimize A without appreciably reducing T − A (see above). Fewer than 5% of the cells in all regions studied were larger than 14.5 μm in diameter (fraction E), the greatest number being in the range of 6.5–14.5 μm (fractions B–D). However, the proportion of cells within the range 6.5–14.5 μm varied for each region studied. Previous studies of cerebellum demonstrated that, based on the developmental state of the starting material, the identity of neuronal subclasses could be made based on perikaryal number, size, morphology, and immunohistochemical analysis before and after culturing (7, 13, 14).

After 1 and 7 days *in vitro,* the DNA content of the cultured cells from the five regions was compared to an equivalent number of freshly prepared cells (Table VII) (15). Plating efficiencies varied between 124% for olfactory bulb

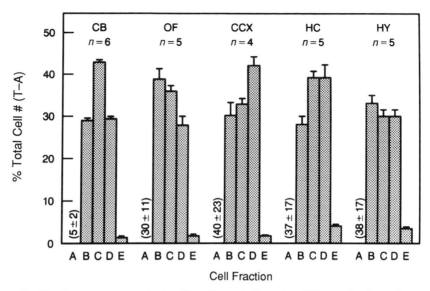

FIG. 1   Coulter counter analysis of perikaryal sizes for different brain regions of 5-day-old rats. See Table II for definition of cell size ranges (A–E) and equivalent volumes. CB, Cerebellum; OF, olfactory bulb; CCX, cerebral cortex; HC, hippocampus; HY, hypothalamus. Note that the values for the subcellular debris (A) are represented as a percentage of the number of ≤ 5.5-μm particles present in the total number of perikarya (T $-$ A $=$ B $+$ C $+$ D $+$ E) and not as a percentage of the total of all particle sizes counted (T $=$ A $+$ B $+$ C $+$ D $+$ E).

TABLE VII   Plating Efficiencies
of Cultures[a]

Region	1 DIV	7 DIV
CB	89.30 ± 0.50 (4)	34.07 ± 1.75 (3)
OF	123.60 ± 13.83 (3)	48.53 ± 4.05 (3)
CCX	48.67 ± 4.00 (3)	29.50 ± 2.65 (3)
HC	62.33 ± 2.94 (3)	22.27 ± 2.83 (3)
HP	63.48 ± 10.80 (3)	56.37 ± 9.93 (3)

[a] DNA content was determined by the method of Zamenhof *et al.* (15). Results were expressed as percentage (mean ± SEM) of DNA in plated cells remaining after 1 and 7 days *in vitro* (DIV). Values in parentheses represent the number of experiments performed. CB, Cerebellum; OF, olfactory bulb; CCX, cerebral cortex; HC, hippocampus; HP, hypothalamus.

and 49% for cerebral cortex at 1 DIV, and between 56% for hypothalamus and 22% for hippocampus at 7 DIV. For all regions studied, DNA content decreased between 1 and 7 DIV, ranging from less than 12% hypothalamus to about 65% for hippocampus, reflecting cell death during this interval.

Figure 2 shows the general morphological characteristics of cells in the cultures prepared from each of the five regions at 1 and 7 DIV. After 1 DIV most cell bodies had either flattened out or remained rounded with extended neurites. At 7 DIV neurite extension became more complex, and there emerged two distinct cell populations: those with rounded, well-defined cell bodies and extended neurites, and others of a flat shape upon which the neurite-extending cells appeared to sit. Indirect immunofluorescence studies

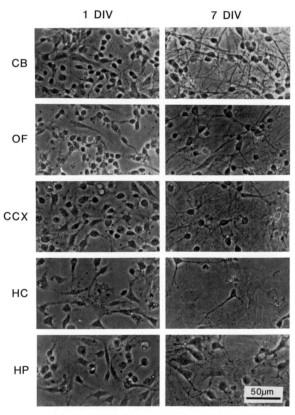

FIG. 2   Cell cultures of isolated perikarya obtained from different brain regions of 5-day-old rat maintained 1 (1 DIV column) and 7 (7 DIV column) days *in vitro*. CB, Cerebellum; OF, olfactory bulb; CCX, cerebral cortex; HC, hippocampus; HP, hypothalamus.

demonstrated that the flat cells stained with antibody against glial acidic fibrillary protein (astrocytes), and that the neurite-containing cells bound tetanus toxin (neurons) [not shown].

Uses of Perikarya and Cultured Cells

Numerous laboratories currently prepare and use cerebellar perikarya (16–20) and cultures (21–24) which have been obtained by methods based on the techniques outlined here. Our own applications include receptor binding studies (25) and regulation of neurotransmitter/neuromodulator release (26–30) from cerebellar neuronal and glial cultures prepared from 7- to 9-day-old rats (Fig. 3). In these experiments all cultures are grown on PDL-coated 22-mm^2 glass coverslips (#1$\frac{1}{2}$) in 35-mm 6-well culture dishes (Costar, Cambridge, MA; #3406, Mark II). Cells for glial cultures are plated at 10^5 cell/cm^2 in glial medium (see above) and used at 17–19 DIV with medium changes every 3–4 days. These cultures are composed almost entirely of type I astrocytes (>95%) plus a few percent oligodendrocytes, macrophages, fibroblasts, type II astrocytes, endothelial cells, and smooth muscle cells (10). Neuronal cultures are plated at 1.5×10^6 cells/cm^2 in neuronal medium (see above) and used at 7–9 DIV without a medium change. The cell composition is largely glutaminergic granule neurons (~90%), GABAergic inhibitory interneurons (stellate and basket cells, 5–7%, shown in Fig. 3e as GAD-positive cells), and a few percentage astrocytes (Fig. 3d, GFAP-positive cells). The high density at which these cells are initially seeded is thought to be responsible for survival of the smaller number of glial cells and greater number of inhibitory interneurons compared to similar cultures of lower cell density. Purkinje perikarya, while present in the cell suspension which is plated, do not survive in these cultures unless obtained from fetal or newborn animals (14, 31).

In studies designed to measure quantitatively substances released from these cells, culture-containing coverslips are mounted in a specially designed perfusion chamber. Here, they can be exposed to alterations in conditions (e.g., K^+ depolarization, drugs, and osmotic and temperature changes) and cellular responses involving the stimulus-coupled release of substances into the medium can be monitored in fractions of collected perfusates (Fig. 4). We have used this experimental setup to follow the release of putative neurotransmitter/neuromodulator substances from both neuronal and glial cerebellar cultures using HPLC as an analytical tool (10, 26–30). This perfusion system has also been used by other investigators to study adenosine receptors in cerebellar cultures (32), and dopamine neurotransmitter activity in cultures of whole brain (33).

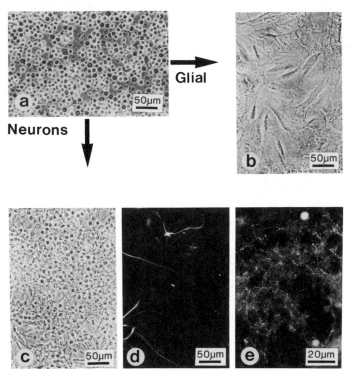

FIG. 3 Cerebellar cultures prepared from 8-day-old rat brain. (a) Freshly prepared cell suspension. (b) Astrocyte (type I) culture at 18 DIV. (c–e) Neuronal cultures at 8 DIV plated at 1.5×10^6 cells/cm^2. (c) Phase photomicrograph, (d) same field as in c showing immunofluorescent labeling of astrocytes using an antibody against glial acidic fibrillary protein (GFAP), and (e) different neuronal field at higher magnification showing immunofluorescent labeling with an antibody against glutamate decarboxylase (GAD) that depicts GABAergic inhibitory interneurons.

In summary, we have described here a simple and rapid method of isolating large numbers of viable perikarya from different regions of the developing CNS. These neural cells may be utilized for a variety of studies either as freshly prepared perikarya, or after being maintained in culture. Moreover, the cellular composition of these preparations may be altered using numerous approaches, such as unit gravity sedimentation (12, 13), immunotoxicity (16), neurotoxicity techniques (34), and by changing cell culture medium conditions. Taken together, the ability to isolate neural cell populations from many brain regions, in combination with the possibilities for manipulating the composition of these populations, represents a powerful tool for use in addressing current problems in neurobiology.

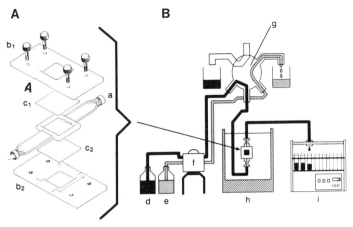

FIG. 4   Culture perfusion chamber and setup. (A) An exploded view of the culture perfusion chamber. Two culture-bearing 22-mm^2 glass coverslips (c_1 and c_2) are placed (facing inward) into recesses of two outer baseplates (b_1 and b_2), and the component carrying the perfusion solutions (a) is placed between the coverslips. All glass-on-metal joints are sealed with inert silicone grease, and the entire assembly is secured by four finger screws. (B) The perfusion setup. Standard and stimulating buffer solutions (d and e) are pumped (f) at 0.4 ml/min through a six-way valve (g) used to direct them in the appropriate sequence to the perfusion chamber, which is mounted vertically in a 37°C water bath (h). Samples of culture perfusates (1 ml) are then obtained for analysis using a fraction collector (i).

Acknowledgments

The author would like to thank Kathleen Tear and Drs. Roderick Pigott, Brian Pearce, Richard Beale, and A. J. Allen, for their substantial contributions to this work. Paul Reimann helped with the photographs, and Marilynn Kirkpatrick with manuscript preparation. Antibodies to GFAP and GAD were kindly provided by Drs. R. Pruss and I. Kopin, respectively. This work was supported in part by NIH grant NS 20632.

References

1. A. A. Moscona, *J. Cell. Comp. Physiol.* **60,** 65 (1962).
2. M. S. Steinberg, *Science* **141,** 401 (1963).
3. D. S. Barclay, L. L. Rakic, J. K. Chaffee, and D. L. Wong, *J. Cell. Physiol.* **81,** 271 (1973).
4. R. S. Lasher and I. S. Zagon, *Brain Res.* **311,** 119 (1984).

5. A. Messer, *Brain Res.* **130,** 1 (1977).
6. G. P. Wilkin, R. Balázs, J. E. Wilson, J. Cohen, and G. R. Dutton, *Brain Res.* **115,** 181 (1976).
7. G. R. Dutton, D. N. Currie, and K. Tear, *J. Neurosci. Methods* **3,** 421 (1981).
8. B. D. Boss, I. Gozes, and W. M. Cowan, *Dev. Brain Res.* **36,** 199 (1987).
9. B. S. Scott and K. C. Fisher, *Exp. Neurol.* **27,** 16 (1970).
10. R. A. Philibert, K. L. Rogers, A. J. Allen, and G. R. Dutton, *J. Neurochem.* **51,** 122 (1988).
11. G. A. Banker and W. M. Cowan, *Brain Res.* **126,** 397 (1977).
12. J. Cohen, R. Balázs, F. Hajós, D. N. Currie, and G. R. Dutton, *Brain Res.* **148,** 313 (1978).
13. J. Garthwaite and R. Balázs, *Adv. Cell. Neurobiol.* **2,** 461 (1981).
14. K. L. Fields, D. N. Currie, and G. R. Dutton, *J. Neurosci.* **2,** 663 (1982).
15. S. Zamenhof, H. Bursztyn, K. Rich, and P. J. Zamenhof, *J. Neurochem.* **11,** 505 (1964).
16. A. L. Gard, A. E. Narrington, and S. E. Pfeiffer, *J. Neurosci. Res.* **20,** 46 (1988).
17. J. Garthwaite and G. Garthwaite, *J. Neurochem.* **48,** 29 (1987).
18. J. Garthwaite, *Br. J. Pharmacol.* **85,** 297 (1985).
19. B. Belhage, G. H. Hausen, A. Schousboe, and E. Meier, *Int. J. Dev. Neurosci.* **6,** 125 (1988).
20. I. Holopainen and P. Kontro, *Neurochem. Int.* **12,** 155 (1988).
21. J. Albrecht, B. Pearce, and S. Murphy, *Eur. J. Pharmacol.* **125,** 463 (1986).
22. J. T. Wolblewski, F. Nicoletti, and E. Costa, *Neuropharmacology* **24,** 919 (1985).
23. V. Gallo, M. T. Ciotti, A. Coletti, F. Aloisi, and G. Levi, *Proc. Natl. Acad. Sci. U.S.A.* **79,** 7919 (1982).
24. R. D. Burgoyne, I. A. Pearce, and M. Cambray-Deakin, *Neurosci. Lett.* **91,** 47 (1988).
25. A. J. Allen and G. R. Dutton, *J. Neurosci. Res.,* in press.
26. K. L. Rogers, R. A. Philibert, A. J. Allen, J. Molitor, E. J. Wilson, and G. R. Dutton, *J. Neurosci. Methods* **22,** 173 (1987).
27. R. A. Philibert and G. R. Dutton, *Neurosci. Lett.* **95,** 323 (1988).
28. R. A. Philibert, K. L. Rogers, and G. R. Dutton, *Neurochem. Res.* **14,** 43 (1989).
29. R. A. Philibert, K. L. Rogers, and G. R. Dutton, *J. Neurosci. Res.* **22,** 167 (1989).
30. R. A. Philibert and G. R. Dutton, *Neurosci. Lett.* **102,** 97 (1989).
31. A. Weber and M. Schachner, *Brain Res.* **311,** 119 (1984).
32. A. C. Dolphin and S. A. Prestwich, *Nature (London)* **336,** 148 (1985).
33. O. Barochovsky and H. F. Bradford, *J. Neurochem.* **48,** 787 (1987).
34. J. Drejer and A. Schousboe, *Neurochem. Res.* **14,** 751 (1989).

[8] Cerebral Cortical Neurons in Primary Culture and Application to Neuropharmacological Studies

Kinya Kuriyama and Seitaro Ohkuma

Introduction

In studies to elucidate the function of the central nervous system (CNS), various cerebral preparations, such as slice, homogenate, and subcellular fractions, have been used. With the exception of cultured cell lines, however, these materials are known to be a mixture of several types of cells: neurons, glias (e.g., astrocytes and oligodendroglias), and endothelial cells constituting intracerebral blood vessels. These facts strongly suggest that neuron-specific changes and/or phenomena may be masked by the use of such a mixture of different cell types. In addition, several neurochemical reports have indicated that the proportion of neurons occupying cerebral tissues is approximately 40% (1), and 60–80% of the protein determined in brain homogenates originates from glial cells (2). These evidences lead to the conclusion that the use of a pure population of neurons rather than mixed cell preparations is more appropriate for analyzing the functional mechanism of neurons.

Two types of neuronal preparations have been used in neurochemical research. One is the cell line, such as neuroblastoma with tumor origin, and the other is primary cultured neurons. In this article, the procedures used to prepare cerebral cortical neurons in primary culture, neurochemical characteristics of these neurons during *in vitro* growth, and their application to pharmacological and/or neurochemical studies are described.

Dissociation and Culture of Neurons

The neopallium obtained from the 15-day-old fetus of the ddy strain mouse is dissected free of meninges and minced with scissors in Ca^{2+}-free Puck's solution following rinsing with the same solution. Then, the minced neopallium is digested by 0.1% (w/v) acetylated trypsin (Sigma Chemical Co., St. Louis, MO) dissolved in Ca^{2+}-free Puck's solution at 37°C for 5 min under a stream of 95% O_2–5% CO_2. After the trypsin treatment, ice-cold modified

Methods in Neurosciences, Volume 2

Eagle's minimum essential medium [MEM containing 2-fold concentration of amino acids, 4-fold concentration of vitamins, 30 mM glucose, 10 mM N-tris(hydroxymethyl)methyl-2-aminoethanesulfonic acid (TES), 10 mM N-2-hydroxyethylpiperazine-N'-2-ethanesulfonic acid (HEPES), carbenicillin (0.1 mg/ml), and streptomycin (0.1 mg/ml)] supplemented with 20% (v/v) horse serum (3, 4) is added for terminating trypsin digestion, and then the tissues are triturated using a Pasteur pipette. The cell suspension thus obtained is centrifuged (900 g, 4°C, 2 min) and the supernatant discarded. The pellet obtained is resuspended in modified MEM without serum and pipetted, followed by filtration through a nylon sieve (mesh size: 60 μm). At this step, the cell number is adjusted to approximately 3×10^6 cells/1 ml of modified MEM. Three milliliters of the cell suspension is then added to a culture dish precoated with poly(L-lysine) (5 μg/1 ml of distilled water) at 37°C for 12–24 hr and incubated at 37°C for 15 min under humidified 95% air–5% CO_2. During this period, living cells are attached to the poly(L-lysine)-coated surface. Following the first incubation, the culture medium is exchanged with 15% fetal calf serum dissolved in modified MEM and incubation continues under the same conditions described above. Three days after the first exchange of medium, cells are exposed to 20 μM cytosine arabinoside dissolved in modified MEM containing 15% horse serum for 24 hr to prevent the proliferation of nonneuronal cells. On the fourth day after the seeding, medium is changed to 15% horse serum in modified MEM without cytosine arabinoside. Culture medium is then changed every 4 days to freshly prepared modified MEM supplemented with 15% horse serum.

For the pretreatment of dishes, poly(D-lysine) and poly(L-ornithine) can also be used instead of poly(L-lysine) and their effect in anchoring cells to the surface of dishes is found to be similar to that of poly(L-lysine), as previously reported (5). Several investigators have also employed fluorodeoxyuridine instead of cytosine arabinoside (6, 7) to prevent the proliferation of nonneuronal cells.

Concerning cell viability, it was found that more than 95% of the cells dissociated by the above procedures had an ability to exclude Trypan blue dye. Contamination of nonneuronal cells, especially astrocytes, was found to be less than 5% of the total cells attached to a culture dish even 14 days after the seeding. The contamination of astrocytes was estimated immunohistochemically using antiglial fibrillary acidic protein (GFAP), a specific marker of astrocytes (3, 8).

Morphological Characteristics of Cultured Neurons

Phase-contrast microscopy (Nikon Diaphoto-TMD) shows that immediately after the isolation cells are well dissociated and round in shape without any neuronal processes. On the first day in culture, the aggregation of cells and the extrusion of fine neuronal processes are observed. The network of fine neuronal processes becomes apparent on the third day after planting, and "bundles" of neuronal processes connected with adjacent cell aggregates are observed. Neuronal processes then become more complex (Fig. 1A) and such morphological features are maintained until the twenty-first day. Several investigators also reported that similar morphological changes in cultured neurons occurred during growth *in vitro* (5, 9, 10).

Scanning electron micrographic observations clearly reveal that neuronal processes extruded from neurons observed by phase-contrast microscopy indeed originate from neuronal cell bodies (3, 11), as reported by other investigators (12). Moreover, an increase in the size of the neuron is also observed (3).

It is well known that one of the most important morphological characteristics of the neuron is the formation of synapses. Transmission electron micrographs reveal that primary cultured neurons used in this study have synaptic formations with asymmetrical thickening of synaptic membrane and vesicle-filled boutons during the seventh to tenth days in culture (Fig. 1B), although these synaptic formations are scarcely found on the third day after seeding. These characteristics of the synaptic formation are in good agreement with those in other reports (13–15).

Biochemical and Pharmacological Characteristics of Primary Cultured Neurons during *in Vitro* Growth

One of the important functions of the neuron is the synthesis of neurotransmitters. Neurons dissociated from the cerebral cortex have a capacity to biosynthesize γ-aminobutyric acid (GABA) and acetylcholine (16). Therefore, we examined the developmental changes in the metabolism of these two neurotransmitters during neuronal growth on poly(L-lysine)-coated surfaces.

Figure 2A shows the developmental changes in GABA content and activity of L-glutamate decarboxylase (GAD), the enzyme biosynthesizing GABA from L-glutamic acid. GABA content and GAD activity are measured according to the methods previously described (17, 18). The content of GABA is found to increase during neuronal cell growth *in vitro* in parallel with the increase in GAD activity (11), which is in agreement with other reports (2, 19–21). Moreover, the immunoreactivity to GAD is localized in neural processes as well as in neural cell bodies, and this immunoreactivity is intensified with the increase in number of days of culture (11). [The anti-GAD antibody used was a gift from Dr. J.-Y. Wu (Pennsylvania State University, Hershey Medical Center, Hershey, PA).]

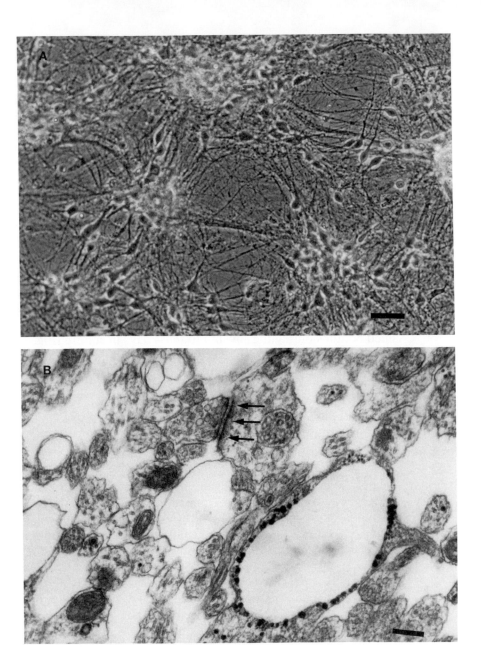

Fig. 1   (A) Phase-contrast micrograph of primary cultured neurons obtained from the neopallium of a 15-day-old fetus at 14 days after inoculation. Neurons aggregate with each other and have fine networks of neuronal processes. Bar, 100 μm. (B) Transmission electron micrograph of primary cultured neurons of a 10-day-old fetus in culture. Typical synaptic formation with asymmetrical thickening of the membrane and vesicle-filled boutons are observed. Arrows show synapse. Bar, 0.2 μm.

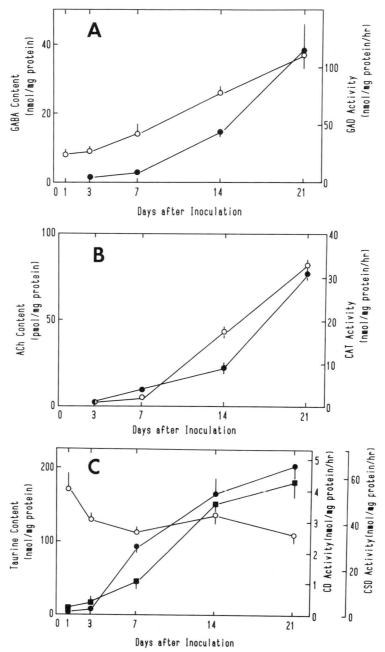

Fig. 2 Developmental changes in the metabolism of γ-aminobutyric acid, acetylcholine, and taurine in primary cultured neurons. (A) γ-Aminobutyric acid (GABA) content (○) and L-glutamate decarboxylase (GAD) activity (●), (B) acetylcholine (ACh) content (○) and choline acetyltransferase (CAT) activity (●), (C) taurine content (○) and activities of cysteine-sulfinate decarboxylase (CSD) (■) and cysteine dioxygenase (CD) (●).

These neurons also possess the capacity to release preloaded [³H]GABA following exposure to 30 mM KCl (11). In addition, the developmental increases in binding sites for [³H]muscimol with high and low affinities and for [³H]flunitrazepam, i.e., radiolabeled ligands specifically bound to GABA$_A$ receptor and the benzodiazepine receptor of the central type, respectively, in particulate fractions obtained from cultured neurons, are observed with neuronal development *in vitro* (Table I) (11). The bindings of [³H]muscimol and [³H]flunitrazepam to the particulate fraction obtained from primary cultured neurons are dose-dependently inhibited by bicuculline (an antagonist for GABA$_A$ receptor) and clonazepam (an agonist for the central type of benzodiazepine receptor), respectively. Similar developmental changes in GABA$_A$ and benzodiazepine receptors in primary cultured neurons have also been reported (22, 23). Furthermore, it has also been observed that [³H]flunitrazepam binding is enhanced in the presence of GABA, even in neurons cultured for 7 days (Fig. 3), which clearly indicates that the functional interaction between these two receptors is present in primary cultured neurons as shown *in vitro* (24), and that such a functional coupling attains its plateau from a relatively early stage of neuronal development.

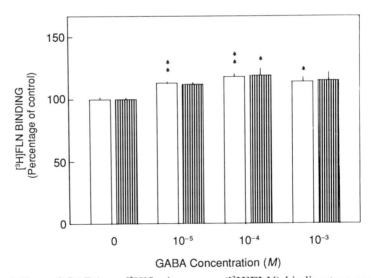

FIG. 3   Effect of GABA on [³H]flunitrazepam ([³H]FLN) binding to a particulate fraction obtained from primary cultured neurons. The [³H]FLN concentration used was 1 nM. The enhancement of [³H]FLN binding by GABA is observed in 7-day-old cultures of neurons. The control values for [³H]FLN binding to particulate fractions obtained from neurons that have been cultured for 7 (□) and 14 (▥) days in the absence of GABA were 326.6 ± 7.8 and 411.7 ± 26.3 fmol/mg protein, respectively. *$p < 0.05$, **$p < 0.02$, compared with each control.

TABLE I Developmental Changes in Kinetic Parameters for [³H]Muscimol, [³H]Flunitrazepam ([³H]FNL), and [³H]Quinuclidinyl Benzilate ([³H]QNB) Bindings[a]

| | [³H]Muscimol | | | | [³H]FLN | | [³H]QNB | |
| | High affinity | | Low affinity | | | | | |
Age	K_d (nM)	B_{max} (fmol/ mg protein)	K_d (nM)	B_{max} (fmol/ mg protein)	K_d (nM)	B_{max} (fmol/ mg protein)	K_d (nM)	B_{max} (fmol/ mg protein)
7 days old	41.7 ± 5.5	178 ± 22	900.2 ± 31.6	652 ± 38	1.27 ± 0.27	970 ± 91	0.25 ± 0.04	137 ± 20
14 days old	42.8 ± 3.5	278 ± 13[b]	1154.8 ± 126.7	1178 ± 76[c]	1.05 ± 0.01	1240 ± 80	0.25 ± 0.03	335 ± 24[c]

[a] Binding to particulate fraction obtained from primary cultured neurons. Each value represents the mean ± SEM obtained from three to seven separate experiments.
[b] $p < 0.01$.
[c] $p < 0.001$.

Acetylcholine (ACh), which is measured by HPLC equipped with immobilized enzyme reactor (25), is also detected in these cultured neurons on the seventh day after seeding, and it shows a gradual increase with the time of incubation (Fig. 2B). The developmental pattern of the activity of choline acetyltransferase (CAT), the enzyme synthesizing ACh and measured by the method of Fonnum (26), is also found to be well correlated with that of ACh content (Fig. 2B) (27). A similar progressive increase in CAT activity has also been reported by Thomas (28).

In the particulate fraction obtained from primary cultured neurons used in this study, the presence of a high-affinity binding site for [^{3}H]quinuclidinyl benzilate ([^{3}H]QNB), a ligand for muscarinic cholinergic receptor, is also found. Furthermore, the number (B_{max} value) of binding sites is found to increase with neuronal growth *in vitro* without altering the affinity (K_d value) (Table I) (27, 29). This binding of [^{3}H]QNB is also inhibited by atropine in a dose-dependent manner.

Taurine (2-aminoethanesulfonic acid) is one of the sulfur-containing amino acids distributed abundantly in the manmmalian brain and it is assumed to play a role as a neuromodulator rather than as a neurotransmitter (30). This amino acid shows a peculiar developmental pattern *in vivo* as well as in primary cultured neurons *in vitro*. Namely, the content of taurine decreases gradually during brain development, especially at the postnatal stage (31), in spite of the increase in activity of the enzymes involved in taurine biosynthesis, such as sulfinoalanine decarboxylase [cysteine sulfinate decarboxylase (CSD)] (32) and cysteine dioxygenase (CD) (33). Similarly, the content of taurine measured by HPLC (17) indeed shows a decrease at the early stage of neuronal culture (Fig. 2C), in addition to the concomitant decreases in cysteinesulfinic acid and cysteic acid (34), which are intermediary metabolites of taurine biosynthesis from cysteine. Moreover, immunohistochemical studies using anti-taurine antibody (4, 35) clearly show that taurine is localized in neuronal cell bodies as well as in neuronal processes and that these immunoreactivities are gradually decreased with neuronal growth *in vitro* (4). In contrast, the activities of CSD and CD show progressive elevations during neuronal development (Fig. 2C). These results suggest that the decrease of taurine observed in developing brain *in vivo* may be due to the decline of this amino acid in neuronal cells.

In the CNS, it is well known that the taurine content is regulated not only by its biosynthesis but also by a sodium- and energy-dependent carrier-mediated transport mechanism. Primary cultured neurons used in this study also possess such a carrier-mediated transport system for taurine.

The uptake of [^{3}H]taurine in primary cultured neurons is significantly suppressed by the withdrawal of Na$^+$ from the incubation medium as well as the addition of metabolic inhibitors, such as 2,4-dinitrophenol and monoiodoacetate. In addition, [³H]taurine uptake is inhibited competitively by β-alanine, guanidinoethane sulfonate, and hypotaurine (36), which are known to be transported by the β-amino acid carrier system (37).

Taking these data together, it seems highly likely that cerebral cortical neurons in primary culture possess neurotransmitter-synthesizing, as well as receptor systems similar to those found in the brain *in vivo* of age-matched animals.

Application of Primary Cultured Neurons to Pharmacological Studies

The effects of long-term (5 days) exposures to agonists and antagonists for muscarinic receptors of primary cultured neurons on [³H]QNB binding and intracellular biosignaling systems coupled with muscarinic receptors were examined as a possible model for pharmacological application of these cells.

Muscarinic agonists and antagonists were added to culture medium between the eighth and thirteenth days of culture. Neurons were then washed three times with Krebs–Ringer bicarbonate buffer (pH 7.4) following the removal of the culture medium by aspiration. For the binding assay of [³H]QNB, the washed cells are homogenized with a Polytron homogenizer and centrifuged at 25,000 g for 20 min at 4°C. The pellet obtained is then resuspended in sodium potassium phosphate buffer (pH 7.4) according to the method previously described (38), followed by centrifugation. After freezing and thawing, the pellet is washed twice by centrifugation as described above, and the particulate fraction obtained is used for binding assays.

When cells are exposed to 10^{-6} M carbachol and 10^{-8} M atropine (at these concentrations, less than 5% of the total number of cells exposed to these drugs are stained by Trypan blue dye) for 1, 3, and 5 days, [³H]QNB binding attains a plateau after exposure to carbachol and atropine for 3 days and a similar magnitude of [³H]QNB binding is found on the fifth day after exposure (Fig. 4). Scatchard analysis shows that the B_{max} value of [³H]QNB binding decreases without changing the K_d value following the exposures to carbachol for 5 days (Table II). The change in muscarinic receptor binding induced by agonist exposure is similar to that reported previously in both *in vivo* (39) and *in vitro* (40, 41) studies. In contrast, the incubation of cells with 10^{-8} M atropine for 5 days induces the elevation of [³H]QNB binding due to the increases in both K_d and B_{max} values (Table II), which is in good agreement with the data previously described (42–44). These results clearly indicate that muscarinic receptors in the primary cultured neurons used in this study are down- and up-regulated following long-term exposures to agonists and antagonists, respectively, as observed *in vivo* (39, 42–44).

One of the well-known intracellular biosignaling systems coupled with

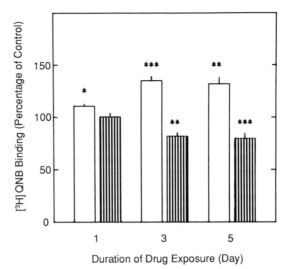

FIG. 4   Time course of changes in [³H]quinuclidinyl benzilate ([³H]QNB) binding to particulate fractions obtained from primary cultured neurons exposed to 10^{-6} M carbachol (▥) and 10^{-8} M (□) atropine for 1 to 5 days. *$p < 0.05$, **$p < 0.01$, ***$p < 0.001$, compared to the values for neurons that were not exposed to carbachol and atropine.

TABLE II   Effect of Long-Term (5 Days) Exposure to Carbachol and Atropine on [³H]Quinuclidinyl Benzilate ([³H]QNB) Binding[a]

| | [³H]QNB binding | |
Drug treatment	K_d (nM)	B_{max} (fmol/mg protein)
None	0.117 ± 0.014	395 ± 7
Carbachol (10^{-6} M)	0.120 ± 0.018	280 ± 7[b]
Atropine (10^{-8} M)	0.182 ± 0.018[c]	577 ± 23[b]

[a] Binding to particulate fraction obtained from primary cultured neurons. Each value represents the mean ± SEM obtained from 6 to 7 separate experiments.
[b] $p < 0.001$, compared with control (nontreated) value.
[c] $p < 0.05$, compared with control (nontreated) value.

muscarinic receptors is phosphoinositide (PI) turnover, which leads to the production of diacylglycerol and inositol 1,4,5-trisphosphate. The former product is known to activate protein kinase C, while the latter triggers the mobilization of Ca^{2+} from intracellular stores (45, 46).

Following the incubation of neurons with 1 μCi [^{3}H]inositol at 37°C for 18 hr, the cells are washed three times with ice-cold Krebs–Ringer bicarbonate buffer (KRB, pH 7.4) and then incubated with 3 ml of KRB containing 10 mM LiCl at 37°C for 2 hr. After the preincubation, carbachol (3 × 10^{-4} M) is added to initiate the reaction. The reaction is terminated by the aspiration of medium and addition of methanol (3.6 ml) to a dish. Neurons are scrapped off and combined with the aspirated KRB buffer and then homogenized under sonication. Then 3.6 ml of chloroform and 1.0 ml of distilled water are added, followed by mixing and centrifugation. An aliquot of the aqueous phase is then subjected to ion-exchange column chromatography to separate [^{3}H]inositol phosphates formed during the incubation (47).

Stimulatory effects of several muscarinic agonists (3 × 10^{-4} M) on PI turnover in primary cultured neurons are examined. Carbachol and methacholine significantly enhance PI turnover, while little stimulation is observed due to bethanechol, oxotremorine, and pilocarpine. Similar characteristics of the stimulatory effect of various muscarinic agonists are also reported for rat brain (48) and astrocytoma (49). These results indicate that primary cultured neurons possess not only the mechanism to hydrolyze phosphoinositides, but also the responsiveness of the PI turnover system to two types of muscarinic agonists, a full agonist and partial agonist, respectively, as shown in the brain *in vivo*.

Following the exposure of primary cultured neurons to carbachol for 5 days, the stimulatory effect of 3 × 10^{-4} M carbachol on the accumulation of [^{3}H]inositol phosphates is reduced to 70% of the control value (without the exposure to carbachol for 5 days) (Fig. 5). The extent of the reduction of carbachol-induced stimulation of PI turnover is in good agreement with that of the muscarinic receptor number estimated by [^{3}H]QNB binding. On the other hand, the [^{3}H]inositol phosphate accumulation induced by 3 × 10^{-4} M carbachol is also found to be decreased as compared with that in nontreated neurons following the exposure of primary cultured neurons to 10^{-8} M atropine for 5 days, despite the significant increase in [^{3}H]QNB binding as compared with that in nontreated neurons (Fig. 4). Although exact mechanisms underlying such a discrepancy between the increase in the number of muscarinic receptors and the attenuation of PI response in atropine-treated neurons are obscure at present, it may indicate the occurrence of functional alterations in the coupling mechanism between the receptor and PI generation systems following a long-term exposure to atropine. Experiments to clarify these points are underway in our laboratory.

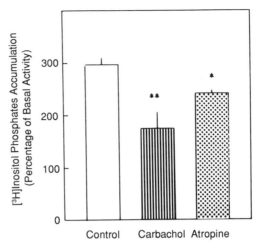

FIG. 5   Effect of carbachol ($3 \times 10^{-4} M$) on phosphoinositide turnover in primary cultured neurons following long-term (5 days) exposures to $10^{-6} M$ carbachol and $10^{-8} M$ atropine. Following the exposure to $10^{-6} M$ carbachol (▥) or $10^{-8} M$ atropine (▨), neurons preincubated with 1 μCi [^{3}H]inositol in modified Eagle's minimum essential medium containing 15% horse serum were washed three times with ice-cold Krebs–Ringer bicarbonate buffer (KRB, pH 7.4) and then incubated for 2 hr with KRB containing 10 mM LiCl. Neurons were then incubated in the presence of $3 \times 10^{-4} M$ carbachol for 45 min. For the assay of [^{3}H]inositol phosphates formed, see the text. The value for [^{3}H]inositol phosphates formed in the absence of $3 \times 10^{-4} M$ carbachol is 5343 $\pm$ 589 dpm/mg protein. *$p < 0.05$, **$p < 0.02$, compared with the value for neurons not exposed to drugs.

Conclusion

Primary cultured neurons dissociated from the neopallium of a 15-day-old mouse fetus by a trypsin treatment (described in the section Dissociation and Culture of Neurons in this chapter) possess typical morphological characteristics, such as synaptic formation, as well as metabolic systems for various neurotransmitters, such as GABA and acetylcholine. This population of neurons also has the binding sites for [^{3}H]muscimol, [^{3}H]flunitrazepam, and [^{3}H]QNB. Moreover, it is found that these receptors are functionally coupled with intracellular biosignaling systems. GABA$_A$ receptor interacts with the benzodiazepine receptor, while muscarinic receptor couples with the PI turnover system. These results indicate that neurons in primary culture have functional as well as morphological characteristics similar to those found in the brain *in vivo*.

It is also noteworthy that muscarinic receptors in primary cultured neurons have a capacity to be "up-" and "down"-regulated following long-term exposures to their agonists and antagonists, respectively. Therefore, these neurons are also assumed to be a suitable experimental system for investigating pharmacological characteristics of neurotransmitter receptors including the occurrence of up- and down-regulations at synapses.

Acknowledgment

This work was supported, in part, by a research grant from the Ministry of Education, Science and Culture, Japan.

References

1. A. Pope, in "Dynamic Properties of Glial Cells" (E. Schoffeniels, G. Frank, L. Hertz, and D. B. Tower, eds.), p. 13. Pergamon, Oxford, 1978.
2. K. Hauser, V. J. Balcar, and R. Bernasconi, *Brain Res. Bull.* **5** (Suppl. 2), 37 (1980).
3. A. C. H. Yu, T. E. Fisher, E. Hertz, J. T. Tildon, A. Schousboe, and L. Hertz, *J. Neurosci.* **11**, 351 (1984).
4. S. Ohkuma, S. Tomono, Y. Tanaka, K. Kuriyama, and T. Mukainaka, *Int. J. Dev. Neurosci.* **4**, 383 (1986).
5. E. Yavin and Z. Yavin, *J. Cell Biol.* **62**, 540 (1974).
6. M. A. Dichter, *Brain Res.* **149**, 279 (1978).
7. E. Goodfrey, P. Nelson, B. Schrier, A. Breuer, and B. Ranson, *Brain Res.* **90**, 1 (1975).
8. K. Kuriyama and S. Ohkuma, in "Model Systems of Development and Aging of the Nervous System" (A. Vernadakis, ed.), p. 43. Nijhoff, The Hague, 1987.
9. P. C. Letourneau, *Dev. Biol.* **44**, 77 (1975).
10. G. A. M. Breen and J. de Vellis, *Dev. Biol.* **41**, 255 (1974).
11. K. Kuriyama, S. Tomono, M. Kishi, T. Mukainaka, and S. Ohkuma, *Brain Res.* **416**, 7 (1987).
12. A. Messer, *Neuroscience (Oxford)* **6**, 2677 (1981).
13. Z. Yavin and E. Yavin, *Exp. Brain Res.* **29**, 137 (1977).
14. J. C. Louis, B. Pettman, J. Courageot, J. F. Rumigny, P. Mandel, and M. Sensenbrenner, *Exp. Brain Res.* **42**, 63 (1981).
15. K. F. Swaiman, E. A. Neale, S. C. Fitzgerald, and P. G. Nelson, *Dev. Brain Res.* **3**, 361 (1982).
16. W. F. Thomas, *Life Sci.* **38**, 297 (1986).
17. S. Ida and K. Kuriyama, *Anal. Biochem.* **130**, 95 (1983).
18. H. Kimura and K. Kuriyama, *Jpn. J. Pharmacol.* **25**, 189 (1975).
19. S. R. Snodgrass, W. F. White, B. Biales, and M. Dichter, *Brain Res.* **190**, 123 (1980).

20. A. C. H. Yu, E. Hertz, and L. Hertz, *J. Neurochem.* **42,** 951 (1984).
21. O. M. Larsson, J. Drejer, E. Kvamme, G. Svenneby, L. Hertz, and A. Schousboe, *Int. J. Dev. Neurosci.* **3,** 177 (1985).
22. J. T. Coyle and S. J. Enna, *Brain Res.* **111,** 119 (1976).
23. K. D. McCarthy and T. K. Harden, *J. Pharmacol. Exp. Ther.* **216,** 183 (1981).
24. R. W. Olsen, *J. Neurochem.* **37,** 1 (1981).
25. K. Fujimori, *J. Chromatogr.* **414,** 167 (1987).
26. F. Fonnum, *J. Neurochem.* **24,** 407 (1975).
27. S. Ohkuma, F.-H. Ma, S. Tomono, M. Kishi, and K. Kuriyama, *Jpn. J. Pharmacol.* **43** (Suppl.), 148P (1987).
28. W. E. Thomas, *Brain Res.* **332,** 79 (1985).
29. Y. Dudai and E. Yavin, *Brain Res.* **155,** 368 (1978).
30. K. Kuriyama, *Fed. Proc., Fed. Am. Soc. Exp. Biol.* **39,** 2680 (1980).
31. H. C. Agrawal, J. M. Davis, and W. A. Himwich, *J. Neurochem.* **13,** 607 (1966).
32. D. K. Rassin and G. E. Gaull, *J. Neurochem.* **24,** 969 (1975).
33. C. H. Misra and J. W. Olney, *Brain Res.* **97,** 117 (1975).
34. K. Kuriyama and S. Ohkuma, *Curr. Top. Nutr. Dis.* **16,** 255 (1987).
35. S. Ida, K. Kuriyama, Y. Tomida, and H. Kimura, *J. Neurosci. Res.* **18,** 626 (1987).
36. M. Kishi, S. Ohkuma, M. Kimori, and K. Kuriyama, *Biochim. Biophys. Acta* **939,** 615 (1988).
37. S. Ohkuma, J. Tamura, K. Kuriyama, and T. Mukainaka, *Cell Biochem. Funct.* **2,** 71 (1984).
38. H. I. Yamamura and S. H. Snyder, *Proc. Natl. Acad. Sci. U.S.A.* **71,** 1725 (1974).
39. J. Ben-Barak, H. Gazit, I. Silman, and Y. Dudai, *Eur. J. Pharmacol.* **74,** 73 (1981).
40. W. L. Klein, N. Nathanson, and M. Nirenberg, *Biochem. Biophys. Res. Commun.* **90,** 506 (1979).
41. J. E. Taylor, E. El-Fakahany, and E. Richelson, *Life Sci.* **25,** 2181 (1979).
42. B. C. Wise, M. Shoji, and J. F. Kuo, *Biochem. Biophys. Res. Commun.* **92,** 1136 (1980).
43. A. Westlind, M. Grynfarb, B. Hedlund, T. Bartai, and K. Fuxe, *Brain Res.* **225,** 131 (1981).
44. M. McKinney and J. T. Coyle, *J. Neurosci.* **2,** 97 (1982).
45. M. J. Berridge and R. F. Irvine, *Nature (London)* **312,** 315 (1984).
46. Y. Nishizuka, *Science* **233,** 305 (1986).
47. M. J. Berridge, R. M. C. Dawson, C. P. Heslop, and R. F. Irvine, *Biochem. J.* **212,** 473 (1983).
48. R. A. Gonzales and F. T. Crews, *J. Neurosci.* **4,** 3120 (1984).
49. M. McKinney, S. Stenstrom, and E. Richelson, *Mol. Pharmacol.* **27,** 223 (1985).

Section II

Purification of Cell Types

[9] Preparation of Highly Purified Populations of Neurons, Astrocytes, and Oligodendrocytes

Russell P. Saneto

Since the initial neural cell culture system developed by Harrison (1), the techniques of cell culture have developed to the point where homogeneous populations of the individual central nervous system (CNS) cell types can be grown in long-term culture. Although the culture methodologies of bulk isolation, cell lines of neural origin, explant, reaggregation, and mixed dissociated cell cultures can be used to examine a particular CNS phenomenon, each procedure has disadvantages for obtaining qualitative and quantitative data on cellular structure and function. To circumvent cellular heterogeneity and phenotypic alterations by transformation, culture systems have been developed where long-term growth of nearly homogeneous populations of CNS cells types is possible. This chapter describes the procedures used in our laboratory for culturing isolated, purified populations of astrocytes, oligodendrocytes, and neurons from the same brain region.

Cell Culture Equipment

Although not always possible, a separate and completely enclosed room should be used for primary culture initiation. This avoids any unnecessary movement around the dissection area and nonspecific laboratory use that might introduce possible contamination. The selection of a tissue culture hood is important for production of quality cultures. The intensity and duration of the tissue dissection procedures make comfort and visibility a high priority, if not a necessity. A large work area that is flat and accessible for pipetting and culture vessel manipulations is also a desirable feature. Cell growth requires constant temperature, humidity, and atmosphere which mimic *in vivo* conditions. A water-jacketed, CO_2 incubator permits such regulation and maintenance of the growth environment. Cell viability requires the correct pH balance of the surrounding growth media. The maintenance of media pH is partially developed by the interaction of CO_2 with the sodium bicarbonate in the basal culture media. An air : CO_2 (95% : 5%) mixture is used, both to maintain the CO_2 level for support of proper pH and allow the correct level of dissolved oxygen in culture media. Although the amount of oxygen found in air, 18%, has been found adequate for the culture system described in this chapter, as more defined populations of neurons are cultured, the need for O_2 regulation will likely become essential. Varying populations of neural cells will likely be found to have varying O_2 requirements, as neurons in general have a high oxygen requirement (2). The ambient temperature inside the incubator must remain constant. We routinely use 36.5°C to maintain our cultures. To minimize the evaporation of media, a relatively high humidity should be maintained in the incubator. A pan of double-distilled water in the incubator will provide proper humidity. Many of the new incubators produce constant humidity; this is a good feature because of possible bacterial or fungal growth in water pans. We routinely use 85% humidity for flasks and 95% humidity for culture dishes.

Cell Culture Technique

Brain areas in general, and individual cell types in particular, develop at various times during developmental ontogeny. For example, the brain stem matures well before the cerebellum, while neurons develop and become postmitotic before glial cell proliferation (3). Therefore, both the developmental age of the animal and the area of brain cultured are important determinants of both the maturation stage and the cellular composition within the culture. Manipulations of animal age and brain area cultured can then be optimized for the desired model system of cell culture.

The ease of controlled breeding, quantity of available tissue, developmental time schedule, and costs are several reasons that newborn rodents have been the tissue source for primary culture of the CNS. We routinely obtain tissue from neonatal Sprague-Dawley rats; however, we have also used Wistar rats, with equivalent results. The developmental age of the animal used to establish CNS cultures is important. Cultures are initiated utilizing 0- to 2-day-old neonatal animals. The finding of the vaginal plug is designated as day zero. If embryonic pups are used, neurons tend to survive the culture period of 7–10 days, and older brain tissues increase the percentage of contaminating "fibroblast-like" cells within the culture.

We use the same brain area, the parietal cortex, for the source of culture material. At 0–2 days postnatal, this area is developmentally immature with respect to glial maturation, which allows for optimal mixed glial cultures. The use of a particular brain region also enhances reproducibility and establishes credibility for extrapolating culture data to *in vivo* events. However, culture precludes homeostatic controls and reduces cellular heterogeneity and interactions found in the animal. Therefore, data derived from *in vitro* manipulations should initially only be regarded as normality *in vitro*. This data then must ultimately be judged relative to reality *in vivo*.

General Precautions for Tissue Dissection

All procedures were developed to ensure maximal cell survival and sterility. Routine sterilization protocols and culture techniques may be found in several reviews (4, 5) and are not given here. Tissues to be dissected should never be allowed to dry. Balanced salt solutions at neutral pH and 37°C should be used whenever possible to avoid ionic losses, to enhance blood removal from dissected material, and to decrease tissue dissociation trauma. Mechanical trauma should also be kept to a minimum. Transported material should be carried and not squeezed by forceps during transfer. Cuts should be made with a sharp instrument rather than by trying to tease tissue apart. Sharp cuts and gentle handling will ensure optimal cell survival.

Establishment of Primary Cultures

Differences in nutrient requirements and adhesion properties of the individual cell types have been utilized for generating purified cell cultures. At the time of cell isolation, neurons have undergone terminal postmitotic differentiation. Taking advantage of this nondividing state and select neuronal nutritional requirements, neurons can be isolated from glial cells. Likewise, by utilizing a different set of nutrient requirements, mixed glial cells can be grown without neuronal contamination. Once mixed glial cells have grown to confluence, adhesion differences between type 1 astrocytes and glial bipotential precursor cells are used to isolate each cell population. Maintenance of isolated cultures can be facilitated by growth in tailor-made serumless, chemically defined medium for each cell type (see the section *Serumless, Chemically Defined Medium,* below). Since each chemically defined medium was formulated for a specific cell population (6–8), optimal culture conditions are maintained for each cell type, thereby enhancing select cell growth. Cultures can also be grown in serum; however, contaminating cell types, usually astrocytes or fibroblasts, will eventually overgrow the culture.

Mixed Glial Culture

The most widely used procedure to isolate various glia populations is that of mixed glial culture (9). We have found that a critical developmental time window for the initiation of mixed glial cultures from the parietal cortex exists. Using 0- to 2-day-old neonatal rat cerebrum, neurons fail to survive after the second medium change. During this time, cells of two distinct morphologies can be seen undergoing proliferation from clusters of cells. There are small phase-dark process-bearing cells residing on top of a phase-gray confluent bed layer of polygonal, flat cells (Fig. 1). We have characterized these cell types, both in mixed and in isolated cell culture. The cells that abut the bed layer of cells are identified by biochemical, ultrastructural, and immunological criteria and are judged to develop into oligodendrocyte progenitor cells when cultured in a serumless, chemically defined medium (7) or into mixed cultures of type 2 astrocytes and oligodendrocytes when cultured in the presence of fetal bovine serum (FBS) (7, 10). Those cells com-

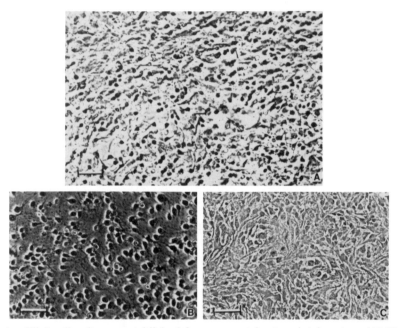

FIG. 1   Glial cell cultures established from neonatal rat parietal cortex. (A) Phase-contrast micrograph represents a 7-day-old mixed glial primary culture: phase-dark, process-bearing cells that are bipotential glial precursor cells, resting on top of a bed layer of phase-gray, polygonal cells that are type 1 astrocytes. Bar, 87 μm. (B) Purified oligodendrocyte progenitor cell culture 24 hr after switching to serumless, chemically defined medium. Bar, 174 μm. (C) Type 1 astrocyte culture after the biopotential glial precursor cells have been removed and type 1 astrocytes replated. Bar, 174 μm.

prising the bed layer of cells are identified by similar criteria to be type 1 astrocytes (6, 11).

Tissue Dissection

1. Typically, 15–30 neonatal rat pups are used to initiate cultures. Since developmental events are rapidly changing in the newborn, similar-aged animals should be used for a single tissue dissection.
2. The head and upper body of a newborn pup are dipped into a beaker filled with 95% (v/v) ethanol, allowing the thumb and forefinger to be immersed also. This allows the pup and finger and thumb to be decontaminated and washed clean of bedding material and blood products.
3. A pair of sterile scissors is used to quickly decapitate the head onto a piece of sterile gauze or paper towel, and the body is subsequently discarded.
4. Another pair of sterile scissors is employed to cut the skin at the midline of the head, cutting from the base of the head to the mideye area.
5. The loosened skin is then pulled back toward the muzzle of the head, thereby exposing the skull. Care should be taken not to touch the exposed skull with the fingers.
6. A third pair of sterile scissors is utilized to cut the skull at the median fissure. It is important to avoid damaging the brain tissue. Slight upward pressure while cutting the skull helps to avoid damage to the brain tissue during this procedure. Contamination is reduced by using each pair of scissors for only its designated function. After each procedure, scissors are dipped in 95% ethanol (separate from the ethanol used for the pup) and allowed to drain on a piece of sterile gauze.
7. Applying slight inward pressure to the skull will raise the cut pieces of skull along the midline sufficiently to allow their removal. Remove the raised portion of the skull by pulling the piece of skull away from the midline with a sterile pair of forceps. The skull is sufficiently soft to be torn away, exposing the brain; however, in slightly older pups, it may be necessary to make a small incision perpendicular to and at the superior end of the midline cut before skull removal.
8. The whole brain is then excised by carefully running a sterile spatula along the bottom and sides of the brain calvarium from the olfactory lobes to the posterior of the midbrain.
9. The brain tissue is subsequently placed in a 35-mm sterile plastic petri dish. We have found that the lid works best, since it allows easy access to the tissue.
10. Parietal cortices are dissected away from the rest of the brain using two

sterile pairs of microforceps. One pair of forceps is used to steady the brain at the median fissure, while, with the other pair of forceps, the cerebral hemisphere is gently pulled away from the brain at the median fissure. The cerebral tissue is now lying superior surface folded onto the surface of the petri dish lid. The parietal cortex is then dissected away using the edge of the forceps. The other cortex is removed in a similar manner.

11. The cortices are immediately immersed in sterile saline solution I (138 mM NaCl, 5.4 mM KCl, 1.1 mM Na$_2$HPO$_4$, 1.1 mM KH$_2$PO$_4$, 22 mM glucose, and 0.9 mM CaCl$_2$) or basal medium (SFM) contained in another sterile petri dish.

12. After all the cortices have been collected, the meninges should be carefully removed. This step is extremely important; the degree of meningeal removal determines the purity of the resulting type 1 astrocyte culture. Each parietal cortex is transferred to another petri dish filled with either saline solution I or SFM. Two pairs of microdissecting forceps (the ones used for cortical removal can be employed) are utilized, one to steady the cortex and the other to remove the meninges and blood vessels. Pull away the meninges from the cortical tissue by beginning with an exposed corner of the membrane on the outer surface. The meninges should pull off in an intact sheet. Turn the tissue over and remove any visible blood vessels.

13. Blot the removed meninges and blood vessels onto a piece of sterilized gauze.

14. Transfer the cleaned tissue to another 35-mm petri dish containing fresh saline solution I or SFM. The use of different petri dishes during parietal cortex isolation and meningeal removal allows blood products and pieces of meningeal tissue to be left behind. Dip both forceps in 95% ethanol and allow to drain.

Dissociation of Cerebral Tissue

The dissociation of tissue into single cells can be accomplished by either trypsinization, mechanical sieving, or mechanical shearing. Each method has advantages and disadvantages. Both trypsinization and mechanical shearing allow a greater degree of reproducibility, while mechanical sieving usually gives greater cell viability. We routinely use the mechanical shearing method as a compromise between the other two methods, with the added advantage of decreasing preparation time. All three techniques have been found to yield similar cellular compositions of mixed glial cultures and nearly equivalent numbers of neurons per number of cells seeded.

Trypsinization Technique

1. Gently aspirate all the cortices and salt solution I or SFM contained in the final 35-mm petri dish through a 10-ml pipette 2–3 times. After the final aspiration, transfer the cellular mixture to a sterile 50-ml screw-capped Erlenmeyer flask. The volume of the tissue suspension should be noted at this step so that the correct dilution of trypsin solution I can be added in step 3.

2. The cell suspension is then gently rotated on a rotary shaker for 15 min (80 rpm, 1.5-in. stroke diameter, 37°C). This gentle agitation further loosens tissue adhesions for enhanced trypsin proteolysis.

3. Trypsin solution I (2.5 g hog pancreas trypsin/100 ml of saline solution I) is added at a final concentration of 10% (v/v) and the cell suspension is gently agitated for an additional 25 min.

4. Trypsinization is halted by the addition of 10 ml of serum-supplemented medium (SSM; 10% (v/v) FBS). The large protein concentration of FBS dilutes the trypsin action on dissociated cells.

5. The disrupted tissue is then gently aspirated through a 10-ml pipette three times and the tissue pieces allowed to settle to the bottom of the flask. Tipping the Erlenmeyer flask at an angle facilitates the settling of the undissociated tissue pieces in a corner of the flask. The flask can be tipped by placing the flask on the edge of several paper towels.

6. Carefully remove the cell suspension, avoiding any disturbance of the settled tissue and filter through Nitex 210 (mesh size: 210 μm; Tetko, Inc. Elmsford, NY). Allow the cell suspension to be filtered by gravity.

7. Add 7 ml of SSM to the undissociated tissue and again aspirate the tissue pieces through a 10-ml pipette three times. The force of the liquid through the end of the pipette should be slightly stronger than in the previous step.

8. The Erlenmeyer flask is again tilted and tissue pieces allowed to settle to the bottom of the flask. The cell suspension is collected and filtered through the same 210 Nitex filter used in step 6. Again, the suspension is allowed to pass through the filter by gravity.

9. For the last pipette titrations, 3 ml of SSM is added to the remaining undissociated tissue and aspirated forcefully through a 10-ml pipette three times. The entire cell suspension is then filtered through the same 210 Nitex filter used in step 6. After the suspension is filtered through the Nitex mesh, 3 ml of fresh SSM is forcefully pushed through the filter.

10. The total filtrate is then passed through a 130 Nitex filter (mesh size: 130 μm; Tetko, Inc.). The filtrate should be allowed to pass through the filter by gravity. After the entire filtrate has passed through the Nitex filter, 3 ml of fresh SSM is forcefully pushed through the filter.

11. Centrifuge the entire filtrate at 800 g for 3–5 min using a clinical tabletop centrifuge at room temperature. Dispose of the supernatant and resuspend the cell pellet in fresh SSM.

12. The cell number is then determined using a hemocytometer. A portion of the cell suspension is added to a 0.4% Trypan Blue solution which has been diluted 1 : 6 (v/v) in phosphate-buffered saline (PBS) containing 1 mM ethylenediaminetetraacetic acid (EDTA). Living cells exclude the colloidal dye Trypan Blue; therefore, an accurate estimation of live cells can be determined. Care should be taken not to incubate cells in the dye solution longer than 10 min. During longer incubation times the dye solution has toxic effects on cell viability. Dead cells appear filled with dye and are blue in color.

Mechanical Sieving Technique

1. This procedure requires a small polyamide nylon mesh bag which is used to "tease" the parietal tissue into single cells. The bag is manufactured from Nitex 210 (mesh size: 210 μm) with the measurements of approximately 1.5 × 3.0 in. Sew three sides of this bag using a very fine stitch. Since this bag is reused, thread should be as strong as possible.

2. Place the sterile Nitex mesh bag in a 100-mm sterile petri dish containing 15–20 ml of SSM.

3. After removal of the meninges and blood vessels (see above), gently aspirate the cortices and pipette the tissue suspension into the moist Nitex mesh bag. This transfer procedure can be facilitated by holding the open end of the mesh bag apart with a pair of sterile forceps while pipetting the tissue suspension. After pipetting, the bag is closed and immersed into the medium-filled petri dish.

4. The tissue is disrupted by using light strokes of a sterile glass rod to tease the tissue through the mesh. Little pressure is used, in fact the weight of the rod itself is usually more than sufficient pressure.

5. When approximately one-half of the tissue has been disrupted, remove the cell suspension and filter through Nitex 210.

6. Add 15 ml of fresh SSM to the petri dish and repeat the teasing procedure for the undissociated tissue. The tissue has a tendency to clump and, unless the bag is turned around several times during this process, tissue asphyxiation can occur.

7. After tissue disruption is complete, elevate the bag above the petri dish and wash the remaining cells into the dish with a stream of fresh SSM. Allow the liquid to drain, touching one corner of the bag against the dish will increase drainage.

8. Filter this cell suspension through the same Nitex 210 filter as in step 5.

The entire filtrate is subsequently filtered through Nitex 130, collected, and centrifuged at 800 g for 3–5 min in a clinical tabletop centrifuge at room temperature. As in the trypsin protocol, the cell suspension should be filtered by gravity. At the end of each filtration, a few milliliters of fresh SSM should be forced through the filter to collect cells caught within the mesh.

9. The cell pellet is resuspended and cell number estimated as described for the trypsinization method.

Mechanical Shearing Technique

1. This tissue disruption method is our technique of choice. Not only is the dissociation faster, but also more reproducible. The speed at which tissues are dissociated, and cells subsequently seeded and allowed to adhere to culture vessel surfaces is related to cell survival and cell elaboration. The longer this process takes, the fewer viable cells are cultured. The mechanical disruption by the Stomacher lab blender (constant speed and pressure) allows more reproducibility within and between primary culture preparations.

2. The sterile plastic bag (Stomacher 80 bag) is loaded with 15–20 ml of SSM and the processed tissue. The bag is then placed into the blender and the tissue disrupted for 2 min at approximately 80% speed. Speed can be controlled by using a variable transformer.

3. The cell solution is then poured through a Nitex 210 filter, being careful to leave all undissociated tissue in the bag. An additional 15 ml of SSM is pipetted into the bag and the remaining tissue is disrupted for an additional 1 min at 80% speed. The resulting cell suspension is passed through the same Nitex 210 filter.

4. An additional 3 ml of fresh SSM is then forcefully passed through the Nitex 210 filter. The entire filtrate is subsequently filtered by gravity through a Nitex 130 filter.

5. After filtration is completed, 3 ml of fresh SSM is forcefully passed through the Nitex 130 filter. The cell suspension is then centrifuged at 800 g for 3–5 min at room temperature. The supernatant is discarded and the cell pellet resuspended with fresh SSM and counted for cell viability and numbers.

Mixed Glial Cultures

The development of mixed glial or neuronal cell cultures diverges at this point. Seeding density, substratum, and culture medium are used to determine the type of culture, mixed glial or neuronal, obtained. This section describes protocols for mixed glial cultures.

1. Two critical parameters, cell seeding density and culture vessel handling, determine the cell type distribution in mixed glial cultures. Initially described by Shein (12), a critical plating cell density is needed for the development of phase-dark process-bearing cells [bipotential glial precursor cells (7, 10)] that lie on top of the phase-gray polygonal flat cells [type 1 astrocytes (9, 11)]. The critical seeding density is based on the appearance of the glial bipotential precursor cells. The ionic charge application to the surface of the culture vessel varies between manufacturers. This charge influences the adhesion of cells to the culture vessel surface and hence cell viability. It is recommended that various product lines be examined for optimal cell growth. After cell seeding, the flasks should not be moved for at least 48 hr and, for best results, 72 hr. This allows complete cell attachment.

2. For optimal mixed glial cell cultures the following cell densities are recommended.
   a. Culture flasks (75-cm^2): 15–18 $\times$ 10^6 cells/11 ml of SSM
   b. Culture dishes (60-mm): 2–2.5 $\times$ 10^6 cells/3 ml of SSM
   c. Culture dishes (35-mm): 1 $\times$ 10^6 cells/2 ml of SSM
   d. Culture plates (24-well): 0.5 $\times$ 10^6 cells/1 ml of SSM
   Culture vessels, flasks, dishes, or plates have undergone a special process to impart a negatively charged surface. Ordinary bacterial petri dishes and plates have not been charged in this manner. All cell culture work should be performed using culture flasks, dishes, or plates.

3. Immediately after cell seeding into the appropriate culture vessel, cultures are incubated at 37°C for 72 hr without disturbance of any type. After this initial culture period, medium is changed every 2 days thereafter until cultures have reached confluence. At this time, cultures have a confluent bed layer of phase-gray, polygonal cells which have numerous phase-dark, process-bearing cells lying on their surfaces (Fig. 1).

Isolation of Bipotential Glial Precursor Cells and Type 1 Astrocytes

1. The length of mixed glial culture growth should be limited to 7–9 days. Cell confluence is usually reached by day 7; however, growth variations can prolong confluence for 1–2 days. Subconfluent cultures have not had enough time for cellular stratification (Fig. 1), while cultures grown for longer periods yield clumps of mixed cell types on cell separation.

2. At the end of the initial period of mixed glial cell growth, medium is changed and flasks placed on a rotary shaker (Labline Junior Orbit

Shaker), secured by fiber tape, and shaken at 200 rpm (1.5 in. stroke diameter) at 37°C. After 1 hr, the media is discarded and fresh SSM added. The flasks are refastened to the rotary shaker and allowed to shake at 250 rpm for an additional 16–18 hr at 37°C. Fresh SSM is added and flasks reshaken for another 16–18 hr. Each cell suspension (bipotential glial precursor cells) is treated as described below and subsequently used for separate experimentation.

3. The resulting cell suspension is filtered through Nitex 33 (mesh size: 33 μm; Tetko, Inc.) and centrifuged at 800 g for 3–5 min at room temperature.

4. The supernatant is discarded and the cell pellet is resuspended in fresh SSM and refiltered through Nitex 17 (mesh size: 17 μm; Tetko, Inc.). This second filtration step increases the purity of bipotential glial precursor cell cultures by removing the contaminating astrocytes which are present almost exclusively in cell clumps.

5. Viable cells are counted and seeded in the appropriate culture vessel.
   a. Culture flask (75-cm^2): 5×10^6 cells/10 ml medium
   b. Culture dish (35-mm): 4×10^5 cells/2 ml medium
   c. Culture plate (24-well): 1×10^5 cells/1 ml medium
   d. Culture plate (96-well): 4×10^4 cells/0.2 ml medium

6. Cells begin to adhere to culture vessel surface within 3 hr; however, it is best not to disturb flasks for at least 18–24 hr. At this time, medium can be switched to serumless, chemically defined medium (ODM) tailored specifically for oligodendrocyte progenitor cell proliferation and maturation (7; Table I). These cultures have been demonstrated to be 95–98% oligodendrocyte progenitor cell cultures by ultrastructural, biochemical, and immunological criteria (7; Fig. 1).

TABLE I Defined Medium Supplements for Primary Neural Cells[a]

Compound	Optimal concentration of supplements		
	Neurons	Type 1 astrocytes	OligoP cells
Hydrocortisone	50 nM	50 nM	
Putrescine	100 μM	100 μM	
Prostaglandin F$_{2\alpha}$	500 ng/ml	500 ng/ml	
Insulin	50 μg/ml	50 μg/ml	5 μg/ml
Transferrin			500 ng/ml
Fibroblast growth factor	500 ng/ml	10 ng/ml	5 ng/ml

[a] Basal medium is Dulbecco's modified Eagle's and Ham's F12 medium in a 1 : 1 (w/w) mix with added pyruvate. Hydrocortisone is the hemisuccinate sodium salt, insulin is isolated from bovine pancreas, transferrin is isolated from human serum, and basic fibroblast growth factor is the homogeneous recombinant peptide.

7. If SSM exposure is continued, cultures become mixed with oligodendro-cytes and type 2 astrocytes (7, 10). The proportion of each cell type varies depending on the batch of FBS and the length of culture. Cultures grown under the conditions of SSM eventually become contaminated with type 1 astrocytes. This contamination can be reduced by changing media and slapping the bottom of the flask sharply with the palm of the hand. The flask is then placed upright to drain and, subsequently, the cell suspension is filtered through Nitex 33 and replated. This purifica-tion procedure should be performed at least every 5–7 days.

8. After removal of the bipotential glial precursor cells, the resulting type 1 astrocyte cultures are approximately 95% homogeneous by phase-con-trast microscopy. Further removal of contaminating precursor cells is accomplished by reshaking the cultures at 100 rpm (1.5 in. stroke radius) for an additional 24–48 hr.

9. At this time, the cultures should have less than 10 phase-dark cells/field as seen using the low-power setting (10×) on a phase microscope. If not, the cultures can be reshaken until the desired purity is obtained. Unfor-tunately, fibroblast-like cell contamination cannot be eliminated in such fashion. These cells remain and contaminate future cultures.

10. For further culture, purified cultures are washed with SFM and exposed to a trypsin solution II (1% Enzar-T; 40× concentrate and 0.1 mM EDTA in Hanks' balanced salt solution that is Ca^{2+}- and Mg^{2+}-free). After cell detachment, fresh SSM is added and cell suspension is centri-fuged at 800 g for 3–5 min at room temperature.

11. After resuspending the cell pellet, viable cells are counted and replated into the appropriate culture vessel.
    a. Culture flask (75-cm^2): $1–2 \times 10^6$ cells/10 ml medium
    b. Culture dish (35-mm): 4×10^5 cells/2 ml medium
    c. Culture plate (24-well): 2×10^4 cells/1 ml medium
    d. Culture plate (96-well): 5×10^3 cells/0.2 ml medium

12. As with bipotential glial precursor cell plating, after seeding, type 1 astrocyte cultures should not be moved for 18–24 hr. At this time, me-dium can be changed to chemically defined medium (ADM, Table I) or SSM. Cultures derived from these cells have been shown to be 98–99% pure type 1 astrocytes by ultrastructural, biochemical, and immunologi-cal criteria (6; Fig. 1).

Neuronal Cultures

1. Dissection of cerebral cortices is performed as described above, and cells are seeded at twice the plating density needed for mixed glial

cultures. The higher cell concentration is likely needed for conditioning of the medium with proper nutrients and trophic factors for neuronal survival. The age of the rat pup used is also more important for initiating neuronal cultures. Pups that are <1 day postnatal enhance neuronal cell survival. In addition, altering the substrata with positively charged compounds like poly(D-lysine) improves neuronal attachment, and therefore survival. The precoating of culture vessels can be done immediately before tissue dissection. A stock solution of polylysine (2.5 μg/ml, MW 30,000–70,000) is added and allowed to coat the vessel surface for approximately 10 min at room temperature. Vessels are then washed three times with SFM. Precoated plates can be stored for short periods of time; we have stored plates up to 48 hr at 4°C without loss of attachment activity.

2. Cells are seeded in the appropriate culture vessel in the presence of SSM with horse serum added [5% (v/v)] and 2 ng/ml of basic fibroblast growth factor (recombinant or homogeneous grade). Cultures are then incubated for 3 days; as with mixed glial cultures, it is best not to move cultures.

3. At this time cultures are washed twice with SFM and neuronal defined medium (NDM, Table I) containing cytosine arabinoside (5 μM) is added. Cytosine arabinoside kills the dividing nonneuronal cells that are stimulated to divide by the NDM. Medium is changed every 3–4 days with added cytosine arabinoside for the initial three medium changes. These cultures have been shown to be approximately 95% neuronal by immunocytochemical detection of neuronal specific marker proteins (8; Fig. 2).

Serumless, Chemically Defined Medium

1. The improvements in cell isolation and culture have allowed factors responsible for cell survival, proliferation, and maturation to be identified. This added knowledge of cell-specific growth components has been used to tailormake serumless, chemically defined media for each cell type. The defined media described in this chapter were developed for the cell populations derived from cerebral cortex. Although cells from other regions will probably grow in these media, one should test the particular medium with each new cell population for maximal cell growth and survival.

2. The ingredients should be made as stock solutions (100–1000×) and stored separately. Defined medium itself should never be stored; we have found a pronounced loss of activity on storage. All supplements

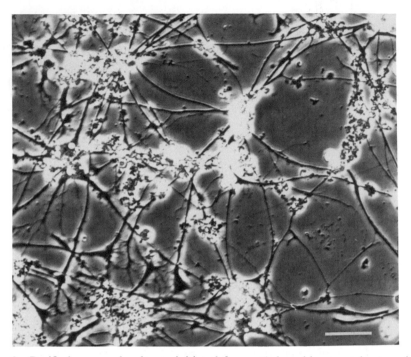

FIG. 2   Purified neuronal cultures initiated from <1-day-old neonatal rat parietal cortex. Phase-contrast micrograph represents a 15-day-old neuronal culture grown in serumless, chemically defined medium. There is still cellular debris from cytosine arabinoside-induced killing of glial cells. Bar, 174 μm.

should be sterilized; we routinely use a 0.22-μm syringe filter for this purpose. The order in which the supplements are added does not change media efficiency, nor is there any reason to recheck the media pH after components have been added.

3. If basal medium is stored for prolonged periods at 4°C, fresh pyruvate should be added at the time of defined medium preparation. Pyruvate is degraded on storage. Both neurons and oligodendrocyte progenitor cells have a pyruvate requirement for survival (7, 13). In addition, only the purest water should be used for media preparation. We use a Milli-Q water purification system with added organic and pyrogen removal cartridges for the water used in basal medium preparation.

Acknowledgments

This work was supported in part by grants from the National Institutes of Health and Medical Research Foundation of Oregon. The author would like to thank Dr. Jean de Vellis, in whose laboratory many of these techniques were developed, and Ms. Ruth Cole, who spent many hours contributing to technical refinements of these methods.

References

1. R. G. Harrison, *Proc. Soc. Exp. Biol. Med.* **4,** 140 (1907).
2. E. Hudspeth, H. Swann, and C. Pomerat, *Tex. Rep. Biol. Med.* **8,** 341 (1950).
3. M. Jacobson, "Developmental Neurobiology." Plenum, New York, 1978.
4. R. I. Freshney, "Culture of Animal Cells: A Journal of Basic Techniques," Liss, New York, 1983.
5. P. F. Kruse and M. K. Patterson (eds.), "Tissue Culture: Methods and Applications." Academic Press, New York, 1973.
6. R. S. Morrison and J. de Vellis, *Proc. Natl. Acad. Sci. U.S.A.* **78,** 7205 (1981).
7. R. P. Saneto and J. de Vellis, *Proc. Natl. Acad. Sci. U.S.A.* **82,** 3509 (1985).
8. R. S. Morrison, A. Sharma, J. de Vellis, and R. A. Bradshaw, *Proc. Natl. Acad. Sci. U.S.A.* **83,** 7537 (1986).
9. K. D. McCarthy and J. de Vellis, *J. Cell Biol.* **85,** 890 (1980).
10. M. C. Raff, R. H. Miller, and M. Nobel, *Nature (London)* **303,** 390 (1983).
11. M. C. Raff, E. R. Abney, J. Cohen, R. Lindsay, and M. Nobel, *J. Neurosci.* **3,** 1289 (1983).
12. H. M. Shein, *Exp. Cell Res.* **40,** 554 (1966).
13. I. Selak, S. D. Skaper, and S. Varon, *J. Neurosci.* **7,** 340 (1985).

[10] Preparation, Enrichment, and Growth of Purified Cultures of Neurons and Photoreceptors from Chick Embryos and from Normal and Mutant Mice

Ruben Adler

Retina as Experimental Tissue for Neurobiological Studies *in Vitro*

Although complex, the retina is a region of the central nervous system (CNS) that is composed of a relatively small number of different cell types. Moreover, most of these cell types have already been fairly well characterized *in vivo,* both anatomically and functionally. As shown in Fig. 1, the retina is organized in well-defined layers, which develop during embryogenesis as neuroepithelial cells become postmitotic, migrate toward the inner (or "vitreal") surface, and express differentiated properties. Neuronal types present in the mature retina include ganglion cells (located in the innermost layer), amacrine, horizontal, bipolar, and interplexiform cells (which are located in the inner nuclear layer), and the highly specialized photoreceptor cells, the rods and cones, located in the outer nuclear layer. Glial cells include the radially oriented cells of Müller, which have the cell body in the inner nuclear layer but extend processes to both inner and outer surfaces of the retina. In some species there are also astrocytes in the retinal ganglion cell layer.

One of the criteria that can be used for the identification of these various cell types *in vivo* is their position within the retina, but this reference point is unavailable in dissociated cell cultures. The information available about structural, chemical, and functional properties of the cells, which could be useful for their identification both *in vivo* and *in vitro,* varies from cell type to cell type, and from species to species. Photoreceptors show many characteristic differentiated properties, including their elongated shape, polarized and compartmentalized pattern of organization, the specialized outer segment, and the expression and distribution of cell-specific macromolecules such as those involved in phototransduction. On the other hand, while the distinctive shape and pattern of nerve processes shown by other retinal neurons *in vivo* have been well known for many years (1), these morphological properties are much less reliable as diagnostic criteria to distinguish neuronal subtypes in cell culture. Ganglion cells, the only retinal neurons with an ex-

Methods in Neurosciences, Volume 2

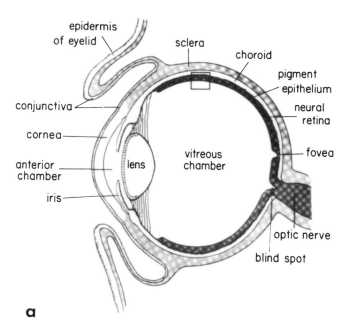

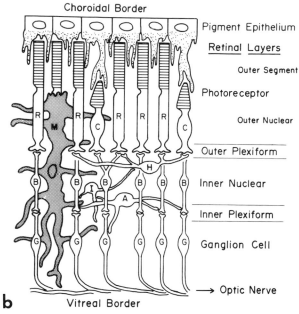

FIG. 1 (a) Diagram of a vertebrate eye. (b) Cellular organization of a portion of the neural retina (□ in a). The main cell types are designated as R, rods; C, cones; H, horizontal cells; B, bipolar cells; I, interplexiform cells; A, amacrine cells; G, ganglion cells; M, Müller cells. [Reproduced with permission from D. Farber and R. Adler, *in* "The Retina: A Model for Cell Biology Studies" (R. Adler and D. Farber, eds.), Part I, pp. 3 and 5. Academic Press, Orlando, 1986.]

traretinal projection, can be identified through their capacity to accumulate fluorescent dyes injected in the midbrain (2). Theoretically, identification of other retinal neurons could be based on their neurotransmitters, particularly since immunocytochemistry and autoradiography can be used both *in vivo* and *in vitro* to investigate neurotransmitter synthetic enzymes and high-affinity uptake mechanisms at the single cell level. However, the occurrence of considerable overlap in the distribution of neurotransmitters across cell types (3, 4) makes it necessary to use them in conjunction with other criteria. Cell type-specific monoclonal antibodies can be of considerable help in this regard, although this is an area in which species differences are notorious. The availability of antibodies against various retinal cell types has been reviewed (5).

Glial cells can be easily distinguished from neurons and photoreceptors based on their "flat," epithelioid configuration. A factor that frequently complicates glial cell identification in cultures from other CNS regions is the presence of other "flat" cells, such as endothelial cells or fibroblasts. This problem is not found with retinas from species such as the chick, which are avascular and free of connective tissue. While the glial fibrillary acidic protein (GFAP) has been much less useful as a marker for cultured retinal Müller cells than for other glial cell types, there are other "glial cell markers" such as glutamine synthetase and carbonic anhydrase (6).

The availability of the probes mentioned above, together with the ease with which the retina can be cleanly dissected from other eye tissues in many species, are among the reasons why the retina has been so extensively used in many laboratories for *in vitro* experiments. Techniques used for retinal tissue include explant, reaggregation, and different types of monolayer cultures (7). Thus, the culture methods described below are just one more type of retinal monolayer culture, developed as a tool for studies of retinal cell survival and differentiation in which intercellular contacts must be kept to a minimum. Technical aspects featured by these cultures include low seeding densities, use of highly adhesive substrata and chemically defined media, selection of conditions allowing selective growth or elimination of various cell types, and amenability of the cultured cells to identification and characterization with a battery of complementary analytical techniques.

Studies with Chick Embryo Retinal Cells

General Considerations

The *in vivo* development of the chick embryo retina has been extensively described (8). As mentioned, the chick retina is avascular and connective tissue-free, and can be cleanly dissected from other eye tissues, thus yielding cell suspensions free of contamination with pigment epithelium, fibroblasts, or endothelial cells. The development of glial cells can also be prevented if dissociated retinal cells are allowed to attach and grow as individual units on highly adhesive substrata (9–12).

Methods

Donor Embryos

The description that follows will be based on studies with 8-day-old chick embryos, the most commonly used stage in our laboratory. At this stage, most retinal cells are already postmitotic, but cell differentiation can be recognized only in the inner retina (8). It must be noted that *in vitro* cell differentiation varies dramatically as a function of the developmental stage of the donor embryos (13) and should, therefore, be carefully controlled using the table of developmental stages described by Hamburger and Hamilton (14).

Neural Retina Dissection

Eggs are incubated with the blunt side pointing up, to facilitate access to the embryo through the air chamber of the egg. The egg surface is cleaned with an alcohol swab, and the shell covering the air chamber is cracked open using blunt, sterile forceps (Appendix D,1,a). Separate curved-tip forceps (Appendix D,1,b) are used to remove the shell membrane, and to break the connections between the embryo and the vascularized chorioallantoid membrane. Using the same forceps, the embryo is lifted by "hooking" it around the neck region without closing the forceps, in order to avoid separating the head from the cell body (if this happens, the head will tend to sink into the egg yolk, and it will become difficult to retrieve it with sterile technique). The embryos are collected in a petri dish containing Hanks' balanced salt solution (HBSS; Appendix C,1). The connective tissue covering the eye is peeled away using forceps, and the eyes are gently rolled out of the socket and transferred to a dish with fresh HBSS. This is the last step that can be carried out without using a dissecting microscope.

The use of transillumination is recommended for dissection of the retina, because it allows easy visualization of the interface between the dark layer of pigmented epithelium (RPE) and the neural retina, which appears as a dull, whitish tissue overlying the shiny vitreous body (Fig. 1). Very sharp, angled watchmaker's forceps (Appendix D,1,c) are used to remove the remaining large pieces of connective tissue attached to the eye ball, and then to dissect the eye tissues external to the retina. While holding the eye cornea side down, a tiny hole is made in the wall of the eye, so that the RPE can be grabbed with the forceps and separated from the retina. The sclera–choroid–pigment epithelium complex can then be dissected, starting near the choroid fissure (the origin of the optic nerve; see Fig. 1) at the back of the eye, and advancing toward the cornea. It is relatively easy to release the RPE and adjacent tissues from most of the retinal surface. However, there is an area of tighter attachment at the choroid fissure, which can be sectioned with the forceps toward the end of the dissection. Grasping one of the RPE flaps, the eye can then be "rolled away" from the RPE by pushing it away from the iris. Given that this is another area of tight attachment between the tissues, it is likely that some RPE fragments will remain attached to the retina after this process is completed; they should be removed later on (see below).

The retina, free of sclera–choroid–RPE but still attached to the vitreous/lens complex, is transferred to a fresh HBSS dish, and positioned "lens side up" (Fig. 1). The lens/vitreous complex is grabbed with one of the watchmaker's forceps, while the retina is pushed away with the other. The vitreous/lens complex is discarded. Pieces of the retina that still show attached pigment epithelium are cut with tungsten needles (Appendix D,1,d) and are discarded. It is important to use the needles in a *cutting,* rather than a *teasing* motion, to avoid excessive trauma to the tissue. The RPE-free retinas are then transferred to yet another dish, containing Ca^{2+}- and Mg^{2+}-free HBSS (CMF; Appendix C,1). The transfer is done either with a wide-bore pipette, or by allowing the individual retinas to sit on the angle of the dissection tweezers (the tissue should neither be grabbed by the tweezers nor hang from them). The retinas are cut into small fragments using tungsten needles, and the fragments are transferred to a 15-ml plastic tube using a siliconized Pasteur pipette (Appendix D,2).

Dissociation

1. Incubate tissue fragments for 10 min at 37°C in CMF (approximately 1–2 ml/retina). During this incubation, thaw trypsin and DNase aliquots (Appendix C,2,3).
2. Aspirate CMF, and incubate at 37°C for 20 min in 0.25% (w/v) trypsin in CMF, containing 100 μg of DNase per milliliters (same solution/tissue ratio). We find that dissociation is better if the tube is *very gently* rotated to resuspend the tissue at the 10-min mark.
3. Discard the trypsin, and gently rinse the tissue once with 0.25% (w/v) soybean trypsin inhibitor (Appendix C,4) and twice with Eagle's basal medium (EBM) containing 1% bovine serum albumin (EBM–BSA; Appendix C,5). Use separate Pasteur pipettes to aspirate trypsin and to dispense fresh EBM–BSA. It is *very important* to avoid generating foam and/or starting the dissociation of the tissue before these rinses are completed.

4. With the tissue suspended in 1–1.5 ml of EBM–BSA, dissociation is accomplished by 20 aspirations with a fire-polished, siliconized Pasteur pipette controlled with a rubber bulb. The pipette should have an opening no larger than 0.1 mm, so that resistance is felt when the solution is forcefully expelled from the pipette. Experimental problems such as the presence of large clumps in the cultures can frequently be tracked down to the use of pipettes with incorrect bore sizes. Foaming can easily occur during this step, and must be prevented by avoiding aspiration of air together with the cell suspension, and by expelling the latter against the wall of the tube.

5. Adjust the volume of the cell suspension to approximately 10 ml, using unsupplemented medium 199.

6. Filter through a sterile Nitex filter (Appendix D,3).

7. To facilitate accurate cell counting with the hemocytometer, the filtered cell suspension must be further diluted with medium to a volume equal to 3–4 ml of suspension per retina.

8. After hemocytometer counting, the cell suspension is further diluted to the desired seeding density. Usual seeding densities used in our laboratory are 8×10^5 cells/35-mm dish (in a final medium volume of 2 ml), 2.4×10^6 cells/60-mm dish (in 6 ml of medium), and $6–9 \times 10^6$ cells/100-mm dish (in 15 ml of medium).

Note: In order to allow use of the same cell suspension for comparison of different media supplements, we routinely prepare seeding stocks in unsupplemented medium 199 at twice the desired final cell density, and seed aliquots in dishes that already contain an equal volume of culture medium with twice the desired final concentration of serum and/or other supplements ($2\times$ stocks). The concentrations of supplements indicated in the Appendix correspond to those in final media, and *must* be doubled to prepare these $2\times$ stocks.

Culture Media

A serum-containing medium is described in Appendix B,1,a. It is important to note that there can be substantial differences between batches of fetal calf serum in their abilities to support cell growth and differentiation. This even applies to different serum lots from the same supplier. In fact, as many as 80% of the serum samples that we test are toxic for retinal neurons and photoreceptors. Screening criteria include cell survival as well as the expression of cell-specific differentiated properties.

More recently, it became possible to grow chick embryo retinal neurons and photoreceptors in serum-free, fully chemically defined medium. An earlier formulation (15), based on the use of medium 199 supplemented with pyruvate, insulin, transferrin, progesterone, linoleic acid, bovine serum albumin, glutamine, and penicillin, supported adequate cell survival, but cell differentiation was not as extensive as that seen in serum-containing media. These limitations have been overcome (16) by modifying, as described in Appendix B,1,b, a medium originally formulated for mouse retinal cells (17, 18) (see below).

Substrata

We use tissue culture plastic dishes or glass coverslips coated with poly-ornithine (PORN; Appendix A,1). It must be noted that retinal cells fail to survive in serum-free medium when they attach to PORN-coated substrata in the absence of special attachment factors. These factors are described in Appendix A,2. Cultures of chick retinal neurons and photoreceptors on collagen-coated substrata were described by Araki (19).

Description of Cultures with Some Considerations on Analytical Techniques

Shortly after culture onset, chick embryo retinal cultures appear as a morphologically homogeneous population of process-free, round cells (Fig. 2A). Cell differentiation is extensive during the next few days. As illustrated in Fig. 2B, after 6 days *in vitro* the cultures show multipolar neurons, cone photoreceptors, and morphologically undifferentiated round cells. Flat, glial-like cells are not present in these cultures.

Although space considerations make it impossible to present detailed protocols describing the analytical methods that have been applied to these cultures, a few general considerations are worth mentioning. As with other monolayer culture preparations, the cells have been amenable to analysis by various microscopical techniques, including transmission and scanning electron microscopy, immunocytochemistry, and autoradiography (11, 20, 21). In addition, the low cell density of the cultures and the absence of flat cells allow dynamic analysis of the development of individual cells, which is particularly efficient using coverslips with a letter-coded, engraved grid (21) (see Appendix A,3). Changes in the lateral mobility of plasma membrane molecules during *in vitro* morphogensis have been analyzed by fluorescence recovery after photobleaching (22).

Cell yields from 8-day-old chick retinas are $80-100 \times 10^6$ cells/embryo, or enough for approximately 120 cultures in 35-mm dishes, or 40 cultures in 60-mm dishes, or 12–16 cultures in 100-mm dishes. Since a trained person can dissect between 5 and 8 embryos in an hour, it is possible to obtain enough material for various types of biochemical studies. Thus, radioisotopic meth-

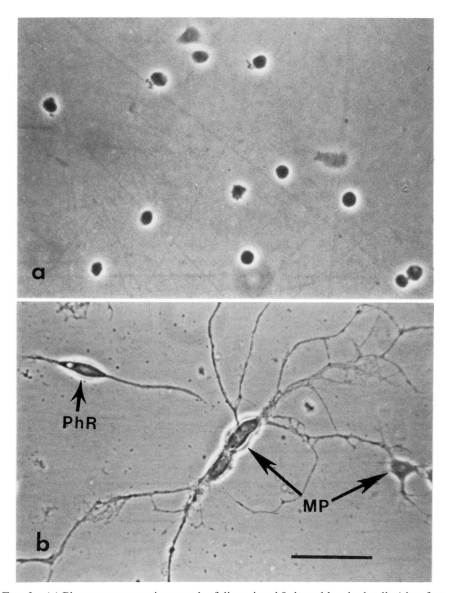

FIG. 2   (a) Phase-contrast micrograph of dissociated 8-day-old retinal cells 1 hr after culture onset. The cells are already attached to the substratum. Most cells are round, free of intercellular contacts, and devoid of processes. (b) A similar culture, grown *in vitro* for 6 days. Multipolar neurons (MP) and a cone photoreceptor (PhR) are seen. Bar, 30 μm. [Reproduced with permission from Madreperla and Adler (21).]

ods have allowed measuring choline acetyltransferase activity and the high-affinity uptake of various putative neurotransmitters in individual 35-mm dishes (23, 24), the melatonin-synthesizing enzyme N-acetyltransferase in 100-mm dishes (25), and the synthesis and subcellular distribution of proteoglycans in pools of four cultures in 100-mm dishes (26).

Generation of Enriched Cell Populations

Selective cell elimination is a well-established method for the generation of cultures enriched for specific cell types (27). This approach can be used for generating enriched populations of cultured photoreceptors (28). In this case, the method is based on the selective toxicity of kainic acid (KA) and β-bungarotoxin (BT), which have been shown to kill various types of retinal neurons without affecting photoreceptor cells (29, 30). The toxins are prepared as concentrated stock solutions in serum-free culture medium, and sterilized by filtration. Aliquots are added to the cultures to obtain the desired final concentrations. The loss of approximately 60% of the nonphotoreceptor neurons is observed when 6-day-old cultures are treated for 8–22 hr with 2 mM KA. Similarly, 1–2 nM β-bungarotoxin causes the loss of approximately 70% of the neurons. The integrity of photoreceptor cells has been corroborated by a variety of techniques, including transmission electron microscopy and the autoradiographic and biochemical analysis of neurotransmitter uptakes (28).

An enriched neuronal preparation can be obtained by selective elimination of photoreceptors by complement-mediated cell lysis using antiopsin antibodies (24). Cultures grown in serum-containing medium must first be rinsed twice, and incubated for 1 hr at 37°C in serum-free medium before the treatment. This is followed by incubation at room temperature for 15 min with antiopsin antiserum [we use a 1 : 100 dilution of sheep antiserum against bovine rhodopsine (31) in the chemically defined medium described in Appendix B,1,b]. The cultures then receive complement at a final concentration of 1.5%. (v/v), and are further incubated for 45–60 min at 37°C. The treatment is terminated by rinsing in fresh medium, and the cells can be further cultured, fixed for microscopical analysis, or harvested for biochemical studies. This treatment results in the lysis of approximately 85% of the photoreceptor cells, without significant changes in nonphotoreceptor neurons. It is critically important to test several batches of complement to investigate their potential toxicity. The possible presence of anticell antibodies in sera used as culture supplements must also be considered.

Mouse Retina Cultures

Interest in the use of the mouse retina for *in vitro* studies has increased due to the availability of mutants affected by photoreceptor degenerations, including *rd/rd* (32), *rds/rds* (33), and the double homozygous *rd,rd/rds,rds* (34). Protocols recently developed in our laboratory allow the growth of retinal neurons and photoreceptors from both wild-type C57/BL mice (17) and from *rd/rd* mice (18). Pilot studies suggest that they are also applicable to mice carrying the *rds* gene.

Dissection

Two-day-old mice are sacrificed by decapitation, and the heads are wrapped in alcohol-soaked pads and kept on ice until dissected. Under the dissecting microscope, the eyelids are removed with one set of forceps (Appendix D,1,b) and the eyes enucleated with a different set of forceps (Appendix D,1,c) in order to preserve sterility. While immersed in a petri dish containing HBSS, the eyes are freed of surrounding loose mesenchyme, and the choroid, sclera, and pigment epithelium are dissected in one step using watchmaker's forceps (Appendix D,1,c). The small size of the mouse eyes makes their dissection more difficult than that of chick embryo eyes, making it necessary to use very sharp forceps (it is advisable to resharpen them before each dissection using a jeweler's stone). The retina is then separated from the vitreous and lens, and transferred to another petri dish with fresh HBSS. As with the chick eye, this dissection technique yields retinas completely free of contamination with other eye tissues, including pigment epithelium. It is advisable to limit dissection times to no more than 45–60 min, allowing the dissection of 4–6 eyes.

Dissociation Procedures

Isolated retinas are transferred to CMF, cut into small fragments using tungsten needles, and incubated at 37°C for 17 min in 0.25% trypsin in CMF containing 100 μg of DNase/ml (Appendix C,2,3) for 17 min at 37°C. This has been empirically determined to be the shortest treatment leading to complete tissue dissociation. Given the sensitivity of mouse retinal cells to trypsin, it is crucial to rinse the tissue twice in a 0.25% solution of soybean trypsin inhibitor in EBM (Appendix C,4), followed by two rinses in EBM–

BSA, and triturated 10–12 times with a narrow-tip Pasteur pipette in 1.5 ml of this same solution. The resulting suspension of single cells is diluted in Dulbecco's modified Eagle's medium (DME), filtered through Nitex, and counted with a hemocytometer. Ninety-five percent of the cells usually exclude Trypan Blue after this procedure.

Culture Conditions

The culture medium is serum-free and chemically defined (Appendix B,2). Cells are seeded in tissue culture plastic dishes (Falcon Plastics, Oxnard, CA) pretreated with polyornithine and schwannoma conditioned medium (Appendix A,2). Usual seeding density is 6×10^5 cells per 35-mm dish, in 2 ml of medium. The cultures are incubated at 36.5°C in a humidified atmosphere of 5.5% CO_2 in air.

Description of Cultures and Some Considerations on Analytical Techniques

As in the case of chick cultures, most cells attach to the substratum as single, unaggregated units. Onset of cell process development is rapid, giving rise to extensive neurite networks. As shown in Fig. 3, during the first week *in vitro* it becomes possible to identify multipolar neurons, rod photoreceptor cells, and process-free, undifferentiated cells. The morphology of the rod photoreceptors present in these cultures is very different from that of chick cones, but their identity has been corroborated by light and electron microscopy, as well as by the immunocytochemical demonstration of opsin and the interphotoreceptor retinoid binding protein (IRBP; 17, 35). The uptake of neurotransmitter-related molecules has also been investigated in these cultures using autoradiographic techniques. It is noteworthy that there is specific degeneration of greater than 90% of the photoreceptor cells during the second week in culture, while less than 20% of the multipolar neurons are affected. This selective photoreceptor degeneration is observed with both wild-type and *rd* cells, suggesting that photoreceptor cells express a specific trophic requirement at that stage (for more details, see Refs. 18 and 36).

Retinas from 2-day-old mice yield only $5–6 \times 10^6$ cells/mouse. Since dissections are usually restricted to three mice at a time, each dissection yields enough cells for 20–30 cultures in 35-mm dishes, or 1–2 cultures in 100-mm dishes. Biochemical studies are thus more limited than in the case of the chick, but are nonetheless possible. High-affinity uptakes of neurotransmit-

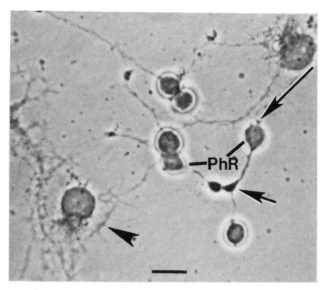

FIG. 3   Mouse retinal cells after 7 days *in vitro*. Photoreceptor cells (PhR) show a short neurite ending in a spherulelike body (short arrow) and an apical structure (long arrow) that electron microscopic studies show to be a cilium. Multipolar neurons show different morphologies (arrowhead). Process-free, round cells are also present. Bar, 10 μm. [Reproduced with permission from Politi *et al.* (17).]

ter molecules can be measured in individual 35-mm cultures, and the cholinergic enzyme choline acetyltransferase has been measured in samples consisting of two cultures in 35-mm dishes (18, 37). Immunochemical determinations of the retinoid binding protein IRBP or of the visual pigment protein opsin using the "slot blot" method have been possible in samples containing 5–10 cultures in 35-mm dishes (35). Proteoglycan synthesis can be investigated by using 1–2 cultures in 100-mm dishes (i.e., the entire yield from one individual dissection; see Ref. 38).

Generation of Enriched Populations of Mouse Photoreceptor Cells

As in the case of chick cells, it is possible to enrich the cultures for photoreceptor cells by selective destruction of multipolar neurons with KA (37). Lower KA concentrations than in the case of chick cultures result in the elimination of as many as 90% of the neurons in approximately 5 hr, without detectable changes in the photoreceptors.

Appendix

A. Substrata

1. Polyornithine

a. We use 20,000–40,000 MW polyornithine (PORN; ICN Pharmaceuticals, Costa Mesa, CA; Cat. #102696 or Sigma, St. Louis, MO; Cat. #P-61012)
b. Buffer: Boric acid/NaOH at 0.15 M each (1.59 g of boric acid, 0.750 g of NaOH, 125 ml deionized water). Adjust pH to 8.4 with HCl
c. Stock polyornithine solution [0.1% (w/v) in borate buffer]: 0.1 g of polyornithine is added to 100 ml of pH 8.4 borate buffer, filter-sterilized, labeled, and refrigerated
d. Working solutions: Optimal concentrations must be determined for each cell type. We routinely use 10–50 μg/ml. Stock solution is diluted with deionized water
e. Coating dishes: One and a half milliliters of polyornithine solution is added to 35-mm tissue culture plastic dishes. Volumes are adjusted proportionally to the surface area of other dishes. The entire surface of the dish must be covered. The dishes are kept for 1–24 hr at room temperature in a dust-free environment, washed twice with 2.0 ml of distilled water, and once with serum-free medium

2. Further Treatments of PORN-Coated Dishes for Serum-Free Cultures

If serum-free medium is to be used, PORN-coated dishes must be preincubated for 3–12 hr with medium containing 2% (v/v) fetal calf serum. If more abundant development of nerve fibers is desirable, this medium should be supplemented with laminin (10 μg/ml) or with 25% (v/v) schwannoma conditioned medium which contains the neurite-promoting factor, PNPF (37). The dishes should be rinsed twice with serum-free medium before cell seeding.

3. Preparation of Glass Coverslips for Cell Culture

Coverslips are placed in porcelain racks and soaked in concentrated nitric acid for 1.5–3 hr, and washed three times, 1 hr each time, by immersing the rack in distilled water. The coverslips are then individually rinsed under running distilled water and are returned to the racks. They are dried in a drying oven and are autoclaved between layers of lens paper in glass petri dishes. They are coated with PORN and other factors as described above. Coverslips with an etched grid are from Bellco (Vineland, NJ; Cat. #1916-92525).

B. Culture Media

1. For Chick Cells

a. Serum-containing medium (11): Medium 199 (i.e., GIBCO Grand Island, NY; #400-1100 EC), supplemented with glutamine (2 mM), penicillin (100,000 U/liter), fetal calf serum (10%), and linoleic acid/BSA (110 mg/ml).

b. Serum-Free Medium (16): Equal parts of medium 199 and Dulbecco's modified Eagle's medium with high pyruvate (DME; i.e., GIBCO #430-1600), with the same supplements indicated below for mouse cells.

2. For Mouse Cells (17)

DME supplemented with HEPES (20 mM), penicillin (100,000 U/liter), glutamine (2 mM), cytidine 5'-diphosphocholine (CDP-choline) (2.56 mg/liter), cytidine 5'-diphosphoethanolamine (CDP-ethanolamine) (1.28 mg/liter), hydrocortisone (100 nM), insulin ($16.6 \times 10^{-7}\ M$), progesterone ($4 \times 10^{-8}\ M$), putrescine ($2 \times 10^{-4}\ M$), selenium ($6 \times 10^{-8}\ M$), and transferrin ($12.5 \times 10^{-8}\ M$).

3. Sources for Medium Supplements

From Sigma: L-glutamine (G-3126), putrescine (P-7505), progesterone (P-0130), linoleic acid–albumin (L-8383), transferrin (T-2252), insulin (I-5500), CDP-choline (C-0256), CDP-ethanolamine (C-1383), sodium selenite (S-1382), hydrocortisone (H-4001).

From Calbiochem (San Diego, CA): HEPES (#391338); from GIBCO: penicillin (#860-1840HI).

C. Other Culture Reagents

1. Hanks' BSS, CMF-HBSS: We purchase 10× stock solutions (i.e., HBSS: Irvine Scientific, Santa Ana, CA; #9222; CMF: ibid #92301).
2. Trypsin (0.25% (w/v) in CMF): From Irvine Scientific, #9338. Solution is aliquoted and store frozen.
3. DNase (100× solution): Dissolve 10 mg of deoxyribonuclease I (Sigma D-4638) in 6.66 ml of CMF. Filter-sterilize, aliquot, freeze. Add to trypsin just before use for tissue dissociation.
4. Soybean trypsin inhibitor (STI; 0.25%): Dissolve 250 mg of STI (Sigma #T-9128, type II) in 100 ml of DME or 199. Filter-sterilize (it is *very* difficult to filter); fractionate in 5-ml aliquots.
5. EBM + 1% BSA: Prepare 1 liter of Eagle's basal medium with Hanks'

salts (Gibco, #420-1100). Add 10 g of bovine serum albumin (Sigma, #A-9647). Stir *slowly* (it foams), filter-sterilize, store refrigerated at 4°C.

D. Miscellaneous Supplies and Protocols

1. Dissecting Tools

a. Dressing forceps, surgical grade, 114 mm (Thomas Scientific, Swedesboro, NJ; #3865-L14).
b. Perry pliers, curved tips, serrated (Biochemical Research Instruments, Inc., Rockville, MD; Cat. #PL312).
c. Angled Dumont tweezers (Biomedical Research, Cat. #10-1060).
d. Tungsten needles: Tungsten wire (0.51 mm in diameter; from Ted Pella, Tustin, CA; Cat. #27-20), electrolytically sharpened. Power supply: high-amperage, low-voltage transformer, of the type frequently used for microscopes; set at 2–10 V. Electrolyte solution: 1–5 M NaOH or KOH. Tungsten wire to be sharpened is used as one electrode, and a piece of carbon (graphite) as the opposite electrode. The tungsten wire, held with an alligator clip, is immersed in the electrolyte solution repeatedly, and for brief periods, to obtain adequate tip. Use approximately 10 V first, then decrease voltage for final surface polishing (check under dissecting microscope). After sharpening, mount needle with epoxy-type resin into a 10- to 11-cm-long piece of glass tubing (i.e., Pyrex 7740 from Corning, Corning, NY; external diameter: 3 mm).

2. Siliconized Pasteur Pipettes

Place pipettes (tip up) in tall cylinder containing Prosil-28 (from American Scientific, Columbia, MD), diluted according to product specifications. Make sure no air bubbles remain inside the pipettes. Wash extensively, dry, cotton-plug, and autoclave.

3. Nitex Filters

Pieces of Nitex nylon mesh (mesh opening: 20 μm; from Tetko, Inc., Elmford, NY) are mounted at one end of a piece of glass tubing (Kimble, Langhorne, PA; #46470; outside diameter 10 ± 0.2 mm), and are kept in place with a plastic ring, cut from a cryotube (i.e., Nunc 363452, from Thomas Scientific).

Acknowledgments

Original studies summarized in this chapter have been supported by USPHS grants EY04859 and 05404, the Alcon Research Foundation, and Research to Prevent

Blindness, Inc. The author is indebted to Dr. A. T. Hewitt for suggestions on the manuscript, to Mrs. D. Golembieski for secretarial assistance, and to Dr. M. Lehar for photographic work.

References

1. S. Ramon y Cajal, "The Structure of the Retina" (S. A. Thorpe and M. Glickstein, trans.). Thomas, Springfield, Illinois, 1972.
2. P. V. Sarthy, B. M. Curtis, and W. A. Catterall, *J. Neurosci.* **3**, 2532 (1983).
3. P. M. Iuvone, *in* "The Retina: A Model for Cell Biology Studies" (R. Adler and D. Farber, eds.), Part II, p. 2. Academic Press, Orlando, Florida, 1986.
4. R. E. Marc, *in* "The Retina: A Model for Cell Biology Studies" (R. Adler and D. Farber, eds.), Part I, p. 17. Academic Press, Orlando, Florida, 1986.
5. K. R. Fry and D. M.-K. Lam, *Prog. Retinal Res.* **8**, 1 (1988).
6. P. Linser, *Am. Zool.* **27**, 161 (1987).
7. R. Adler, *Prog. Retinal Res.* **6**, 1 (1987).
8. G. Grun, *Adv. Anat. Embryol. Cell Biol.* **78**, 7 (1982).
9. R. Adler, M. Manthorpe, and S. Varon, *Dev. Biol.* **69**, 424 (1979).
10. R. Adler, P. J. Magistretti, A. G. Hyndman, and W. J. Shoemaker, *Dev. Neurosci.* **5**, 27 (1982).
11. R. Adler, J. D. Lindsey, and C. L. Elsner, *J. Cell Biol.* **99**, 1173 (1984).
12. R. Adler, *in* "Handbook of Nervous System and Muscle Factor" (J. R. Perez-Polo, ed.), p. 151. CRC Press, Boca Raton, Florida, 1987.
13. R. Adler and M. Hatlee, *Science* **243**, 391 (1989).
14. V. Hamburger and L. Hamilton, *J. Morphol.* **88**, 49 (1951).
15. J. D. Lindsey and R. Adler, *Invest. Ophthalmol. Visual Sci. (Suppl.)* **27**, 329 (1986).
16. R. Adler and L. E. Politi, manuscript in preparation.
17. L. E. Politi, M. Lehar, and R. Adler, *Invest. Ophthalmol. Visual Sci. (Suppl.)* **29**, 534 (1988).
18. L. E. Politi and R. Adler, *Exp. Eye Res.* **47**, 269 (1988).
19. M. Araki, *Dev. Biol.* **103**, 313 (1984).
20. R. Adler, *Dev. Biol.* **117**, 520 (1986).
21. S. A. Madreperla and R. Adler, *Dev. Biol.* **131**, 149 (1989).
22. S. A. Madreperla, M. Edidin, and R. Adler, *J. Cell Biol.* **107**, 783a (1989).
23. M. Pessin and R. Adler, *J. Neurosci. Res.* **14**, 317 (1985).
24. L. E. Politi and R. Adler, *Invest. Ophthalmol. Visual Sci.* **28**, 118 (1987).
25. P. M. Iuvone, G. Avendano, and R. Adler, *Invest. Ophthalmol. Visual Sci. (Suppl.)* **30**, 123 (1989).
26. L. Needham, R. Adler, and A. T. Hewitt, *Dev. Biol.* **126**, 304 (1988).
27. A. E. Schaffner and R. L. Schnaar, *in* "Current Methods in Cellular Neurobiology" (J. Barker and J. McKeivy, eds.), p. 131. Wiley, New York, 1983.
28. L. E. Politi and R. Adler, *Invest. Ophthalmol. Visual Sci.* **27**, 656 (1986).
29. I. G. Morgan, *Prog. Retinal Res.* **2**, 249 (1983).

30. N. Hirokawa, *J. Comp. Neurol.* **180,** 149 (1978).
31. D. S. Papermaster and B. G. Schneider, *in* "Cell Biology of the Eye" (D. McDevitt, ed.), p. 475. Academic Press, New York, 1982.
32. M. M. LaVail, *Invest. Ophthalmol. Visual Sci.* **21,** 630 (1981).
33. R. K. Hawkins, H. G. Jansen, and S. Sanyal, *Exp. Eye Res.* **41,** 701 (1985).
34. S. Sanyal, *in* "Degenerative Retinal Disorders: Clinical and Laboratory Investigations" (J. Hollyfield, R. E. Anderson, and M. M. LaVail, eds.), p. 175. Liss, New York, 1987.
35. L. E. Politi, L. E. Lee, B. Wiggert, G. Chader, and R. Adler, *Invest. Ophthalmol. Visual Sci. (Suppl.)* **14,** 672 (1988).
36. R. Adler and L. E. Politi, *in* "Inherited and Environmentally Induced Retinal Degenerations" (M. Lavail, ed.), p. 167. Liss, New York, 1989.
37. R. Adler, J. Jerdan, and A. T. Hewitt, *Dev. Biol.* **112,** 100 (1985).
38. A. T. Hewitt, L. E. Politi, F. Murillo-Lopez, and R. Adler, *Invest. Ophthalmol. Visual Sci. (Suppl.)* **30,** 489 (1989).

Section III

Bulk Isolation

[11]   Bulk Isolation of Mouse Oligodendrocytes by Gradient Centrifugations

Liane Bologa and Norbert Herschkowitz

Development of Oligodendrocyte Bulk Isolation Procedures

Thorough biochemical studies of any particular cell type require the availability of a pure cellular population. Ideally, the procedure for obtaining the cells should not be complicated and should yield reasonable quantities of material that would be of service in cellular neurochemistry research. Although of great interest for neurochemists, owing to the complex microarchitecture of the brain and to the intertwined network of cellular processes, the development of techniques for preparation of pure brain cells in bulk has been a lengthy process because of the many technical problems.

Several methods have been described in the literature for the isolation of neurons, astrocytes, and oligodendrocytes. The first important contribution, attributed to Korey and co-workers almost 35 years ago, concerned a crude isolation of glia from white matter (1). This technique has since been extensively developed and modified by other investigators. Ten years later, Rose (2) succeeded in isolating mechanically dissociated rat brain cells. The cells were suspended in a medium of 10% (w/v) Ficoll, 100 mM KCl, and 10 mM potassium phosphate buffer, pH 7.4, and centrifuged for 120 min at 0°C and 53,000 g on a Ficoll/sucrose gradient. Glia cells were collected on 30% Ficoll, and neurons were collected on 1.45 M sucrose. Hamberger et $al.$ (3) preincubated rabbit cortex as source tissue in a medium containing 120 mM NaCl, 20 mM glucose, 2.5 mM MgCl$_2$, 2.5 mM ADP, 2% Ficoll, 35 mM Tris-chloride, and 5 mM sodium phosphate buffer, pH 7.6. Investigators from the same laboratory, as an alternative, used 0.32 M sucrose, Tris buffer, EDTA, and Ficoll (4). The mixed cell suspension was also centrifuged on Ficoll/sucrose gradients. The neuronal fraction was collected between 40% (w/v) sucrose and 30% Ficoll, and the glial fraction between 15 and 12.5% Ficoll. Another procedure was devised by Johnson and Sellinger (5). Rat cortices were minced in the absence of digestive enzymes in a hypotonic medium consisting of 7.5% poly(vinylpyrrolidone), 10 mM CaCl$_2$, and 1% (w/v) bovine serum albumin (BSA). After repeated sievings, the cells were successively centrifuged at 0–4°C on three different gradients, the first consisting of 1.0 and 1.75 M sucrose (75,000 g, 30 min), the second of 30% Ficoll, 1.2 M sucrose, and 1.65 M sucrose (20,000 rpm, 30 min), and the third of 1.3 and

1.65 M sucrose (5,000 rpm, 20 min). Neuronal perikarya formed a pellet at the end of the first centrifugation; glia were collected at the 1.65 M sucrose interface. Norton and Poduslo (6) and Poduslo and Norton (7) preincubated minced rat cerebral tissue with 1% trypsin at 37°C for 90 min. The single cell suspension was centrifuged on two successive sucrose gradients, the first consisting of 0.9, 1.35, 1.55, and 2 M sucrose (3,300 g, 10 min), and the second of 0.9 and 1.4 M sucrose. Neurons were collected at the 2 M sucrose interface and did not require further purification. The crude glial layer collected at the 1.35 M sucrose interface was centrifuged on the second gradient and yielded pure astrocytes at the 0.9 M sucrose interface.

In order to avoid the possibly deleterious effect exerted on the cells by the high concentration of solutes used to form density gradients, Flangas (8) used centrifugal elutriation. Elutriation is a process of particle separation according to their rate of sedimentation while a liquid medium or gas containing the suspended particles is flowed upward against gravity. Particles whose sedimentation rates are less than the upward flow velocity are washed away from the larger, heavier particles. Six-day-old rat cerebra prepared as a 10% (v/v) cell suspension in 3% buffered Ficoll were fractionated in a Beckman CR-3 elutriator rotor. Pure neurons were recovered after a single passage through the elutriator at 2400 rpm using serial flow rates from 10 to 30 ml/min for 20 min. Glia were found in the overflow after a second passage by reelutriation through the rotor chambers at 5030 rpm at a rate of 11–22 ml/min for 30 min, 31–57 ml/min for 12 min, and 80 ml/min for 3 min. Schengrund and Repman (9) used the elutriation procedure to isolate cells from embryonic rat cerebra. The cells obtained were viable (recovery averaged to 70%), and could be cultivated. At 21 days *in vitro,* the cultures consisted of mixed cell populations.

As the interest in the viability of isolated cells increased, other techniques that preserved cellular integrity were also sought. Cohen and co-workers (10) isolated viable perikarya from developing rat cerebellum by incubating the minced tissue in Krebs–Ringer phosphate buffer (supplemented with BSA, 3 mg/ml, pH 7.4) that contained, successively, trypsin (0.5–1 mg/ml), DNase (2 μg/ml), soybean trypsin inhibitor in a concentration equivalent to that of the trypsin, and 2 mM EDTA (Ca^{2+}- and Mg^{2+}-free) prior to centrifugation (50 g, 5 min) on 4% (w/v) BSA in Krebs–Ringer buffer. Cerebral neurons that preserved their morphology as well as the proximal part of their processes were isolated from rat brain pretreated by *in situ* perfusion with a hyperosmotic solution containing hyaluronidase (460 U/mg) and collagenase (100 U/mg) prior to centrifugation on a discontinuous sucrose gradient. The neurons were collected at the 2 M sucrose interface (11). Another technique for isolating integer rat brain astrocytes and neurons was developed by Farooq and Norton (12) by using a single-cell suspension (obtained by incubation of brain slices with 0.1% (w/v) acetylated trypsin, sieving, and differential centrifugation) that was centrifuged (8500 g, 5 min) on a 10, 22, 28, and 32% Ficoll gradient. Neurons were collected as a pellet, while astrocytes and some contaminants were found at the 22% Ficoll interface. Schnitzer and Schachner (13) isolated cells from early postnatal mouse cerebellar cortex by discontinuous BSA gradient centrifugation. A 75% viable glial-enriched cell fraction (60% astrocytes, 6% oligodendrocytes) that also contained fibroblasts and small neurons (putative stellate and basket cells) was collected at the 15% BSA interface.

A different concept of cell isolation has been presented by Dvorak *et al.* (14), who employed affinity methods for the purification of neurons from chick sympathetic ganglia. Briefly, a samall water-jacketed glass column containing α-bungarotoxin-coated Sepharose 6MB was constructed, and a suspension of dissociated sympathetic ganglia cells was passed through the column. Nonneuronal cells were eluted with Ca^{2+}- and Mg^{2+}-free phosphate-buffered saline (PBS). Ninety five percent pure neuronal cells were eluted after incubation with DNasc (4 μg/ml) and 0.1% trypsin for 2–3 min at 37°C. These cells could be cultured.

Oligodendroglia were first isolated by Fewster *et al.* (15, 16) from rat and bovine white matter using gradients of 20 and 30% Ficoll over 1.35 M sucrose, or 20, 30, and 43% Ficoll. Rat oligodendrocytes were collected at the 1.35 M sucrose interface, and bovine oligodendrocytes were collected at the 43% Ficoll interface. Iqbal and Tellez-Nagel (17) and Iqbal *et al.* (18) have used a combination of the techniques of Blomstrand and Hamberger (4) and Norton and Poduslo (6) for isolating cells from human postmortem tissue or from rat brain after incubation without enzymes. Poduslo and Norton (19) isolated oligodendroglia from calf white matter. Minced corpus callosum and centrum semiovale tissue were dissociated after incubation for 90 min at 37°C with 0.1% trypsin dissolved in a special medium consisting of glucose, fructose, and BSA in a 10 mM KH_2PO_4/NaOH buffer, pH 6 (hexose–albumin phosphate medium; HAP). The single-cell suspension was layered onto a discontinuous gradient of 1.4 and 1.55 M sucrose dissolved in the above medium and centrifuged at 3400 g for 20 min. Oligodendrocytes were recovered from the 1.55 M sucrose layer and from the pellet. This technique, which has been widely adopted by many laboratories (20–27), furnishes highly enriched preparations of oligodendroglia. The cells appeared both structurally intact (24, 28, 29) and metabolically active (20–23, 25–27, 30, 31). Since this technique is nearly identical to the one developed in the same laboratory for the isolation of neurons and astrocytes (6), the starting material required consists of dissected white matter. Despite this particularity, which favors the work with brains from larger animals, in a few cases, the procedure has also been applied to dissected rat brain white matter (23, 25).

Another technique has been used by Szuchet *et al.* (32), who succeeded in isolating intact, viable cells that were fractionated into two oligodendroglial subgroups. For this, trypsinized ovine white matter was disrupted by passage through a series of screens, the cells were freed of myelin by centrifugation in 0.9 *M* sucrose at 850 *g* for 10 min, the pellet was resuspended in 0.9 *M* sucrose, applied to a linear sucrose gradient (1.0–1.2 *M*), and centrifuged at 277 *g* for 40 min. All centrifugations were done at 0–4°C.

A different approach for obtaining viable cells originated from the idea that hyperosmotic chokes to the cells could be avoided by using gradients of isosmotic Percoll [poly(vinylpyrrolidone)-coated silica gel] as a separation medium. This medium was developed by Wolff and Pertoft (33) for the isolation of HeLa cells and later on applied to the isolation of other cell types (34). Using Percoll, Gebicke-Härter and co-workers obtained viable oligodendrocytes from white matter of young cat (35) or adult pig brain (36). Dissociated cells were incorporated in 25% Percoll, deposited under a 16.6% Percoll, and centrifuged for 30 min at 10,000 *g*. In this study (as well as in all the others using Percoll gradients), oligodendrocytes were found to float as a cloudy mass between the myelin and the erythrocyte rings. Of the dispersed cells, 80–99% (80–95%, respectively) could be classified as oligodendrocytes by transmission electron microscopy and immunocytochemical studies. Pleasure *et al.* (37) and Lisak *et al.* (38) isolated viable oligodendrocytes from minced calf cerebral white matter by trypsinization at pH 7.4, screening, and centrifuging for 15 min on a preformed 50% isosmotic Percoll gradient. A similar procedure has been used by the same research group to obtain viable oligodendrocytes from rat corpus callosum (39). The Percoll density gradient centrifugation (30 and 50%, respectively) even allowed Kim *et al.* (40) and Korn-Lubetzki *et al.* (41) to obtain viable oligodendrocytes from adult human brain obtained at autopsy.

In all the reports mentioned above, oligodendrocyte isolation involved as a first step dissection of the white matter out of the whole brain. While the brain of larger animals (bovine, ovine) has been used with predilection for this type of experiments, the usage of smaller animals has been reported as well (23, 25). The separation of gray matter from white matter, however, becomes very cumbersome when small animals such as developing rats and mice are involved; therefore, techniques not requiring this dissection step were devised. Chao and Rumsby (42) succeeded in isolating all three major brain cell types from the same rat brain by incubating a part of the biological material with 0.1% trypsin in HAP medium, pH 7.4, for 60 min at 37°C. This additional step led to a selective lysis of astrocytes and neurons, while oligodendrocytes maintained their integrity and could be further purified. Snyder *et al.* (43) found that oligodendroglia can be obtained from several species with little or no loss in yield and purity using balanced salt solutions at pH 7.4. This technique was used for the isolation of oligodendrocytes from undissected rat forebrain. The brain tissue was finely minced and incubated for 30 min at 37°C in 0.1% trypsin, 10 μg/ml DNase, and 25 mM HEPES in Hanks' balanced salt solution (BSS), pH 7.2. After dissociation, the cells were incorporated in 35% sucrose and layered over a gradient of 45 and 53% sucrose and centrifuged at 3065 g and 0–4°C for 15 min. All sucrose solutions were prepared in Hanks' BSS containing 25 mM HEPES. Oligodendrocytes were recovered from the whole volume (including the pellet) beneath the red-cell layer situated below the 53% sucrose interface. Koper *et al.* (44) isolated viable oligodendrocytes that displayed a 70% plating efficiency after isolation, and a purity of 67 ± 10% after 10 days in culture. These cells were obtained from 5- to 10-day-old rat pups by trypsinization and Percoll gradient centrifugation at 9150 g without prior dissection of the white matter. The Percoll gradient was performed by layering a suspension of dissociated cells in 25% Percoll under 15 ml of 20% Percoll. Kohsaka and co-workers (45) obtained viable mouse oligodendrocytes by using a 40%, *in situ* self-generated Percoll gradient centrifugation (60 min at 1500 g). These cells originated from 7-day-old BALB/c mouse brains, exhibited a purity of 85%, and could express myelin basic protein when transplanted into the corpus striatum of 4-week-old shiverer mutant mice.

Owing to the availability of myelin-deficient mouse mutants, a better knowledge of mouse oligodendrocyte properties is of particular interest. In order to perform antigenic and biochemical studies on mouse oligodendrocytes (46), we have developed a technique aimed at the bulk isolation of these cells. Prior experience of the procedures of Poduslo and Norton (19) and of Chao and Rumsby (42) has been of particular help in the development of our method, which is described below.

Isolation of Mouse Oligodendrocytes by Sucrose Gradient Centrifugation

Reagents

The following reagents are needed: KH_2PO_4, NaOH, glucose, fructose, BSA, EDTA, acetylated trypsin, trypsin inhibitor, fetal calf serum (FCS), sucrose, NaCl. The reagents used were from Sigma (St. Louis, MO) and Merck (Darmstadt, FRG). This does not imply that reagents from other sources would not be adequate.

Equipment

Surgical instruments for dissecting the brains: three pairs of scissors/forceps (for decapitation and dipping of the heads in ethanol, for cutting the skin, and for cutting the skull); one pair of recurved forceps for collecting the brains; one pair of forceps plus one razor blade for brain chopping; one 5-ml syringe plus one long (2/80 mm) needle for trituration; four plastic funnels; nylon cloth screens (mesh size: 180 and 75 μm), folded and fixed in the shape of the funnels; one 1-ml pipetman with plastic tips; one shaking water bath at 37°C; one swing-out rotor refrigeration centrifuge; one magnetic stirrer; usual laboratory glassware and pipettes.

Solutions

The quantities are given for the isolation of oligodendrocytes from 20 brains of 10-day-old mice (10 brains per centrifuge tube). The following solutions are necessary.

0.4 M KH$_2$PO$_4$ solution: 10 ml

100 mM KH$_2$PO$_4$ stock buffer: 40 ml, prepared from 10 ml of 0.4 M KH$_2$PO$_4$, 1.5 ml of 0.4 N NaOH, and 40 ml of H$_2$O

10 mM (working solution) hexose–phosphate (HP) medium: 275 ml, prepared from 27.5 ml of KH$_2$PO$_4$ buffer stock solution, 13.75 g of glucose (5%), 13.75 g of fructose (5%), and 275 ml of H$_2$O

HAP medium: we adopted the isolation medium consisting of hexose, albumin, and phosphate (HAP) described by Poduslo and Norton (19). We needed 210 ml that was prepared from 210 ml of HP medium and 21 g of BSA (final concentration of BSA, 1%); 80 ml of this medium was reserved for the preparation of sucrose solutions

HAP medium containing EDTA: 130 ml, prepared from 130 ml of HAP medium supplemented with EDTA to a final concentration of 10 mM; this is used for suspending the cells after trypsin removal and gradient centrifugations

Acetylated trypsin solution: 60 ml, prepared from HP supplemented with 0.05% acetylated trypsin. We chose acetylated trypsin because it was shown to be less damaging to the cell membrane during the isolation process (25). The pH of this solution was adjusted to 7.4 since it was shown by Chao and Rumsby (42) that incubation of minced rat brain tissue with 0.1% trypsin in HAP medium at pH 7.4

(60 min, 37°C) leads to the lysis of astrocytes and neurons while oligodendrocytes maintain their integrity

Trypsin inhibitor: 3 ml, prepared in HP; the concentration of this solution has to be calculated as a function of the activity of trypsin

Sucrose solutions in HAP: for the first gradient centrifugation, 0.9 and 1.55 M, 20 ml each; for the second gradient centrifugation, 1.2 and 1.75 M, 20 ml each

FCS: 10 ml

NaCl 9‰–10 mM EDTA: 2 ml

Procedure

Before starting, switch on the water bath. It is important that the procedure is carried out rapidly and the cells are maintained at 4°C throughout (except for trypsin incubation); therefore working in the coldroom or on ice is recommended. Twenty animals are decapitated and the heads are placed on an absorbent paper towel so that the blood is drained away as much as possible. Cerebra are dissected out and collected in two petri dishes placed on crushed ice (10 cerebra per petri dish). The cerebral tissue is minced as finely as possible with a razor blade and transferred to two 50-ml conical centrifuge tubes, each containing 30 ml of acetylated trypsin solution (0.05% in HP, pH 7.4). The contents of the two tubes are to be treated in parallel in an identical manner. The minced tissue is triturated by 10 medium-speed aspiration/repelling cycles with a 5-ml syringe equipped with a 2/80-mm needle, then incubated for 60 min in the shaking water bath at 37°C. The role of the trituration step is to increase the yield of isolated cells. Since neurons could be protected inside the tissue fragments from the lysing effect of the trypsin, to avoid any neuronal contamination it is important that this step takes place before the trypsinization. At the end of the incubation period, the tubes are placed on crushed ice and 1.5 ml of trypsin inhibitor solution and 5 ml of FCS are added to each tube. Subsequently, the cell suspension is filtered by pouring it through nylon cloth sieves (mesh size: 180 and 75 μm) placed over funnels. The trypsin is removed by a 5-min centrifugation at 110 g in a refrigerated centrifuge. The supernatant is discarded and the pellet is resuspended in 20 ml of HAP–EDTA. The two 20-ml cell suspensions are now being placed over the first sucrose gradient, which was prepared in 50-ml conical centrifuge tubes shortly before the removal of the trypsin solution was completed. It is important that the gradient is not prepared long in advance. To prepare the gradient, we found it very handy to deposit the upper sucrose layer (10 ml of 0.9 M sucrose in HAP) by touching the lower

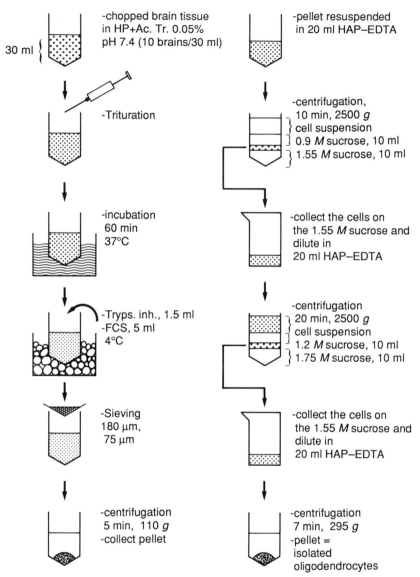

FIG. 1   Procedure for the isolation of mouse oligodendrocytes by sucrose gradient centrifugation.

layer (10 ml of 1.55 M sucrose in HAP) with the widely cut plastic tip of an automatic pipette. The cell suspension is deposited in the same way. This enabled us to prepare sharply delimited gradients within a couple of minutes. The tubes are then centrifuged for 10 min at 2500 g. The 25-ml HAP and 10-ml 0.9 M sucrose layers are discarded by aspiration with a vacuum attached Pasteur pipette that has been equipped at its tip with an obliquely cut plastic tube that permits the admission of air during the aspiration process. This is important for the maintenance of the distances between different layers during aspiration. It should also be noted that the layers are more visible if illuminated from behind. The cellular ring over the 1.55 M sucrose is collected with a pipette in a beaker and diluted dropwise under agitation on a magnetic stirrer with 20 ml of HAP–EDTA. The cell suspension is layered on a second sucrose gradient (10 ml of 1.2 M sucrose over 10 ml of 1.75 M sucrose) and centrifuged for 20 min at 2500 g. Isolated oligodendrocytes are recovered as a cellular ring at the 1.75 M sucrose interface. The collection and the dilution of these cells take place as above. Then the cells are spun for 7 min at 295 g and the pellet is resuspended in 1 ml of NaCl 9‰–EDTA for further analysis. An outline of this procedure is shown in Fig. 1.

Isolation of Mouse Oligodendrocytes by *in Situ* Self-Generated Percoll Gradient Centrifugation

Reagents

Same as for sucrose gradient cell isolation, plus commercial Percoll solution (Pharmacia, Uppsala, Sweden) and PBS tablets (Flow Laboratories, McLean, VA).

Equipment

Same as for sucrose gradient cell isolation, plus an ultracentrifuge with appropriate centrifuge tubes.

Solutions

The quantities are given for the isolation of oligodendrocytes from 12 brains of 10-day-old mice (6 brains per centrifuge tube). Many of the solutions used are similar to those used for the sucrose gradient cell isolation procedure.

0.4 *M* KH$_2$PO$_4$ solution: 1 ml

KH$_2$PO$_4$ buffer stock solution: 20 ml, prepared from 5 ml of 0.4 *M* KH$_2$PO$_4$, 750 μl of 0.4 *N* NaOH, and 20 ml of H$_2$O

HP medium: 165 ml, prepared from 16.5 ml of KH$_2$PO$_4$ buffer stock solution, 8.25 g of glucose, 8.25 g of fructose, and 165 ml of H$_2$O

HAP–EDTA medium: 100 ml, prepared from HP supplemented with 1% BSA and 10 m*M* EDTA

Acetylated trypsin solution: 60 ml, prepared from HP plus 0.05% acetylated trypsin

Trypsin inhibitor: 3 ml, prepared in HP

FCS: 10 ml

NaCl 9‰: 2 ml

PBS, 1×: 80 ml

PBS, 10×: 2 ml

Isosmotic Percoll: 20 ml, prepared from 18 ml of Percoll commercial solution and 2 ml of 10× PBS

Procedure

Until after trypsin solution removal, the procedure is identical to that for the isolation of oligodendrocytes by sucrose gradient centrifugation (see above). After removal of the trypsin solution, each pellet is resuspended in 3 ml of HAP–EDTA and mixed in a 26-ml round-bottomed Beckman centrifuge tube with 4.4 ml of isosmotic Percoll and 18.6 ml of PBS to obtain a 17% isosmotic Percoll solution. This is then centrifuged for 20 min at 20,000 *g* and 15°C. By this centrifugation, the first *in situ* self-generated Percoll gradient is formed. At the end of the centrifugation, the cloudy mixed cell population floating about 2 ml below the myelin layer is collected, diluted 5-fold with HAP–EDTA, and centrifuged for 5 min at 295 *g*. Each pellet is then suspended in 3 ml of HAP and mixed with 5.4 ml of isosmotic Percoll and 17.4 ml of PBS to obtain a final concentration of 21% Percoll. The tubes are centrifuged as above to form the second *in situ* self-generated gradient. Isolated oligodendrocytes were collected between the debris and erythrocytes layers, were diluted 5-fold with HAP–EDTA, and spun at 295 *g* for 5 min. The pelleted cells were suspended in NaCl 9‰ for further analysis.

Observation

If the cultivation of isolated cells is intended, the HP medium and the PBS should contain antibiotic/antimycotic solutions (GIBCO, Grand Island, NY)

and be autoclaved. The HAP should be sterilized by filtration, all the instruments should be sterilized, and all the manipulations should be done sterilely. At the end of the isolation procedure, the cells are suspended in tissue culture medium.

Characteristics of Isolated Oligodendrocytes

Since first devised, the isolation of oligodendroctyes aimed at the acquisition of new data on this particular brain cell type. Earlier studies that used sucrose gradients dealt mainly with the biochemical properties of oligodendrocytes. For example, extensive analysis of proteins and nucleic acids (16, 18, 43), protein profiles and peptide maps (18), *in vitro* protein synthesis (25), estimation of enzyme activities (46), lipid and nucleic acid analysis (19), biosynthesis of lipids (23, 47), plasma membrane isolation (48), and ultrastructure studies (18, 28, 42, 43, 47) were performed, and antisera to the isolated cells were raised (46, 49). An exception is given in the report of Szuchet *et al.* (47), who used oligodendrocytes obtained by sucrose gradients also for culture purposes. Viable cells that were isolated by Percoll gradients were used mainly for culture and antigenic marker expression studies (36, 39, 40, 41, 44). Pleasure *et al.* (37) demonstrated lipid biosynthesis, and Kohsaka *et al.* (45) successfully transplanted Percoll-isolated oligodendrocytes. Owing to the multitude of various techniques that have all been devised for specific purposes, it is not possible to establish a hierarchy as to their usefulness. The reader is prompted to choose the appropriate technique in accordance with his/her goals.

We were interested in developing procedures for the isolation of mouse oligodendrocytes that would allow (1) biochemical studies, for which a good cellular recovery is required, and (2) cultivation of the isolated cells, for which the viability of the cells is a prerequisite. Purity of the preparation is essential for both purposes. From this point of view, each of the isolation procedures we described above has its advantages and drawbacks. The great advantage of the sucrose gradient isolation procedure resides in the large number of cells yielded. Thus, this technique is irreplaceable for biochemical studies. However, usually the cells obtained do not survive and cannot be cultivated for longer than a couple of days. In contrast, the efficiency of the Percoll isolation procedure is only 10% of that of the sucrose procedure. However, the cells survive and can subsequently be cultivated; thus, the Percoll method should be used when cell cultivation is intended.

When mouse oligodendrocytes were isolated by the sucrose gradient centrifugation technique, the following layers were obtained. At the end of the first gradient centrifugation, myelin floated over the 0.9 M sucrose, an oligodendrocyte-enriched mixed cell population formed a ring at the 1.55 *M* sucrose interface, and erythrocytes were pelleted. At the end of the second gradient centrifugation, isolated oligodendrocytes formed a ring at the 1.75 *M* sucrose interface. The viability of these cells varied between 38 and 60% by the Trypan blue exclusion test, and dropped to 25% after 16 hr of cultivation. The yield of isolated oligodendrocytes was 21.1×10^6 cells per gram of fresh brain tissue (mean value of nine experiments). The increased number of cells obtained versus that found by other investigators (7, 42) may be explained by the trituration step introduced by us. The cerebroside-sulfotransferase (CST) activity of this cell population was comparable to that of whole-brain microsomes, and it was about double the amount found in whole-brain homogenate (50). When tested for purity by indirect immunofluorescence using rabbit antigalactocerebroside (GC) serum (51), 95% of the isolated cells were revealed to be oligodendrocytes (Fig. 2). These cells expressed on their surface an antigenic molecule (other than GC) that was resistant to acetone, trypsin, and neuraminidase, and apparently did not contain L-fucose and mannose within its epitope. This antigenic compound was detected with an antibody raised in rabbits to mouse oligodendrocytes

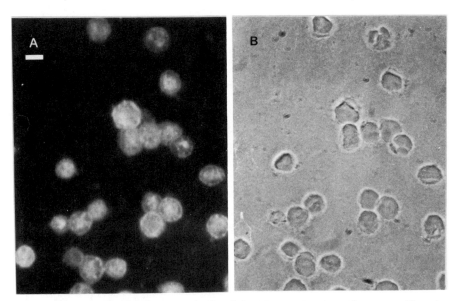

FIG. 2 Mouse oligodendrocytes isolated by the sucrose gradient centrifugation method and immunostained with rabbit anti-GC serum. (A) Immunofluorescence; (B) phase contrast of the same field as in a. Bar, 8.62 μm.

that were isolated by the above-described sucrose gradient centrifugation procedure (46).

When mouse oligodendrocytes were isolated by the *in situ* self-generated isosmotic Percoll gradient procedure, the following layers were obtained at the end of the first centrifugation, counting from the top of the tube: (a) small debris above the myelin; (b) myelin, debris, and agglomeration of debris; (c) first layer under the myelin, comprising small and large debris and a few cells; (d) second layer under the myelin, comprising round cells and small debris; (e) erythrocytes. These layers are shown schematically in Fig. 3. The actual content of the layers was photographed and it is presented in Fig. 4. At the end of the second centrifugation we obtained: (a) debris, (b) oligodendrocytes, (c) erythrocytes. Of these cells, 96–98% were GC-positive. The viability of isolated oligodendrocytes was over 90% and these cells could be cultivated. The yield of isolated cells was on average 2.6×10^6 cells/g, and therefore further biochemical studies were precluded.

Since only a few reports from the literature deal with the isolation of mouse oligodendrocytes (45), and moreover the three parameters we tried to pinpoint (yield, purity, viability) are not always given, a comparison of our techniques with those published by others is difficult. It is, however, feasible if attempts to isolate oligodendrocytes from other species are taken into consideration. Such comparisons are presented in Tables I and II. The methods we report here are highly reproducible and have a number of advantages. The sucrose gradient cell isolation procedure yields 2- to 10-fold more oligodendrocytes per gram of wet brain tissue as compared to other techniques, without incurring additional difficulties or costs. An exception is

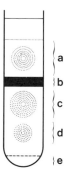

FIG. 3 Layers obtained by the first Percoll gradient centrifugation. (a) Small debris above the myelin; (b) myelin, debris, and agglomeration of debris; (c) first layer under the myelin, comprising small and large debris and a few cells; (d) second layer under the myelin, comprising round cells and small debris; (e) erythrocytes.

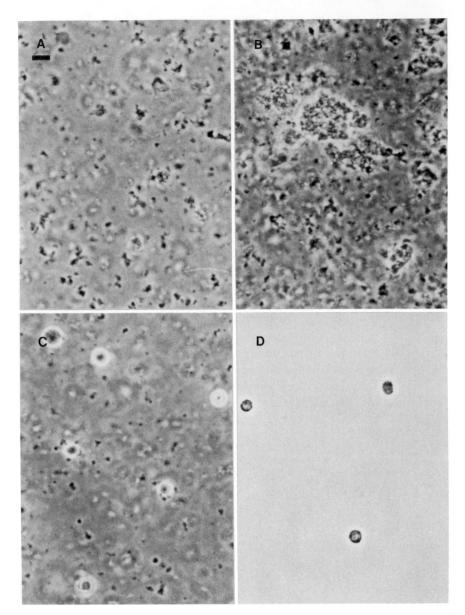

FIG. 4   Phase-contrast micrographs of the layers obtained during the Percoll gradient centrifugation procedure for mouse oligodendrocyte isolation. (A–C) First gradient centrifugation. (A) Small debris above the myelin; (B) myelin, debris, and agglomeration of debris; (C) second layer under the myelin, comprising round cells and small debris. (D) isolated oligodendrocytes from the middle layer of the second gradient centrifugation. Bar, 13.7 μm.

TABLE I Comparison of Different Techniques for Oligodendrocyte Isolation from Dissected White Matter (WM) by Gradient Centrifugation

Source	Gradient	Yield (cells/g)	Purity[a]	Viability	Reference
Calf WM	Sucrose, discontinuous	10.9×10^6	95% (morphology)		b
Bovine WM	Ficoll, discontinuous	52×10^6	95% (LM, TEM)		c
Rat WM	Sucrose, discontinuous	11.4×10^6			d
Ovine WM	Sucrose, linear	3×10^6	97% (GC$^+$)	Viable, cultivable	e
Cat WM	Percoll, discontinuous	1.5×10^6	80–90% (GC$^+$, TEM)	Viable, cultivable	f
Calf WM	Percoll, preformed	0.75×10^6	95% (TEM, GC$^+$)	80–95%	g
Rat corpus callosum (rcc)	Percoll, preformed	$0.5–1 \times 10^6$/10 rcc	90–95% (GC$^+$)	90%	h
Human WM	Percoll, in situ self-generated	$25–50 \times 10^4$	95%	80–90%	i
Pig WM	Percoll, discontinuous	3.2×10^6	80% (GC$^+$ after 6 weeks)	Viable, cultivable	j

[a] LM, Light microscopy; TEM, transmission electron microscopy; GC, galactocerebroside.
[b] S. E. Poduslo and W. T. Norton, *J. Neurochem.* **19**, 727 (1972).
[c] M. E. Fewster, S. K. Blackstone, and T. J. Ihrig, *Brain Res.* **63**, 263 (1973).
[d] N. L. Banik and M. E. Smith, *Neurosci. Lett.* **2**, 235 (1976).
[e] S. Szuchet, B. G. W. Arnason, and P. E. Polak, *J. Neurosci. Methods* **3**, 7 (1980).
[f] P. J. Gebicke-Härter, H.-H. Althaus, P. Schwartz, and V. Neuhoff, *Brain Res.* **227**, 497 (1981).
[g] D. Pleasure, M. Hardy, G. Johnson, R. Lisak, and D. Silberberg, *J. Neurochem.* **37**, 452 (1981).
[h] M. Hirayama, D. H. Silberberg, R. P. Lisak, and D. Pleasure, *J. Neuropathol. Exp. Neurol.* **42**, 16 (1983).
[i] S. U. Kim, Y. Sato, D. H. Silberberg, D. E. Pleasure, and L. B. Rorke, *J. Neurol. Sci.* **62**, 295 (1983).
[j] P. J. Gebicke-Härter, H.-H. Althaus, I. Rittner, and V. Neuhoff, *J. Neurochem.* **42**, 357 (1984).

TABLE II Comparison of Different Techniques for Oligodendrocyte Isolation from Whole-Brain Tissue by Gradient Centrifugation

Source	Gradient	Yield (cells/g)	Purity	Viability	Reference
Rat, adult whole brain	Sucrose, discontinuous	3.6×10^6	60–70% (morphology)	Exclude Trypan Blue for 120 min	[a]
Rat, 10 days old	Sucrose, discontinuous	7.1×10^6	90% (morphology)	80–90% exclude Trypan Blue	[b]
Rat, 1–10 days old	Percoll discontinuous	$2–4 \times 10^6$/brain	Mixed cultures after 21 days	70–80% (attachment)	[c]
Mouse brain, 7 days old	Percoll, in situ self-generated		85% (GC$^+$)	95% exclude Trypan Blue	[d]
Mouse brain, 10 days old	Sucrose, discontinuous	21.1×10^6	95% (GC$^+$)	38–60% exclude Trypan Blue	Text
Mouse brain, 10 days old	Percoll, in situ self-generated	2.6×10^6	96–98% (GC$^+$)	90% cultivable, exclude Trypan Blue	Text

[a] S.-W. Chao and M. Rumsby, *Brain Res.* **124**, 347 (1977).

[b] D. S. Snyder, C. S. Raine, M. Farooq, and W. T. Norton, *J. Neurochem.* **34**, 1614 (1980).

[c] J. W. Koper, M. Lopes-Cardozo, H. J. Romijn, and L. M. G. van Golde, *J. Neurosci. Methods* **10**, 157 (1984).

[d] S. Kohsaka, K. Yoshida, Y. Inoue, T. Shinozaki, H. Takayama, H. Inoue, K. Mikoshiba, K. Takamatsu, M. Otani, and S. Toya, *Brain Res.* **372**, 137 (1986).

made by the method of Iqbal *et al.* (18) which yields 52×10^6 cells/g, but this technique requires dissected white matter as the starting material and thus it is not applicable to mouse oligodendrocyte isolation. The Percoll gradient cell isolation procedure yields a number of cells that is comparable to that obtained from dissected white matter by Gebicke-Harter *et al.* (35, 36) and is 3.3 times higher than the quantities of cells obtained by Pleasure *et al.* (37) and by Lisak *et al.* (38). The yield and purity of the cells obtained by sucrose gradient centrifugation, and the viability and purity of those obtained by using Percoll define these methods as useful tools for studying the biochemistry of mouse oligodendrocytes.

Acknowledgments

This work was supported by a grant from the Swiss Multiple Sclerosis Society and a grant from the Swiss National Science Foundation (3.156-0.88).

References

1. S. R. Korey, M. Orchen, and M. Brotz, *J. Neuropathol. Exp. Neurol.* **17,** 430 (1958).
2. S. R. P. Rose, *Biochem. J.* **102,** 33 (1967).
3. A. Hamberger, O. Eriksson, and K. Norrby, *Exp. Cell Res.* **67,** 380 (1971).
4. C. Blomstrand and A. Hamberger, *J. Neurochem.* **16,** 1401 (1969).
5. D. E. Johnson and O. Z. Sellinger, *J. Neurochem.* **18,** 1445 (1971).
6. W. T. Norton and S. E. Poduslo, *Science* **167,** 1144 (1970).
7. S. E. Poduslo and W. T. Norton, *in* "Methods in Enzymology" (J. M. Lowenstein, ed.), Vol. 35, p. 561. Academic Press, New York, 1975.
8. A. L. Flangas, *Prep. Biochem.* **4,** 165 (1974).
9. C.-L. Schengrund and M. A. Repman, *J. Neurochem.* **33,** 283 (1979).
10. J. Cohen, G. R. Dutton, G. P. Wilkin, J. E. Wilson, and R. Balázs, *J. Neurochem.* **23,** 899 (1974).
11. H.-H. Althaus, W. B. Huttner, and V. Neuhoff, *Hoppe-Seyler's Z. Physiol. Chem.* **358,** 1155 (1977).
12. M. Farooq and W. T. Norton, *J. Neurochem.* **31,** 887 (1978).
13. J. Schnitzer and M. Schachner, *J. Neuroimmunol.* **1,** 457 (1981).
14. D. J. Dvorak, E. Gipps, and C. Kidson, *Nature (London)* **271,** 565 (1978).
15. M. E. Fewster, A. B. Scheibel, and J. F. Mead, *Brain Res.* **6,** 401 (1967).
16. M. E. Fewster, S. K. Blackstone, and T. J. Ihrig, *Brain Res.* **63,** 263 (1973).
17. K. Iqbal and I. Tellez-Nagel, *Brain Res.* **45,** 296 (1972).
18. K. Iqbal, I. Grundke-Iqbal, and H. M. Wisniewski, *J. Neurochem.* **28,** 707 (1977).

19. S. E. Poduslo and W. T. Norton, *J. Neurochem.* **19**, 727 (1972).
20. S. R. Cohen and J. Bernsohn, *Brain Res.* **60**, 521 (1973).
21. S. R. Cohen and J. Bernsohn, *J. Neurochem.* **30**, 661 (1978).
22. J. A. Benjamins, M. Guarnieri, K. Miller, M. Sonneborn, and G. M. McKhann, *J. Neurochem.* **23**, 751 (1974).
23. D. S. Deshmukh, T. J. Flynn, and R. A. Pieringer, *J. Neurochem.* **22**, 479 (1974).
24. B. D. Trapp, B. Dwyer, and J. Bernsohn, *Neurobiology* **5**, 235 (1975).
25. N. L. Banik and M. E. Smith, *Neurosci. Lett.* **2**, 235 (1976).
26. D. Pleasure, O. Abramsky, D. Silberberg, B. Quinn, J. Parris, and T. Saida, *Brain Res.* **134**, 377 (1977).
27. D. Pleasure, C. Lichtman, S. Eastman, M. Lieb, O. Abramsky, and D. Silberberg, *J. Neurochem.* **32**, 1447 (1979).
28. C. S. Raine, S. E. Poduslo, and W. T. Norton, *Brain Res.* **27**, 11 (1971).
29. C. S. Raine, U. Traugott, K. Iqbal, D. S. Snyder, S. R. Cohen, M. Farooq, and W. T. Norton, *Brain Res.* **142**, 85 (1978).
30. S. E. Poduslo and G. M. McKhann, *Neurosci. Lett.* **5**, 159 (1977).
31. S. E. Poduslo, K. Miller, and G. M. McKhann, *J. Biol. Chem.* **253**, 1592 (1978).
32. S. Szuchet, B. G. W. Arnason, and P. E. Polak, *J. Neurosci. Methods* **3**, 7 (1980).
33. D. A. Wolff and H. Pertoft, *J. Cell Biol.* **55**, 579 (1972).
34. F. Gmelig-Meyling and T. A. Waldmann, *J. Immunol. Methods* **33**, 1 (1980).
35. P. J. Gebicke-Härter, H.-H. Althaus, P. Schwartz, and V. Neuhoff, *Brain Res.* **227**, 497 (1981).
36. P. J. Gebicke-Härter, H.-H. Althaus, I. Rittner, and V. Neuhoff, *J. Neurochem.* **42**, 357 (1984).
37. D. Pleasure, M. Hardy, G. Johnson, R. Lisak, and D. Silberberg, *J. Neurochem.* **37**, 452 (1981).
38. R. P. Lisak, D. E. Pleasure, D. H. Silberberg, M. C. Manning, and T. Saida, *Brain Res.* **233**, 107 (1981).
39. M. Hirayama, D. H. Silberberg, R. P. Lisak, and D. Pleasure, *J. Neuropathol. Exp. Neurol.* **42**, 16 (1983).
40. S. U. Kim, Y. Sato, D. H. Silberberg, D. E. Pleasure, and L. B. Rorke, *J. Neurol. Sci.* **62**, 295 (1983).
41. I. Korn-Lubetzki, H. Ovadia, U. Wald, and O. Abramsky, *Neurosci. Lett.* **69**, 25 (1986).
42. S.-W. Chao and M. Rumsby, *Brain Res.* **124**, 347 (1977).
43. D. S. Snyder, C. S. Raine, M. Farooq, and W. T. Norton, *J. Neurochem.* **34**, 1614 (1980).
44. J. W. Koper, M. Lopes-Cardozo, H. J. Romjin, and L. M. G. van Golde, *J. Neurosci. Methods* **10**, 157 (1984).
45. S. Kohsaka, K. Yoshida, Y. Inoue, T. Shinozaki, H. Takayama, H. Inoue, K. Mikoshiba, K. Takamatsu, M. Otani, and S. Toya, *Brain Res.* **372**, 137 (1986).
46. S. L. Bologa, H. P. Siegrist, and N. Herschkowitz, *Neurosci. Lett.* **22**, 131 (1981).
47. S. Szuchet, K. Stefansson, R. L. Wollmann, G. Dawson, and B. G. W. Arnason, *Brain Res.* **200**, 151 (1980).

48. S. E. Poduslo, *J. Neurochem.* **24,** 647 (1975).
49. S. E. Poduslo, H. F. McFarland, and G. M. McKhann, *Science* **197,** 270 (1977).
50. H. P. Siegrist, S. L. Bologa, T. Burkart, U. Wiesmann, K. Hofmann, and N. Herschkowitz, *J. Neurosci. Res.* **6,** 293 (1981).
51. S. L. Bologa, H. P. Siegrist, A. Z'graggen, K. Hofmann, U. Wiesmann, D. Dahl, and N. Herschkowitz, *Brain Res.* **210,** 217 (1981).

[12] Bulk Isolation and Culture of Oligodendroglia from Mature Brain

William T. Norton and Muhammad Farooq

Methods exist for the bulk preparation from the mature central nervous system (CNS) of astrocytes (1–3), neurons (1–3), oligodendrocytes (4–11), and vascular endothelial cells (e.g., 12, 13). With existing techniques only the latter two cell types can be maintained in culture, although there has been some success in obtaining small numbers of viable neurons from young developing rats (14). Astrocytes can be cultured from the adult brain (15–17), but it is probable that such cells derive from immature glial precursor cells present in the adult CNS, rather than from preexisting differentiated cells (17, 18).

The various methods for the isolation and subsequent cell culture of mature oligodendroglia differ in particulars, such as the animal species used, the composition of the isolation medium, and the composition of the density gradients used for purification. They all derive in principle, however, from an earlier technique (4) that produced oligodendroglia in high yield and purity but which did not survive well in culture, probably because of the unphysiological medium used during isolation. Cells obtained by these newer techniques from mature animals are fully differentiated; they can be kept in culture for weeks to months, and they retain their differentiated properties for the entire period (9, 10, 17–21). Thus, these preparations permit investigations that may not be possible with cultures derived from

Methods in Neurosciences, Volume 2

neonates, which contain a mixture of astrocytes, microglia, glial progenitor cells, and oligodendrocytes in various stages of differentiation, or with oligodendrocytes purified from these cultures (22).

Most investigators (17, 18, 21) find that cultures of mature oligodendroglia soon become contaminated with rapidly growing astrocytes and/or fibroblasts (9, 10). This problem, however, does not seem to have been encountered with cultures of oligodendrocytes from lamb brain (20). These astrocytes apparently derive from a small population of glial precursor cells that coisolate with the oligodendrocytes (17, 18). The growth of rapidly dividing cells can be suppressed by adding a mitotic inhibitor to the medium (21). However, it may eventually be possible to destroy the precursor cells selectively to avoid this problem.

The method described here has been developed in our laboratory and is used on a routine basis to isolate oligodendroglia from bovine and rat brains. The following protocol has been improved and simplified from the procedures originally described (6, 8). Although the published procedures work well, we have found they contain unnecessary steps and thus take longer to complete.

The great advantage of the procedure is that is can be used with undissected rat forebrain. We have found that, during incubation in our physiological medium at pH 7.3, the neurons and astrocytes lyse but the oligodendrocytes remain intact (6). This greatly simplifies the purification of these cells. However, we generally use dissected white matter when isolating bovine cells because this dissection is rapid and easy and gives an increased yield.

Isolation of Oligodendroglia from Bovine Brain

The procedure consists of three steps: (1) incubation of minced tissue with trypsin, (2) disaggregation through screens to form a cell suspension, and (3) purification of the cells by centrifugation on a sucrose density gradient.

Materials

Trypsin (type III, crystallized two times, from bovine pancreas), HEPES (N-1-hydroxyethylpiperazine-N'-ethanesulfonic acid), and deoxyribonuclease (DNase I, from bovine pancreas) were obtained from Sigma Chemical Co. (St. Louis, MO). Reagent grade glucose and sucrose were obtained from Fisher Scientific Co. (Fairlawn, NJ) and Hanks' balanced salt solution and calf serum from Grand Island Biological Co. (Grand Island, New York). Nitex nylon screens were obtained from TETKO Inc. (Elmsford, NY).

The isolation medium consists of Hanks' balanced salt solution containing 35 mM glucose, 10 μg/ml of DNase, and 25 mM HEPES, pH 7.3. Trypsin is added to this during the first step only. Calf serum is buffered by adding solid HEPES to 25 mM and adjusting the pH to 7.3 with 1 M NaOH. The stock solution for sucrose gradients is 70% (w/v) sucrose made up in isolation medium. This is then diluted with isolation medium to obtain 44% (w/v) and 48% (w/v) sucrose in medium.

Incubation

Bovine brains, obtained from freshly killed animals at a local slaughter-house, are placed in plastic bags on ice and brought to the laboratory. We have obtained satisfactory preparations from brains used as long as 4 hr after killing. Generally, we use 100 g of white matter, dissected from three brains, for each preparation, although 200 g can be processed in 1 day, and of course amounts smaller than 100 g can be used with appropriate adjustments in volumes of reagents. The white matter is finely minced with a tissue slicer blade on a cooled glass plate and divided into 50-g portions. Each portion is added to a 500-ml Erlenmeyer flask to which is added 150 ml of medium containing 0.1% (w/v) trypsin. The flasks are incubated at 37°C with shaking for 30 min. The flasks are cooled in ice and all further steps performed at 0–4°C. After allowing the minced tissue to settle for about 5 min, the supernatant is aspirated and discarded, and 75 ml of ice-cold medium plus 25 ml of cold buffered calf serum are added to each flask. The purpose of the calf serum is to inactivate the residual trypsin.

Disaggregation

A piece of nylon screen cloth with 145-μm openings (100 mesh) is stretched over a 24-cm-diameter plastic funnel and taped tight. The cloth is moistened with medium and both portions of the trypsinized white matter are poured on the screen. About 300 ml of fresh medium is added to the white matter on the screen and allowed to wash through. These washings are discarded. The tissue is then spread over the screen (we use the bottom of a small glass beaker for this) and, with gentle strokes, but without vacuum, is forced through the screen. To facilitate this process, small amounts of medium are frequently added to the top of the screen. At the end of the screening step a red layer of capillaries is seen adhering to the top of the screen. The tissue on the underside of the screen is scraped into the funnel and washed into the receiving flask with medium and the screen is discarded. The cell suspension is then filtered twice through a stainless steel screen with 74-μm openings (200 mesh) under slight vacuum, and finally through a 200-mesh nylon screen laid over the 200-mesh steel screen. The final filtrate is made up with medium to 175 ml/100 g of starting tissue.

Density Gradient Centrifugation

To 175 ml of cell suspension in medium is added an equal volume of 70% sucrose in medium to give a cell suspension in 35% (w/v) sucrose in medium. Equal volumes of the cell suspension are layered on each of two sucrose gradients prepared in 250-ml plastic centrifuge bottles. The gradients consist of 25 ml of 44% sucrose in medium layered over 50 ml of 48% sucrose in medium. The interface between the cell suspension and the 44% sucrose layer is disturbed by stirring the boundary with a Pasteur pipette to give a partially continuous zone. The bottles are centrifuged at 3600 g (3600 rpm in a Sorvall HG-4 rotor) for 14 min at 4°C. The oligodendroglia form a thin pellet on the bottom of the bottle and there is a myelin-rich layer on top. This layer, the 44% sucrose layer, and the supernatant directly above the pellet are aspirated carefully and discarded.

The cells are pooled in 100 ml of medium and filtered through a nylon screen having 25-μm openings (460 mesh) to remove capillary fragments. Aliquots can be taken at this stage for cell counts and light microscopic examination. If the cells are desired for biochemical studies, they can be concentrated by centrifugation at 600 g, reconstituted to any convenient volume, or stored as a frozen pellet. If desired for cell culture, they must be transferred to tissue culture medium as described below. This entire procedure, from receiving the brains to obtaining a purified cell preparation, takes about 3 hr.

Isolation of Rat Brain Oligodendroglia

This procedure is nearly identical to that described for bovine brain, except that whole rat forebrain is used, the preparations are usually performed on a smaller scale, and changes in the composition of the gradient are sometimes desirable.

We generally use 30-day-old animals, although older animals can also be used. The preparations from animals younger than 30 days contain large amounts of glial precursor cells (see below). Usually, 10–20 animals (10–20 g of tissue) are processed at a time. The rats are decapitated, and the brains removed and trimmed of olfactory bulbs, cerebellum, and brain stem. The forebrains are minced and incubated as described above, using 3 ml of trypsinization medium per gram of tissue. Other volumes are reduced accordingly, and a 9-cm-diameter funnel is used for the screening step. The density gradient for purifying the cells can be prepared in one bottle. The gradient consists of, from the bottom up: 52% (w/v) sucrose in medium, 48% (w/v) sucrose in medium, and the cell suspension in 35% sucrose in medium. Typically, the following volumes are used: 50 ml of 52% sucrose in medium, 25 ml of 48% sucrose in medium, and 100 ml of cell suspension. Note that these solutions are more dense than those used for the bovine cells. This is to ensure more complete removal of erythrocytes. If 48 and 44% sucrose are used for the bottom two layers of the gradient, a maximum yield of oligodendrocytes can be obtained, but they are contaminated with erythrocytes. The interface between the cell suspension and the middle layer is disturbed as described above. After centrifugation at 3600 g for 15 min, the entire volume below the red-cell layer (which is below the interface of 48–52% sucrose layers) and the pellet are collected as the oligodendrocyte-enriched preparation. This can be diluted with medium, filtered through the 460-mesh screen, and concentrated by centrifugation as described above.

Properties of Isolated Cells

Bovine Oligodendroglia

Examination by phase microscopy shows that more than 90% of the preparation consists of small (6–12 μm diameter) phase-bright round cells. There are 6–8% phase-dark cells and free nuclei, a few red cells, and capillary fragments. The phase-bright cells exclude Trypan blue, whereas the phase-dark cells do not. No other cell types, such as astrocytes, neurons, or ependymal cells, can be detected. Ultrastructural examination shows that the vast majority of cells satisfies all *in situ* criteria for oligodendrocytes (8). The yield is 8×10^6 cells/g white matter, having a protein content of 33 pg/cell. Thus the average preparation of 8×10^8 cells from 100 g white matter contains 26 mg of protein from a single cell type (8). Since cell culture requires only 10×10^6 cells per 60-mm dish, this number of cells, after accounting for losses in transferring to tissue culture medium, would be sufficient for 50 dishes (see below).

Rat Cells

The microscopic appearance of these cells is very similar to that of the bovine cells (6). Small round phase-bright cells constitute 90% of the preparation. There are 3–6% red blood cells, 4–5% phase-dark cells and nuclei, occasional capillary fragments, and ependymal cells.

The yield of rat oligodendrocytes is about $6-8 \times 10^6$ cells/rat forebrain from 30- or 60-day-old animals. Thus, $60-80 \times 10^6$ cells containing 2–3 mg of protein can be obtained from 10 animals, enough to set up 5–10 60-mm culture dishes (18). Although we have published that oligodendroglia can also be isolated from 10-day-old animals, we now know that such preparations contain a high percentage of glial precursor cells (18, 23).

This isolation procedure also works well with guinea pigs as described. We believe it should be generally applicable to other species, although some variation in the gradients may be necessary.

Cell Culture (17, 18, 21)

Our standard tissue culture medium consists of Eagle's minimum essential medium (MEM) with Earle's salts, $1\times$ penicillin–streptomycin–fungizone mixture, 2 mM glutamine, 15% heat-inactivated calf serum (all from GIBCO, Grand Island, NY), and 0.5% (w/v) glucose. In some cases, 0.8×10^{-5} M cytosine 1-β-D-arabinofuranoside (cytosine arabinoside, Sigma) is incorporated in the medium. Cells are grown in Falcon plastic tissue culture dishes or flasks coated with poly(L-lysine) (PLL, from Sigma). Approximately 3 ml of a solution of 40 μg/ml of PLL in sterile water is added to each 60-mm dish and allowed to stand for 30 min. The solution is aspirated from the dishes and they are allowed to air-dry in the hood before use.

Cell preparations that have been concentrated by centrifugation as described above must be transferred from our isolation medium to tissue culture medium before plating. This is done by suspending them in a mixture of isolation medium : MEM (1 : 1), centrifuging, and then taking them up in tissue culture medium at a concentration of $10-20 \times 10^6$ cells/ml. The cells should be recounted at this stage since there can be a 30–50% loss of cells during the washing and centrifugation steps. They are then plated at a density of approximately 4×10^5 cells/cm^2 (about 10×10^6 cells per 60-mm dish). The cultures are maintained at 37°C in 5% CO_2 and the medium is changed every 3–4 days.

Bovine Cells

Approximately 75% of the cells attach and survive in culture, although they do not multiply (21). After 1 day in culture, 95% of the cells can be identified as oligodendroglia by immunocytochemical staining for the markers galactosylceramide and myelin basic protein (18). The remaining cells appear to be glial precursor cells which coisolate with oligodendrocytes and which eventually generate astrocytes (17, 18). Cultures containing different cell populations can be obtained from these parent cultures depending on the culture medium and how they are manipulated.

In the MEM–calf serum medium the oligodendrocytes appear as small round cells that begin to extend small processes in less than a week. At 6 days *in vitro* (DIV), the cultures still consist of about 90% oligodendrocytes. By this time, however, larger, bipolar cells have begun to grow, which will eventually become the predominant cell type, with clumps of oligodendrocytes growing on top of them. These large flat cells are usually mostly astrocytes, but fibroblast-type cells predominant in some cultures (17, 21).

The overgrowth of astrocytes and fibroblasts can be suppressed by including 0.8×10^{-5} M cytosine arabinoside in the cultures, beginning at 4–5 DIV. In this medium, cultures that consist of 90% oligodendrocytes can be maintained for up to 4 months (21). These cells form small clumps that elaborate an extensive network of processes throughout the dish. All cells of this morphology are positive for galactosylceramide and myelin basic protein (17, 18, 21), and have ultrastructural characteristics of mature oligodendrocytes (21). Moreover, intracellular vacuoles can be found in older cultures that have multilamellar walls with alternating major and minor dense lines resembling myelin (21).

If cultures are switched from MEM–calf serum medium to a defined, serum-free medium during the first week, the cultures consist of only astrocytes and oligodendrocytes (17). The latter cells can be removed to yield pure astrocyte cultures (17). These cells appear to derive from the glial precursor cells originally present in the cell isolates and not from contaminating astrocytes (18). Thus, if it is important for any investigation that the cultures contain the minimum number of nonoligodendroglial cells, the cultures in MEM–calf serum must be used within the first 6 DIV, or mitotic inhibitors must be included in the medium.

Rat Cells

Our experience with these cells is more limited then with bovine cells. The plating efficiency of rat oligodendrocytes is lower by a factor of 4–5 compared to bovine cells, and they become contaminated with astrocytes much more rapidly (18). Oligodendrocyte cultures from 30-day-old rats are, at 1 DIV, 90% oligodendrocytes and 10% glial precursor cells. In MEM–calf serum they are still >80% oligodendrocytes at 3 DIV, but by 4 DIV this figure has dropped to 55%. Cytosine arabinoside is less successful in inhibiting this overgrowth of astrocytes and appears to be toxic to the oligodendrocytes. It is probable that, with careful selection of growth media, substrata, mitotic inhibitors, or cell selection techniques these cultures could be significantly improved.

References

1. W. T. Norton and S. E. Poduslo, *Science* **167,** 1144 (1970).
2. M. Farooq and W. T. Norton, *J. Neurochem.* **31,** 887 (1978).
3. H.-H. Althaus, W. B. Huttner, and V. Neuhoff, *Hoppe-Seyler's Z. Physiol. Chem.* **358,** 1155 (1977).
4. S. E. Poduslo and W. T. Norton, *J. Neurochem.* **19,** 727 (1972).
5. S. Szuchet, B. G. W. Arnason, and P. E. Polak, *J. Neurosci. Methods* **3,** 7 (1980).
6. D. S. Snyder, C. S. Raine, M. Farooq, and W. T. Norton, *J. Neurochem.* **34,** 1614 (1980).
7. P. J. Gebicke-Härter, H.-H. Althaus, P. Schwartz, and V. Neuhoff, *Dev. Brain Res.* **1,** 497 (1981).
8. M. Farooq, W. Cammer, D. S. Snyder, C. S. Raine, and W. T. Norton, *J. Neurochem.* **36,** 431 (1981).
9. R. P. Lisak, D. E. Pleasure, D. H. Silberberg, M. C. Manning, and T. Saida, *Brain Res.* **223,** 107 (1981).
10. P. J. Gebicke-Härter, H.-H. Althaus, I. Rittner, and V. Neuhoff, *J. Neurochem.* **42,** 357 (1984).
11. L. Bologa and N. Herschkowitz, this volume [11].
12. A. L. Betz and G. W. Goldstein, *in* "Handbook of Neurochemistry" (A. Lajtha, ed.), Vol. 7, p. 465. Plenum, New York, 1984.
13. M. Spatz and B. B. Mrsulja, *Adv. Cell. Neurobiol.* **3,** 311 (1982).
14. J. E. Heuttner and R. W. Baughman, *J. Neurosci.* **6,** 3044 (1986).
15. V. K. Singh and D. Van Alstyne, *Brain Res.* **155,** 418 (1978).
16. R. M. Lindsay, P. C. Barber, M. R. C. Sherwood, J. Zimmer, and G. Raisman, *Brain Res.* **243,** 329 (1982).
17. W. T. Norton, M. Farooq, F.-C. Chiu, and J. E. Bottenstein, *Glia* **1,** 403 (1988).
18. W. T. Norton and M. Farooq, *J. Neurosci.* **9,** 769 (1989).
19. S. Szuchet, K. Stefansson, R. L. Wolman, G. Dawson, and B. G. W. Arnason, *Brain Res.* **200,** 151 (1980).
20. S. Szuchet and K. Stefansson, *Adv. Cell. Neurobiol.* **1,** 313 (1980).
21. W. T. Norton, M. Farooq, K. L. Fields, and C. S. Raine, *Brain Res.* **270,** 295 (1983).
22. R. P. Saneto, this volume [9].
23. M. J. Brammer, *Adv. Biosci.* **61,** 287 (1986).

Section IV

Special Approaches

[13] Measurement of Pulsatile Hormone Release from Perifused Pituitary Cells Immobilized on Microcarriers

James R. Hansen and P. Michael Conn

Neurochemical signals regulate pituitary hormone release by alterations in their pattern of presentation. The frequency and duration of exposure of target cells to neuroendocrine substances are often as significant as hormone concentration. Cells grown in culture plates are useful for the identification of signal transduction pathways, as well as dose–response studies, but their application to the study of dynamic cellular events is limited. Perifusion of pituitary cells grown on microcarriers, though, permits control of the frequency, duration, and magnitude of the signal that is presented to the cells, and responses are measured in an environment devoid of toxic cell products and substances that may exert feedback effects. These benefits, along with the ability to introduce sequential treatments during a single experiment, have made it possible to identify a role, which could not be measured in static cultures, for intracellular-derived calcium during the early minutes of gonadotropin-releasing hormone (GnRH)-stimulated luteinizing hormone (LH) release from pituitary gonadotropes. Application of the methods described in this article to the study of other neuroendocrine coupling mechanisms should provide a powerful tool for the resolution of the dynamic molecular and cellular events that underlie these processes.

Preparation of Cell Cultures

Figure 1 shows a summary of the procedures involved in preparation of cell cultures for perifusion.

Pituitary Dispersion

Following cervical dislocation and decapitation, pituitaries are removed from weanling (25- to 30-day-old) female Sprague-Dawley (Harlan, Indianapolis, IN) rats and collected in a 50-ml conical centrifuge tube (Corning, Corning, NY) containing fresh, sterile media (M199/BSA): M199 (GIBCO,

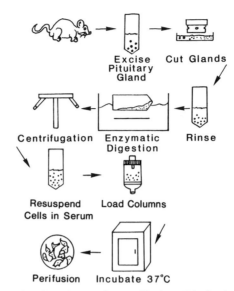

FIG. 1 Preparation of cell cultures for perifusion. Pituitaries are removed from female weanling rats, cut into pieces, and enzymatically dissociated as described in the text. Cells are incubated in microcarrier-containing chambers at 37°C for 48 hr prior to perifusion.

Grand Island, NY), 0.3% (w/v) BSA (Fraction V; Sigma, St. Louis, MO), 10 mM HEPES (Sigma), and 10 μg/ml of gentamicin sulfate (Sigma), pH 7.4. The pituitaries are rinsed several times with M199/BSA and placed in a petri dish, where each pituitary is cut into 6–8 pieces using a sterile razor blade. The pituitary pieces are allowed to settle in fresh M199/BSA in a sterile centrifuge tube. The M199/BSA is decanted and replaced twice with fresh M199/BSA to remove lysed cells and their products.

A 10-ml portion of 0.25% (w/v) collagenase (CLS II, 126 U/mg; Worthington, Freehold, NJ) and 0.10% (w/v) hyaluronidase (Sigma) in M199/BSA is filtered through a 0.45-μm membrane (HAWP; Millipore, Bedford, MA) and added to the decanted pituitary pieces. The conical tube is capped, placed on its side in a 37°C water bath, and shaken at 100 cycles/min in a Dubnoff metabolic shaking incubator (GCA Precision Scientific, Chicago, IL). At 3-min intervals, the tissue suspension is gently passed five times in and out of a 10-ml disposable pipette. After 15 min, the tissue fragments are allowed to settle and the supernatant is passed through organza cloth (Nitex). The tissue fragments are resuspended in another 10-ml portion of enzymes and the procedure is repeated a second time. The combined organza cloth cell filtrate is brought to a final volume of 50 ml with M199–BSA.

After centrifugation of the cell filtrate at 225 g for 10 min at 23°C, the supernatant is discarded and the pellet is resuspended (2.8 pituitaries/ml) in culture medium: M199/BSA with 10% (w/v) horse serum and 2.5% (w/v) fetal calf serum (M.A. Bioproducts, Walkersville, MD). A cell suspension aliquot of 0.55 ml ($\sim10^6$ cells) is delivered to each cell chamber. Culture medium (0.45 ml) is added to bring the final volume of each cell chamber to 1.0 ml. The cell chambers are gently shaken to mix the cell suspension and the microcarriers.

Cell viability, which is assessed by Trypan blue dye exclusion, is typically in excess of 95% at the completion of the dispersion.

Cell Chamber

Figure 2 shows the cell chamber, which is constructed using a disposable 3-ml syringe (Becton-Dickinson & Co., Rutherford, NJ). The syringe is cut at the 1.8-ml mark (3.1 cm from the end) using a miniature electric saw (model No. 395; Dremel, Racine, WI), and then fitted with a porous 1.6-mm-thick (70 μm pore size) polyethylene platform (punched from a sheet using a #4 cork borer; Scientific Products, McGaw Park, IL) that supports 16.7 mg of

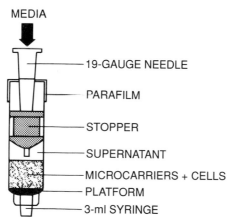

FIG. 2 Construction of a cell chamber. The cell chamber is constructed from a 3-ml disposable syringe that is fitted with a porous polyethylene platform, which supports the Cytodex 1 microcarriers that provide a matrix for cell attachment and growth. A 19-gauge hypodermic needle is inserted through a rubber stopper, which was removed from the syringe plunger, and broken off just beyond the exit point.

Cytodex 1 microcarriers (Pharmacia, Piscataway, NJ). The microcarriers are autoclaved, then swollen for 60 min in Dulbecco's phosphate-buffered saline (PBS) without calcium chloride (Irvine Scientific, Santa Anna, CA), and rinsed three times with culture medium prior to the introduction of the cell suspension. A disposable 19-gauge hypodermic needle (Becton-Dickinson) is inserted through a rubber stopper, which is removed from the syringe plunger, and is broken off just beyond the exit point. The modified stopper is introduced into the cell chamber, which is covered at the inlet with Parafilm (American National Can, Greenwich, CT) and at the outlet by Parafilm and the plastic cover that accompanied the syringe.

Incubation

Cell chambers are incubated in a water-saturated atmosphere maintained at 37°C. After 24 hr, the supernatant is drained and replaced with fresh culture medium. Cell attachment to the microcarriers is virtually complete after 24 hr since very few cells are observed when the cell chamber effluent is examined microscopically. The cells are incubated for an additional 24 hr prior to perifusion in order to allow the cells to recover from the enzymatic digestion.

Perifusion of Cell Cultures

Perifusion Apparatus and Conditions

The perifusion apparatus is shown in Fig. 3. Depending on the motivation of the investigator, up to 10 cell chambers may be simultaneously perifused

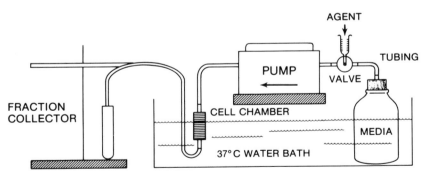

FIG. 3   Diagram of the perifusion apparatus.

using this system. Media reservoirs are connected to plastic three-way stop-cocks by flexible plastic tubing (Tygon; Norton Specialty Plastics Division, Akron, OH). Each stopcock is connected to a cell chamber by the same plastic tubing. A peristaltic pump (Manostat Cassette Jr., New York, NY) is located between the media reservoirs and cell chambers. The cell chambers, which are immersed in the same 37°C water bath as the media reservoirs, are connected to a fraction collector (model FC-220; Gilson, Middleton, WI) by polyethylene tubing (PE-60; Intramedic Clay Adams, Parsippany, NJ). The fraction collector was modified to collect 10 fractions simultaneously, which are usually 0.25 ml (1 min) or 0.75 ml (3 min). The void volume from the media reservoir to the cell chamber is 0.88 ml and from the cell chamber to the fraction collector is 0.37 ml.

After rinsing the tubing with media for 15 min, cell chambers are introduced into each tubing circuit and perifused with M199/BSA at 0.25 ml/min for 90 min to remove metabolic products from the cell supernatant. Achievement of basal hormone release is confirmed by measurement of LH in two 0.75-ml fractions that are collected at the completion of the 90-min acclimation period.

During the perifusion, prewarmed (37°C) treatment solutions are introduced through the stopcocks from disposable 5-ml plastic syringes (Becton-Dickinson). When pharmacological agents are used, these substances are infused individually for 9 min and then together with GnRH. This method of introduction permits observation of any effect the agent alone may have on basal LH release.

Signal–Response Characteristics

The pattern of secretagogue presentation dramatically influences the responsiveness of target cells. In the case of GnRH, for example, infusion of intermittent pulses maintains cell responsiveness, while continuous infusion of the peptide produces desensitization (1). As a result, it is important to consider the physiological pattern of secretagogue presentation and hormone release in planning perifusion experiments.

The physical characteristics of the perifusion system determine the shape of the signal that is presented to the cells. It is desirable to have a small void volume so that changes in the signal are sharply demarcated; the ideal signal has a square-wave conformation. Figure 4 shows the signal profile of ^{125}I-labeled GnRH when it is continuously infused in our system. The interval between the time of ^{125}I-labeled GnRH introduction and its detection is a function of the dead volume of 1.25 ml (5 min) in the system. The ^{125}I-labeled GnRH profile has the steep initial portion and subsequent plateau that are

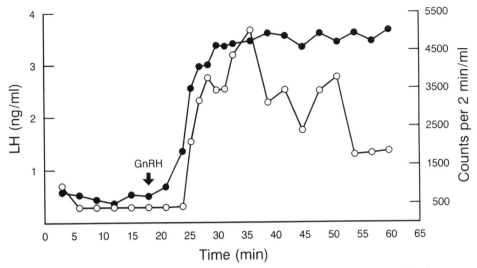

FIG. 4 Delivery profile of continuously infused GnRH. After 48 hr of culture on Cytodex 1 microcarriers, pituitary cells in parallel circuits received a continuous infusion (0.25 ml/min) of 10^{-7} M ^{125}I-labeled GnRH or 10^{-6} M GnRH. The ^{125}I-labeled GnRH signal profile was determined by measurement of counts per 2 min (●). LH release (○) in response to 10^{-6} M GnRH was assessed by radioimmunoassay.

typical of a square wave. Consequently, GnRH-stimulated LH release is rapid and immediately apparent.

Continuous-infusion and multiple-pulse paradigms have been used in our system to study signal transduction mechanisms in the gonadotrope.

Continuous Infusion

Delivery of a sustained pulse permits identification and resolution of cellular events that occur during the initial phase of signal transduction. In our laboratory, this type of paradigm, which is illustrated in Fig. 5, permitted identification of a role for intracellular-derived calcium during early GnRH-stimulated LH release (2). As shown in Fig. 5, LH release in response to 10^{-9} M GnRH occurred rapidly, peaked within a few minutes, and then gradually declined over the 60-min observation period. Chelation of extracellular calcium using ethylene glycol bis(β-aminoethyl ether)N,N,N',N'-tetraacetic acid (EGTA; Sigma) did not affect the initial rate or peak amplitude of LH release produced by GnRH. However, the profile of the LH curve after the first few minutes of GnRH-stimulated release was dramatically altered in the presence of EGTA. LH rapidly declined and reached basal levels within 15 min following the achievement of peak release. Con-

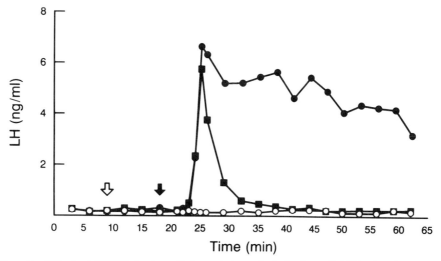

Fig. 5 Effect of EGTA (extracellular calcium chelation) on GnRH-stimulated LH release from continuously perifused pituitary cells. After 48 hr of culture on Cytodex 1 microcarriers, pituitary cells received a continuous infusion (0.25 ml/min) of 10^{-9} M GnRH (●), 10^{-9} M GnRH + 3 mM EGTA (■), or M199/BSA (○). When EGTA was present, it was infused for 9 min before the introduction of GnRH. Open and closed arrows indicate when EGTA and GnRH delivery began, respectively. LH release was measured by radioimmunoassay.

centrations of EGTA ranging from 1.5 mM (300 μM free Ca^{2+}) to 3.0 mM (45 nM free Ca^{2+}) were used. Calculation of the free Ca^{2+} concentration was done with the aid of a computer program that uses affinity constants for the binding of Ca^{2+} and Mg^{2+} by EGTA (3). The area under the LH curve was inversely related to the EGTA concentration. LH curve area increased from 8 to 28% of control (10^{-9} M GnRH) when the concentration of EGTA was decreased from 3 to 1.5 mM.

Calcium channel blockade by methoxyverapamil (D600; Knoll Pharmaceuticals, Whippany, NJ) also affected GnRH-stimulated LH release. The effect of 10^{-4} M D600 on 10^{-9} M GnRH-stimulated LH release is shown in Fig. 6. The LH release curve in the presence of D600 differs from the one seen with EGTA in two respects. First, the peak amplitude of LH release relative to control (GnRH) was reduced by D600 and, second, achievement of basal LH release occurred more slowly when D600 was present.

Together, the observations from the EGTA and D600 experiments indicate that uninterrupted extracellular Ca^{2+} mobilization is necessary for sustained LH release from the gonadotrope in response to GnRH. These results are consistent with the findings of studies that were done in static cell prepa-

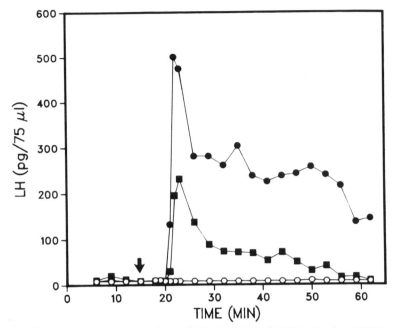

FIG. 6   Effect of D600 (calcium channel blockade) on GnRH-stimulated LH release from continuously perifused pituitary cells. After 48 hr of culture on Cytodex 1 microcarriers, pituitary cells received a continuous infusion (0.25 ml/min) of 10^{-9} M GnRH (●), 10^{-9} M GnRH + 10^{-4} M D600 (■), or M199/BSA (○). When D600 was present, it was infused for 9 min before the introduction of GnRH. Arrow indicates when GnRH delivery began. Results are representative of three separate experiments. [Reproduced with permission from J. R. Hansen, C. A. McArdle, and P. M. Conn, *Mol. Endocrinol.* **1,** 808 (1987), © by The Endocrine Society.]

rations (4, 5). The data shown in Figs. 5 and 6, though, provide evidence for the involvement of a nonextracellular Ca^{2+}-dependent cellular mechanism during early GnRH-stimulated LH release. Further studies have shown that this mechanism is dependent on the mobilization of Ca^{2+} from an intracellular location (2, 6, 7). Thus, delivery of a continuous infusion of GnRH to immobilized pituitary cells while concomitantly monitoring LH release made it possible to identify an early cellular event in the gonadotrope that was not previously appreciated due to the limitations of the static cell system.

The continuous infusion paradigm has also been useful for the study of desensitization, which occurs in many secretory cells due to sustained agonist exposure. Figures 4, 5, and 6 show that a continuous infusion of GnRH results in decreased LH release over time. Delivery of intermittent pulses of

GnRH, though, maintains gonadotrope responsiveness, as shown in Fig. 7. Use of a continuous infusion of GnRH, or more frequent pulses, results in desensitization and thereby permits evaluation of the potential involvement of various cellular mechanisms in this interesting phenomenon, which underlies the clinical utility of GnRH analogs in the treatment of gonadal steroid-dependent conditions, such as prostate cancer and central precocious puberty (8).

Multiple Pulses

Intermittent pulses are useful for the examination of cellular processes that are mainly regulated through changes in the frequency and magnitude of a given signal.

Figure 7 illustrates the pattern of LH release that is observed in response to 5-min pulses of 10^{-9} M GnRH every 40 min. Well-defined LH peaks, which are highly reproducible between cell chambers in parallel circuits (columns), are produced by pulsatile GnRH. The delay in LH release that is observed following the introduction of GnRH is a function of the dead volume in the system. A small dead volume is advantageous, since it facilitates

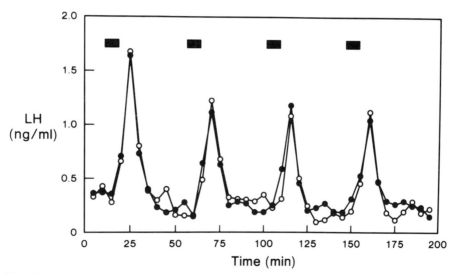

FIG. 7 LH release in response to intermittent pulses of GnRH. After 48 hr of culture on Cytodex 1 microcarriers, pituitary cells received 5-min pulses of 10^{-9} M GnRH at the times indicated by the bars (■). The delay in response is a function of the dead volume in the system. LH release was assessed by radioimmunoassay. (●) Column A and (○) column B.

immediate detection of hormone release and rapid removal of the secreta-gogue at the completion of a pulse. These benefits permit the study of transient cellular events that occur in response to episodic signals such as GnRH and other neuroendocrine peptides in the absence of issues related to the clearance of hormone from blood. It is also possible to assess the effects of various treatments on interpulse basal hormone release.

Assessment of Cell Response

Radioimmunoassay

The hormone content of collected fractions may be determined by radioimmunoassay (RIA). In our laboratory, LH is measured. Rat LH standard (RP-2) is obtained from the National Pituitary Agency (Baltimore, MD). LH antiserum (C-102) is prepared and characterized by previously described methods (9). Highly purified rat LH (LH I-7; National Institute of Diabetes and Digestive and Kidney Diseases, National Institutes of Health, Bethesda, MD) is iodinated by a modification of the method of Hunter and Greenwood (10). Immobilized protein A is used to separate free and bound hormone (11). RIA data are analyzed by the four-parametric logistic method (12). Intra- and interassay coefficients of variation are 5 and 7%, respectively.

Other Methods

Perifusion of cells immobilized on microcarriers provides flexibility in the pattern of signal presentation as well as monitoring of response.

The intracellular level of hormones such as LH may be determined after disruption of the cells on the microcarriers. Measurement of the intracellular level of a given hormone is helpful when one wants to evaluate whether observed treatment effects are associated with hormone depletion. Such an issue is pertinent when pituitary cells are treated with 500 nM phorbol 12-myristate 13-acetate (PMA) to down-regulate protein kinase C (PKC) activity. Measurement of intracellular LH in pituitary cells treated for 6 hr with 500 nM PMA in 0.1% dimethyl sulfoxide (DMSO)/M199/BSA revealed a 25% decrease in Triton X-100-extractable LH when compared to control cells, which received only 0.1% dimethyl sulfoxide DMSO/M199/BSA (1). This observation is of importance when on interprets the data from experiments involving GnRH-stimulated LH release from PMA-pretreated (PKC-down regulated) cells. In this setting, it is necessary to normalize LH output in terms of the amount of LH that was available for release at a given time. Normalized results may be stated as percentage of control or fractional efflux, which is calculated using a spreadsheet program.

Disruption of the cells on microcarriers is accomplished in our laboratory using two methods. The choice of method depends on what the investigator plans to measure. The first method involves solubilization of the cells using 0.1% Triton X-100 in M199/BSA. At the completion of perifusion, the supernatant is drained from the cell chamber, which is capped at the outlet using the plastic cover that accompanied the syringe. The microcarriers and cells from each chamber are suspended in 0.1 ml of 0.1% Triton X-100/M199/BSA and transferred to a 15-ml conical centrifuge tube (Corning) using a Pasteur pipette. The suspension and transfer are repeated three times, which removes all of the microcarriers and cells from the cell chamber. Using 0.1% Triton X-100/M199/BSA, the total volume of each centrifuge tube is brought to 10.0 ml. The centrifuge tube is shaken intermittently while sitting at room temperature for 10 min. After at least 24 hr in the freezer, the microcarrier plus cell suspension is thawed, shaken vigorously, and centrifuged at 750 g for 10 min in order to pellet the microcarriers. The supernatant, which contains the disrupted cells and their contents, is then used for RIA of hormone (e.g., LH).

The second method for disruption of the cells on microcarriers utilizes an extraction buffer, which is prepared as shown in Table I. Following perifusion and drainage of supernatant, the microcarriers and cells of each cell chamber are suspended in 1.0 ml of warm PBS, and then removed with a Pasteur pipette and washed with 1.0 ml of extraction buffer in a 15-ml conical centrifuge tube. The washing procedure with extraction buffer is repeated three times and 14.5 μl (12 μg/ml) of leupeptin is added to each tube. The suspension of microcarriers and cells is sonicated for 5 sec using a Sonifier cell disruptor (Branson Instruments, Inc., Melville, NY) at an output control setting of 7 (110 W maximum) prior to rotation of the centrifuge tubes on a platform (Labquake Shaker, Labindustries, Inc., Berkeley, CA) for at least

TABLE I   Extraction Buffer for Removal of
Cells from Microcarriers

Buffer component[a]	Amount	Concentration (mM)
Tris-HCl (pH 7.5)	0.6056 g	25
Sucrose	17.116 g	0.25
EGTA	0.19 g	2.5
EDTA	0.1488 g	2
2-Mercaptoethanol	7 μl	50
PMSF	2 ml (of 0.1 M stock)	1
Triton X-100	0.6 g	—

[a] The components are dissolved in deionized water, which is used to bring the buffer to a final volume of 200 ml. PMSF, Phenylmethylsulfonyl fluoride.

30 min at 4°C. Afterward, the microcarriers are pelleted by centrifugation at 750 g for 10 min. The supernatant is then analyzed for the intracellular substance of interest. In our laboratory, this method has been successfully used in collaboration with Dr. William Andrews to measure changes in PKC activity in response to intermittent pulses of GnRH (unpublished data).

Data Analysis

Simultaneous perifusion of multiple cell chambers in parallel circuits allows one to measure the relative effect of various treatment agents. This approach is valid if constancy is achieved in terms of cell numbers, microcarrier mass, and flow rate between cell chambers. In our system, one million pituitary cells are added to 16.7 mg of Cytodex 1 microcarriers and the perifusion flow rate is maintained at 0.25 ml/min. Twelve columns are simultaneously prepared for each experiment using cells from the same pituitary dispersion. A high degree of reproducibility is achieved (see Fig. 7). Intra- and interexperimental coefficients of variation are 14 and 16%, respectively.

Area under Curve

Some investigators use peak amplitude of hormone release to make comparisons between treatment groups. We believe, though, that the integrated area under the hormone release curve is a better indicator of the total amount of hormone released per secretory event since some treatments alter release rates and the profile of the curve while leaving the peak amplitude unchanged (see Fig. 5).

The integrated area under the curve is calculated using a spreadsheet program, which was written in our laboratory, that sums the amounts of LH released during the individual collection periods. Basal release in defined as the level of LH release that occurs prior to the onset of stimulated LH release. Basal release is deducted from the total LH release for each time period. The net values for the collection periods are summed to obtain the area under the LH curve. This may be expressed as follows.

$$\text{Area under LH curve} = \sum_{i=1}^{24} (\text{stimulated LH} - \text{basal LH})$$

where i is the collection period.

Computer programs that facilitate detection of peaks and calculation of secretory rates during pulsatile hormone release are available (13, 14). These programs, such as the "Detect" package developed by Rodbard and colleagues (13), offer an objective basis for the evaluation of serial hormone levels over time. As a result, it is possible to analyze the data obtained from perifusion experiments in a more refined manner that encourages recognition of complex neuroendocrine mechanisms.

Statistics

Integrated LH curve areas for replicate experiments are expressed as the mean ± SEM. Differences between control and treatment groups are assessed using nonparametric, one-way analysis of variance (ANOVA). The Kruskal–Wallis test is used to compare the areas under the LH curves as a result of the various treatments. Multiple comparison of treatments against a single control is performed using Dunnett's test. $P < 0.05$ is considered significant in both tests.

General Comments

Perifusion of cells on microcarriers is a labor-intensive method that requires meticulous precision, patience, and large RIAs.

Sterile technique is essential, given the lengthy time course of some perifusion experiments. In our laboratory, cell cultures and perifusion reagents are prepared in a laminar flow hood. Gentamicin is added to the M199/BSA and culture media, and both are sterilized by filtration. The concentration of gentamicin that is used, though, will only eradicate the few bacteria that may enter the M199/BSA during the dispersion; it will not prevent overwhelming infections. At the completion of each experiment, the tubing of the perifusion apparatus is flushed with deionized water and then with sodium azide in deionized water (0.5 mg/ml), which remains in the lines during the interval between experiments. Care must be taken to flush the azide solution from the lines at the beginning of each experiment since it is cytotoxic. The water bath for the media reservoirs and cell chambers is drained after each experiment. The metabolic shaking incubator used during dispersions is also periodically emptied and wiped with 70% ethanol, as is the cell incubator.

Tubing connections must be airtight during perifusion experiments. If air enters the system, it damages the cells and alters the flow rate. Alteration of the flow rate produces variability that is typically expressed as fluctuating basal hormone release. The timing of secretagogue introduction is also affected, and this makes it difficult to reliably evaluate differences between treatment groups. Consistency is the key to successful perifusion!

Acknowledgments

We are grateful to Dr. Leon Burmeister for recommendations regarding statistical analysis of the perifusion data. We thank Jody Janovick for excellent technical help, and Sue Birely for expert secretarial assistance.

This work was supported by NIH Grant HD-19899, Training Grant for Diabetes Mellitus and Endocrinology LH-07344, and the Mellon Foundation.

References

1. E. Knobil, *Recent Prog. Horm. Res.* **36,** 53 (1980).
2. J. R. Hansen, C. A. McArdle, and P. M. Conn, *Mol. Endocrinol.* **1,** 808 (1987).
3. M. L. Pressler and P. W. Schindler, *Experientia* **39,** 639 (1983).
4. C. R. Hopkins and A. M. Walker, *Mol. Cell. Endocrinol.* **12,** 189 (1978).
5. J. Marian and P. M. Conn, *Mol. Pharmacol.* **16,** 196 (1979).
6. Z. Naor, A. Capponi, M. Rossier, D. Ayalan, and R. Limor, *Mol. Endocrinol.* **2,** 512 (1988).
7. J. P. Chang, S. S. Stojilkovic, J. S. Graeter, and K. Catt, *Endocrinology* (*Baltimore*) **123,** 87 (1988).
8. M. Filicori and C. Flamigni, *Drugs* **35,** 63 (1988).
9. W. A. Smith, R. L. Cooper, and P. M. Conn, *Endocrinology* (*Baltimore*) **111,** 1843 (1982).
10. W. M. Hunter and F. C. Greenwood, *Nature* (*London*) **194,** 495 (1962).
11. R. Gupta and D. L. Morton, *Clin. Chem.* **25,** 752 (1979).
12. D. Rodbard and D. M. Hutt, "Radioimmunoassay and Related Procedures in Medicine." UNIPUB, New York, 1973.
13. K. E. Oerter, V. Guardabasso, and D. Rodbard, *Comput. Biomed. Res.* **19,** 170 (1986).
14. R. J. Urban, W. S. Evans, A. D. Rogol, D. L. Kaiser, M. L. Johnson, and J. D. Veldhuis, *Endocr. Rev.* **9,** 3 (1988).

[14] Cultivation of Nerve and Muscle Cells on Microcarriers

Abraham Shahar

Introduction

My colleagues and I have introduced a new approach for culturing cells of the central nervous system (CNS), myoblasts, and nerve–muscle cells on microcarriers (MCs) (1, 2). The rationale behind introducing MCs to primary neuronal and muscle cultures is to provide these cells with a tridimensional support for growth and differentiation in a pattern close to the *in vivo* situation.

Neuronal and muscle cells attach to the MCs to form aggregates which remain floating in the nutrient medium. Such aggregates can be regarded as functional units and can be sampled at any time during cultivation without interfering with the ongoing culture.

In this chapter, the MC culture techniques for neuronal and muscular cells are compared with the conventional methods.

Conventional Culture Methods

Cultures of Central Nervous System

Cell culture of the CNS are obtained from fetal or neonatal material. When cultured as organotypic explants of 1 mm³ or 400-μm-thick slices, fetal material is employed mainly for spinal cord cultures (3), while neonatal tissue is used for culturing different brain areas (4). Because of their thickness, organotypic cultures do not always allow a clear visualization of neurons; however, they can be cultured for several months, reaching an advanced stage of maturation and myelination. They have been therefore widely employed to study several aspects of neuronal and glial cell development and differentiation.

Dissociated CNS cells are cultured either as monolayers on coated substrates (5, 6) or in rotating systems which allow cell suspensions to form floating aggregates (7, 8).

Monolayer cultures do not simulate, in their growth *in vitro*, the tridimensional organization of the CNS structure *in vivo*. Thus, neurons remain single or in groups and lay randomly over a layer of dividing nonneuronal elements. During cultivation neurons show intensive sprouting and formation of synapses but do not usually reach the stage of myelination. Nevertheless, monolayers are the cultures of choice for microscopic examination of cells and extracellular environment. Furthermore, they are highly accessible for morphological, immunocytochemical, and electrophysiological studies. It is, however, difficult to sample monolayer cultures for ultrastructural or biochemical analyses without destroying the ongoing culture at any time during cultivation.

When CNS cells are rotated under appropriate conditions they aggregate. Neuronal and glial elements rearrange themselves in tridimensional structures which facilitate cell contact, cell recognition, and sorting out of cells (9). In their reorganization pattern, the aggregates resemble organotypic cultures and their cells reach maturation and myelination. The advantages of aggregates over monolayers are that the amount of material in aggregates is sufficient for biochemical and pharmacological analyses and that sampling during cultivation is possible without interfering with the ongoing culture. On the other hand, when aggregates reach a certain size, the compact growth of their peripheral cells prevents optimal nutrition of the cells in the center of the aggregate, leading to degenerative phenomena (10).

Muscle Cultures

Dissociated myoblasts are obtained from embryonic or newborn skeletal muscles and are usually cultivated in the form of monolayers on coated substrates (11, 12). During cultivation, myoblasts fuse into multinucleated myotubes which become striated and contract spontaneously. The biochemical myogenesis in culture consists of the formation of creatine kinase, a cytoplasmic protein indicative of muscle differentiation, and acetylcholine receptors and acetylcholinesterase, which are membrane proteins influenced by muscle contractions and the state of innervation.

Although there is a great similarity between the process of myogenesis in culture and *in vivo,* myotubes in culture are usually randomly oriented in a bidimensional pattern rather than being packed parallel to each other in tridimensional bundles as *in vivo*. Furthermore, muscle monolayer cultures are difficult to sample without interfering with the ongoing culture. In addition, these cultures are short-lived because they peel off the dish after 2–3 weeks of cultivation due to intensive contractions of the muscle fibers.

Autologous Nerve–Muscle Cocultures

The traditional way of coculturing nerve and muscle cells is to establish first a monolayer of myoblasts from one embryo, and then, once the cells are differentiated, to add neuronal tissue (usually spinal cord) from another embryo, either as explants (13, 14) or as dissociated cells (15, 16). Explants from both tissues have also been successfully cocultured (17, 18). The cultured tissues in all three types of coculture are always obtained from different animals: myoblasts from mature fetuses or neonates and spinal cord from younger embryos.

Shahar *et al.* have recently described a method in which neuronal and muscular tissue grow and differentiate in a common culture made from the same embryo (19). Such autologous nerve–muscle cultures are obtained from spinal cords which are dissected with their meninges and dorsal root ganglia (DRG) from a 13- to 14-day-old rat fetus and cultured as monolayers.

The source of myoblasts in these cultures is probably from the remains of somites adherent to the meninges. The possibility of myoblasts from such young embryos becoming striated and contracting in cultures is probably due to the presence and influence of the neuronal tissue, with which they also form neuromuscular junctions.

Features and Choice of Microcarriers

By the concept of MCs we mean small solid particles, spherical or cylindrical in shape, that are made of dextran, polyacrylamide, gelatin, polystyrene, or glass (20). A great variety of MCs are available commercially (Table I). They can be divided into three categories.

1. Positively charged MCs. These are either positively charged throughout their matrix or have a layer of charged groups distributed over the outer surface. All the MCs in this category are porous in nature and thus enable penetration of the nutrient medium. Mammalian cells which are negatively charged on their surface are electrostatically attracted to the positively charged MCs.

2. Collagen-coated MCs and MCs made of gelatin. Collagen-coated MCs include dextran beads coated with a covalently bound denatured collagen. In the second group, the entire matrix of the MCs is composed of cross-linked gelatin. Collagen and gelatin are among the most commonly used substrates which combine both the properties of cell adhesion and cell nutrition.

TABLE I   Properties of Commercially Available Microcarriers

Type of microcarriers	Registered trade name (manufacturer)	Shape and dimensions (μm)
Positively charged dextran	Biocarrier (Bio-Rad, Richmond, CA)	Beads 120–180
	Cytodex 1 (Pharmacia, Uppsala, Sweden)	Beads 131–220
	Dormacell (Pfeifer & Langen, Germany)	Beads 140–240
	Microdex (Dextran Products, Canada)	Beads 150
	Superbeads (Flow Labs, U.S.A.)	Beads 135–205
Positively charged cellulose	DE-52, DE-53 (Whatman, England)	Cylinders 40–50 × 80–400
	DEAE-, QAE-, or TEAE-cellulose (Sigma, St. Louis, MO)	Cylinders 10–20 × 10–800
Surface-charged dextran	Cytodex 2 (Pharmacia, Uppsala, Sweden)	Beads 114–198
Collagen-coated	Cytodex 3 (Pharmacia, Uppsala, Sweden)	Beads 133–215
	Collagen-Coated Bioplas (SoloHill England, U.S.A.)	Beads 90–150 or 150–215
Gelatin	Gelibeads (KC Biological, Lenexa, KS)	Beads 115–235
	Ventragel (Ventrex, U.S.A.)	Beads 150–250
Polystyrene	Biosilon (Nunc, Denmark)	Beads 160–300
	Cytospheres (Lux, U.S.A.)	Beads 160–230
	Bioglas (SoloHill England, U.S.A.)	Beads 90–150 or 150–212
Glass	Bioglas (SoloHill England, U.S.A.)	Beads 90–150 or 150–212

3. Polystyrene and glass MCs. The polystyrene hydrophobic beads are of tissue culture type treated so as to provide them with a low negative charge on the surface. The glass spheres are plastic beads with a glass coating.

In deciding which type of MCs to use for neuronal and muscle cultures, it is necessary to take into consideration the main features of these cells and their pattern of growth and differentiation in culture.

For example, DRG neurons are difficult to culture on MCs because their spherical perikarya do not attach well to either beaded or cylindrical MCs. In addition, in culture, these nerve cells regenerate usually only one process each, and these do not interconnect to form a network so as to permit aggregation of MCs.

On the other hand, CNS neurons are most suitable for MC cultures since they have rather flat multipolar somas, each of which regenerates several processes. These processes interconnect to establish a well-organized network, permitting the adhesion of MCs to form aggregates.

A tridimensional arrangement of the nervous tissue within the MCs aggregates is better achieved with cylindrical MCs rather than with beads. Beads are transparent and permit observation of the attached cells by phase-contrast microscopy (Fig. 1A), but their spherical and limited surface is probably not suitable for nerve fibers to grow in their usual growth pattern. Instead, they develop into a sparse network composed of single coiled fibers, which in many MCs retract and easily detach from the beaded surface (Fig. 2A).

In contrast, cylindrical MCs form well-established aggregates which are held together by a dense network of fibers, resembling a ball of wool yarn (Figs. 1B, 2B, 3A and B). The better organization of CNS cells on cylindrical MCs is probably achieved because of the elongated surface which these MCs provide and which is desirable for nerve cell regeneration.

It should be mentioned that, in cultures in which the meninges have not been carefully removed, one can find aggregates of MCs which are covered entirely by glial and meningeal elements (Fig. 3B). The sealing coat of the flat cells in these aggregates is usually composed of several layers, preventing penetration of nutrient medium into the center of the aggregates and thus

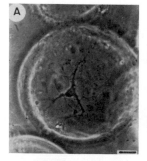

FIG. 1   Phase-contrast micrograph of dissociated brain after 4 days in culture. (A) One neuron attached to a transparent Cytodex 1 bead. Bar, 50 μm. (B) Neuronal cells form an aggregate with DE-53 cylindrical MCs. Bar, 200 μm.

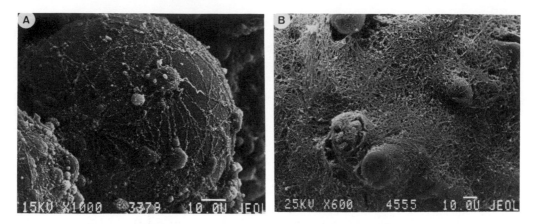

FIG. 2   Scanning electron micrographs (SEMs) of dissociated brain cells 10 days *in vitro*. (A) Cytodex 1 bead covered with single coiled nerve fibers. (B) Part of an aggregate of DE-53 MCs entirely covered by a network of nerve fibers.

inhibiting the growth of neuronal elements which are not present in these aggregates.

The use of cylindrical MCs, rather than the beads used by others (21), is also recommended for muscle MC cultures. This is due to the fact that the myoblasts fuse in culture into elongated myotubes and therefore need elongated substrates. The muscle fibers are organized on the cylindrical MCs in

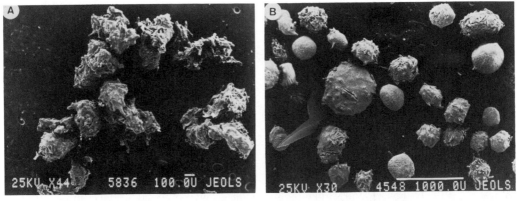

FIG. 3   SEMs of brain cells after 10 days in MC cultures. (A) Aggregates covered mainly with neuronal tissue. (B) Many "smooth" aggregates composed of flat cells.

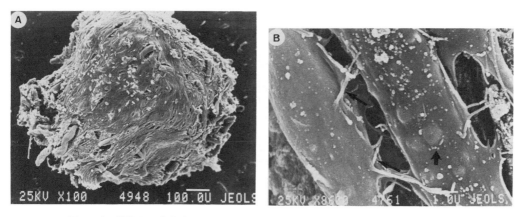

FIG. 4 SEMs of 7-day muscle MC cultures. (A) Orientation of myotubes in an aggregate. (B) Tangled lateral microvilli (long arrows) and nuclear swellings (short arrow) of myotubes.

bundles of myotubes which have the same orientation, laying parallel to each other in a pattern which mimics the *in vivo* situation (Fig. 4).

Cylindrical MCs are also most suitable for autologous nerve–muscle co-cultures. In these cultures, both tissues differentiate in about the same time. However, they organize in a different way: myotubes form the first layer, which covers the MCs, while neuronal elements, single or in groups, sprout to form a network above the muscle layer (Fig. 5).

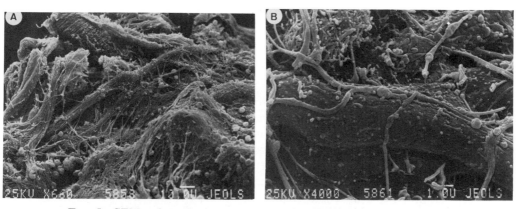

FIG. 5 SEMs of autologous nerve–muscle MC culture 7 days *in vitro*. (A) Dense network of nerve fibers around myotubes. (B) Engulfment of a myotube by single nerve fibers.

Microcarrier Culture Technique

Handling of Microcarriers

The following procedures are recommended for handling MCs (usually cylindrical DE-53) before and during cultivation.

1. Since MCs tend to stick to glass, they should be handled with either plastic or siliconized glass instruments.
2. When MCs are in solution they precipitate rapidly. Mixing is therefore essential in order to get an even distribution of MCs in the solution. Use small-volume pipettes since the MCs tend to settle in the lower part of the pipette.
3. Sterilization of MCs is carried out by autoclaving. It is recommended that a stock solution [150 mg MCs in 100 ml of phosphate-buffered saline (PBS)], which can be kept in the refrigerator for months, be prepared for sterilization.
4. The final concentration of MCs in the culture is 3–5 mg for 1×10^6 cells in 1–1.5 ml of nutrient medium. It is advisable to wash the MCs twice with medium before mixing them with the cells.
5. When medium has to be changed, the culture dish is inclined to allow deposition of cell–MC aggregates in one place, so that the medium can be aspirated from the other end and replaced with a fresh one. After a few weeks in culture, the large aggregates settle and stick to the plastic, where they continue to grow like small explants.
6. In processing aggregates for transmission electron microscopy (TEM), the consistency of the MCs should be considered, and therefore embedding is performed in a harder epoxy than that usually used for cells alone.

Formation of Aggregates

In both neuronal and muscle MC cultures, attachment of cells to the MCs occurs shortly after seeding. Due to absorption of phenol red from the medium, the MCs exhibit a pink color. There is a tendency for MCs bearing cells to aggregate, each clump composed of several MCs. These aggregates, which float in the medium, are much larger in size in muscle and nerve–muscle cultures than in CNS cell culture. In the latter, the aggregates become more tightly interconnected by the ramified network of nerve fibers that sprouts during the first days of cultivation.

The consolidation and organization of the aggregates in muscle cultures are achieved after myoblasts have completed their fusion into myotubes.

When the myotubes composing the aggregates become striated, the whole aggregate, or parts of it, starts to contract. The formation of a large number of aggregates indicates the maintenance of good culture conditions, otherwise the cells would not attach to the MCs and aggregates would not form.

Neuronal Microcarrier Cultures

Dissociated cerebral (22–24) and spinal cord (25) cells are grown in two ways: (1) in stationary cultures in 32-mm uncoated plastic dishes containing 1×10^6 cells with 5 mg of cylindrical DE-53 MCs in 1.5 ml of medium per dish or (2) in rotating cultures either in 50-ml Erlenmeyer shaker flasks containing $6–8 \times 10^6$ cells in 10 ml of medium with 40 mg of MCs with rotatory shaking at 150 rotations/min or in spinner flasks (Model 1965-00100 Bellco) containing $6–8 \times 10^7$ cells in 100 ml of medium with 16 mg of MCs and stirred at 40 rotations/min. Stationary cultures are incubated in a CO_2 incubator, while suspended cultures are pregassed with 5% CO_2 in air and maintained by closing the flask with a rubber stopper. All cultures are incubated at $36.5 \pm 0.5°C$ for several weeks. The culture medium for cerebral neurons consists of 72% Eagle's basal medium, 15% heat-inactivated fetal bovine serum, 10% egg ultrafiltrate, 1% glucose [from a 50% (w/v) solution to provide a final concentration of 600 mg], 1% of 2 mM L-glutamine, and 1% of 16 μg/ml gentamicin.

For spinal cord cells, the culture medium is composed of 73.5% Eagle's basal medium, 20% heat-inactivated horse serum, 1% L-glutamine (2 mM), 2.5% of a 20% (w/v) dextrose solution, and 1% gentamicin.

Growth and differentiation of neuronal cells in the aggregate are characterized, during the first week in culture, mainly by intensive fiber regeneration along with active cell division of meningeal and glial elements. In TEM, bundles of naked axons of different diameters, as well as scattered glial cells and groups of neurons are observed to organize themselves tightly along the MCs, filling up every vacant space (Fig. 6B). Cells adhere to each other at different sites along their membrane by tight junction-like structures (Fig. 6A). These points of contact might be considered as sites for ion exchange and are similar to the punta adherence junctions described in aggregating cultures (8).

The following 2–3 weeks in culture are characterized mainly by growth in size of the perikarya, formation of many mature synapses, and active myelination (Fig. 7). In scanning electron microscopy (SEM) single or groups of perikarya become evident in different areas at the periphery of the aggregates. The synapses are axosomatic and axodendritic of the cholinergic type. They contain mainly clear vesicles. However, in some synapses, a few

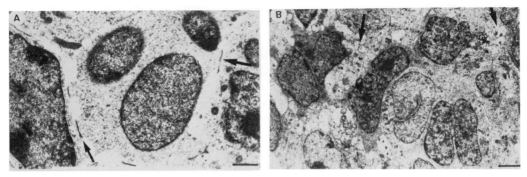

FIG. 6   TEM of a 4-day culture of brain cells on DE-53. (A) Cellular junctions (arrows). Bar, 1 μm. (B) Bundles of naked axons (arrows). Bar, 3 μm.

electron-dense core vesicles are apparent (Fig. 7A). Most of the axons exhibit typical compact multilamellar myelin. However, a thin myelin sheath, composed of only a few lamellae, is also found around a few perikarya and around a structure which does not have typical axonal features (Fig. 7B and C).

Muscle Microcarrier Cultures

Myoblasts are mechanically dissociated from the thigh muscles of 11- to 12-day-old embryos of white Leghorn chickens or from newborn rats. The

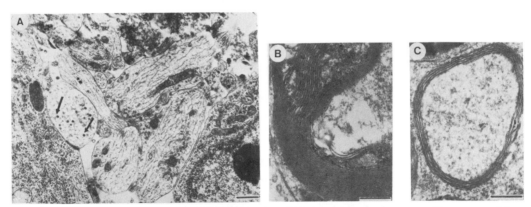

FIG. 7   TEMs showing the following. (A) Axosomatic synapse with core vesicles (arrows). Bar, 1 μm. (B) Multilamellar myelin sheath. Bar, 200 μm. (C) A myelin sheath composed of a few lamellae. Bar, 200 μm.

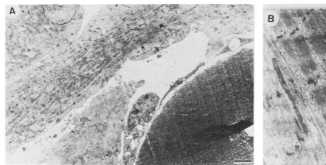
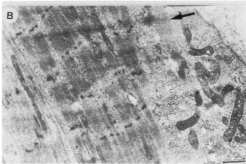

FIG. 8 Myotubes exhibit characteristic cross-striation after 14 days cultivation on MCs. Honeycomblike endoplasmic reticulum is seen in B (arrow). (A) Bar, 2 μm. (B) Bar, 1 μm.

culture medium consists of 58% high-glucose Dulbecco's modified Eagle's medium (MEM) supplemented with 10% heat-inactivated horse serum, 2% chick embryo extract, and 1% gentamicin.

The growth pattern of dissociated myoblasts on cylindrical DE-53 MCs (26) is basically similar to that of monolayer cultures. During the first 2–4 days, an active division of myoblasts takes place. At the end of the first week, fusion of myoblasts into multinucleated myotubes occurs. After the first week, the myotubes, which were flat and thin, become thicker and cylindrical. Each myotube exhibits on its sides elongated microvilli which are located at equal distances to interconnect with the adjacent fibers. Several swellings along the fiber indicate nuclear location (Fig. 4B). In TEM, fibers show a characteristic cross-striation, mitochondria aligned along with myofibrils, and typical honeycomblike sarcoplasmic reticulum (Fig. 8B). Biochemical differentiation of muscle cultures is measured using creatine kinase and acetylcholine receptor as markers. The levels of both proteins are found to be slightly higher in MC cultures than in monolayers. The synthesis of these two proteins can be measured in MC cultures for months, but monolayer cultures peel off the dish after 2–3 weeks, due to active spontaneous muscle contractions.

Autologous Nerve–Muscle Cocultures on Microcarriers

These cultures develop from dissociated spinal cords of 14-day-old rat fetuses (27). The culture medium is composed of 80% Eagle's minimum essential medium, 10% fetal calf serum, and 10% horse serum (both heat-inactivated), 5 mg/ml of glucose, 0.3 mg/ml glutamine, and 13 μg/ml of gentamicin. The neuronal tissue is the first to grow (within the first week) with its regular pattern—regeneration of nerve fibers concomitantly with division of nonneuronal elements. Unlike muscle cultures, the fusion of myoblasts into myotubes occurs in nerve–muscle cocultures only toward the second week *in vitro* (i.e., 7–10 days *in vitro*). At that time, myotubes become striated and contraction in the aggregates can be observed. This period of muscle differentiation is also characterized by a dramatic increase in the level of acetylcholine receptor (measured by I[125]-labeled bungarotoxin binding to these cultures) as compared to the level in muscle MC cultures (Fig. 9). The acetylcholine receptors and acetylcholinesterase activity are organized in sites which indicate existence of nerve–muscle interconnections. The existence of such connections is also indicated by the reverse inhibition of muscle contractions which are induced by *d*-tubocurarine. Although no

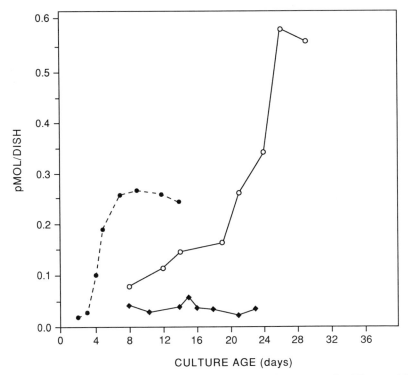

FIG. 9   The level of acetylcholine receptor in cultures in nerve cells (■), myoblasts (●), and autologous nerve–muscle cells (○). Each point represents the mean of three culture dishes.

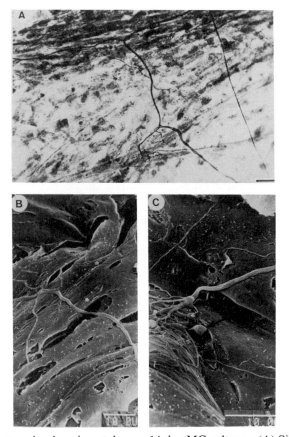

FIG. 10 Nerve terminations in autologous 14-day MC cultures. (A) Silver impregnation. Bar, 50 μm. (B and C) SEM showing the termination of a sensitive cell in B and a motor ending with characteristic swellings (arrow) in C.

end-plate structures can be identified by TEM, typical sensory and motor nerve endings on the muscle fiber are observed with SEM (Fig. 10B and C).

Conclusions

The MC technique for nerve and muscle cultures provides an attractive alternative to the monolayer procedure because of the following advantages.

1. Availability of a high surface-to-volume ratio enables mass cultivation of cells.

2. Separate or reciprocal growth and differentiation of cells from both tissues into organized functional units which remain floating in the nutrient medium.

3. The possibility of harvesting the floating units for biochemical analysis and morphological evaluation any time during cultivation without interfering with the ongoing culture.

4. Cells grown on MCs can be maintained for a longer period in culture, in larger numbers, and more efficiently.

5. DE-53 MCs are commercially available, they are inexpensive, and easy to handle.

During their long-term cultivation on MCs, neuronal and muscle cells become mature functional structures. They therefore provide an excellent *in vitro* tool for acute and chronic exposures to toxicological agents. Furthermore, cell–MC aggregates, which can be sampled during cultivation, can be used for implantation into injured or dystrophic tissue in order to investigate the role played by transplanted embryonic material in adult tissue regeneration. The MCs in the implanted entities serve as identifiable markers after implantation.

References

1. A. Shahar and S. Reuveny, *Adv. Biochem. Eng.* **34,** 33 (1987).
2. A. Shahar, S. Reuveny, A. Mizrahi, and A. Shainberg, *J. Acad. Med. Torino* **147,** 33 (1984).
3. A. Shahar, G. Frankel, Y. David, and A. Friedmann, *J. Neurosci. Res.* **16,** 671 (1986).
4. B. H. Gahwiler, *Neuroscience (Oxford)* **11,** 751 (1984).
5. Z. Yavin and E. Yavin, *Exp. Brain Res.* **29,** 137 (1977).
6. M. Sensenbrenner, *in* "Cell, Tissue, and Organ Cultures in Neurobiology" (S. Federoff and L. Hertz, eds.), p. 191. Academic Press, New York, 1977.
7. P. Honegger and E. Richelson, *Brain Res.* **109,** 335 (1976).
8. N. W. Seeds, G. Ramirez, and M. J. Marko, *in* "Cell Culture and Its Application" (R. T. Acton and J. D. Lynn, eds.), p. 23. Academic Press, New York, 1977.
9. N. W. Seeds and S. C. Haffke, *Dev. Neurosci.* **1,** 69 (1978).
10. J. M. Matthieu, P. Honegger, B. D. Trapp, S. R. Cohen, and H. D. Webster, *Neuroscience (Oxford)* **3,** 565 (1978).
11. D. Yaffe, *Curr. Top. Dev. Biol.* **4,** 37 (1969).
12. A. Shainberg, G. Yagil, and D. Yaffe, *Dev. Biol.* **25,** 1 (1971).
13. N. Robbins and T. Yonezawa, *Science* **172,** 395 (1971).
14. Y. Kidokoro and F. G. Klier, *Dev. Biol.* **77,** 52 (1980).
15. A. Shainberg, A. Shahar, M. Burstein, and E. Giacobini, *in* "Tissue Culture in

Neurobiology'' (E. Giacobini, A. Vernadakis, and A. Shahar, eds.), p. 25. Raven, New York, 1980.
16. S. De La Porte, P. Courbin, J. Chapron, D. Hantaz-Ambroise, and J. Koenig, *Biol. Cell* **56,** 181 (1986).
17. E. R. Paterson and S. M. Crain, *Z. Zellforsch.* **106,** 1 (1970).
18. M. Ecob, *J. Neurol. Sci.* **58,** 1 (1983).
19. A. Shahar, M. Bidder, Y. David, A. Amir, and A. Shainberg, *in* ''Model Systems in Neurotoxicology: Alternative Approach to Animal Testing'' (A. Shahar and A. M. Goldberg, eds.), p. 45. Liss, New York, 1987.
20. S. Reuveny, *Adv. Biotechnol. Processes* **2,** 1 (1983).
21. R. Pawlowski, V. Szigeti, R. Loyd, and R. J. Przybylski, *Eur. J. Cell Biol.* **35,** 296 (1984).
22. A. Shahar, S. Reuveny, A. Amir, M. Kotler, and A. Mizrahi, *J. Neurosci. Res.* **9,** 339 (1983).
23. R. Bjerkvig, S. K. Steinsvag, and D. D. Laerumj, *In Vitro Cell Dev. Biol.* **22,** 180 (1986).
24. R. Bjerkvig, *In Vitro Cell Dev. Biol.* **22,** 193 (1986).
25. A. Shahar, A. Amir, S. Reuveny, L. Silberstein, and A. Mizrahi, *Dev. Biol. Stand.* **55,** 25 (1984).
26. A. Shainberg, A. Issac, S. Reuveny, A. Mizrahi, and A. Shahar, *Cell Biol. Int. Res.* **7,** 27 (1983).
27. A. Shahar, A. Mizrahi, S. Reuveny, T. Zinman, and A. Shainberg, *Dev. Biol. Stand.* **60,** 263 (1985).

[15] Monolayer and Three-Dimensional Culture of Rat and Human Central Nervous System: Normal and Malignant Cells and Their Interactions

Ole Didrik Laerum and Rolf Bjerkvig

Introduction

Since the pioneering work of Ross Harrison in 1907 (1), cell and tissue culture has become an obligatory tool in modern neurobiological research. From the use of clotted lymph and crude tissue extracts, media have become defined and synthesized according to the actual needs of the cultured cells. By combining different nutritional components, trace elements, and growth factors, biological selection of different subpopulations from the nervous system can be achieved.

General techniques for cell culture have become simpler and more straightforward. Methods are highly standardized, and all the components and equipment are commercially available. These facts result in more appropriate division of time and effort, with less being spent on preparation of the cultures, and more devoted to the actual experiments. Furthermore, modern freezing techniques have made storage of even normal, differentiated cell populations from the central nervous system (CNS) rather simple (2). Careful dissection and cell separation methods have enabled the culture of specific cell types or cells from defined brain areas. The use of mixed populations has made direct cell interaction studies possible. In addition, signal molecules can give clues to more distant regulatory interactions. (For general surveys, see Refs. 3–6.) Use of different staining techniques in immunohistochemistry or immunofluorescence of a multitude of specific markers for different types of neural cells has greatly improved the possibilities for characterizing cells (7, 8). Data are also available on how primary cultures can be obtained from defined brain areas and how the maturity of the developing brain will affect *in vitro* growth (9). This also applies to the time lag from the death of the animal until explantation is done (10). Since cell death is a naturally occurring process during neural development, viability and growth in culture are also dependent on the state of the cells as affected by the previous *in vivo* conditions (11).

In this chapter, we review our own work in the field of cell and tissue culture of the CNS. Since early in the 1970s we have been engaged in different types of culture methods for the CNS. These include both new applications of standard tissue culture methods as well as establishment of new methods for specific purposes. In particular, we have been investigating the differences between two- and three-dimensional cultures, i.e., between monolayer and organ cultures, and have compared them to the *in vivo* conditions, including diffusion chamber culture and transplantation studies. The methodology is emphasized in our description, although various applications are discussed. We also review our studies that are related to malignant transformation of neural cells in culture and different cell properties which are involved in tumor cell invasiveness.

It is our impression that there has been an increasing use of cultured malignant glioma cells for general neurobiological studies. This is based on the principle that cellular processes taking place in cultured neoplastic cells widely reflect normal functions. This trend, combined with the advantage that they can be kept as continuous cultures with a high degree of homogeneity, has given researchers in neurobiology and neurochemistry close connections to cancer research.

Monolayer Cultures

General Features

Cell culture cannot replace the complex conditions in the brain. Therefore, it is mandatory to evaluate whether the functions which are investigated *in vitro* really reflect *in vivo* properties of the same cells. An advantage of monolayer cultures is that they are easily propagated on a directly observable surface. A major disadvantage is that the differentiation pattern *in vitro* may be entirely different from the *in vivo* situation. For example, fetal and newborn rat brain cells will form a monolayer on a plastic surface which comprises various numbers of differentiated glial cells and neurons on an underlayer of flat epithelioid neuroblasts. After a few passages, only the epithelioid cells will be present. However, they can be induced to differentiate into morphologically recognizable astrocytes by adding different substances, e.g., glia maturation factor (12, 13), protein kinase C activators (14), and 12-*O*-tetradecanoylphorbol-13-acetate (TPA), and dibutyryl cyclic AMP (unpublished observations).

When compared to three-dimensional culture systems, such as organ culture and reaggregated cultures, monolayers have the advantage that large numbers of cells can be obtained. Furthermore, oxygenation and nourishment of cells are more easily accomplished in monolayer cultures as compared to organ cultures, where oxygen and nutritional gradients are frequently present (15).

Using various procedures, two-dimensional microcultures can reveal valuable information about progenitor cells in the nervous system, including information about the propagation of bi- or multipotential glial progenitors in single-cell microculture as well as the use of limiting dilution analysis in microwell chambers (16, 17). Extensive metabolic and other biochemical studies have also been performed on primary cultures from defined brain regions (18).

Fetal Rat Brain Cells

The basis for our studies on monolayer cultures has been a standardized explantation and culture procedure for fetal rat brain cells in monolayers. The basic method is as follows. Brains are dissected from fetuses of the inbred rat strain BD-IX at the eighteenth day of gestation, placed in a petri dish containing medium (see below), and cleaned of any adhering tissue. The brain tissue is then cut into small pieces by the use of two scalpels and dissociated with 0.025% (w/v) trypsin in phosphate-buffered saline at 37°C for 15 min. The cell suspension is washed, centrifuged for 5 min at (125 g), and resuspended in growth medium. The cells from one litter of rats are plated in 5–6 dishes with 1×10^6 viable cells per dish. The growth medium is Dulbecco's modified Eagle's medium (Flow Laboratories, Glasgow, Scotland) fortified with 10% (w/v) newborn calf serum and 4-fold the concentration of nonessential amino acids, 100 IU/ml penicillin, and 100 μg/ml streptomycin. The cells are kept at 37°C in a tissue culture incubator (100% relative humidity and air containing 5% CO_2), and the medium is renewed every 2–3 days. At confluency the cells are trypsinized and passaged 1 : 2 to 1 : 10 depending on the rate of growth. This method has been the basis for most of our studies on both normal brain cells and neoplastic cell lines (for further details, see Ref. 19). For monolayer studies on fetal brain cells undergoing neoplastic transformation *in vitro* the following procedure is used. After dissection, the pooled brains of one litter (6–10 per experiment) are cut into fragments and passed through a stainless steel grid (mesh width: 100 μm). The resulting cell suspension is then seeded into 10-cm tissue culture dishes (1–2 $\times$ 10^6 cells/dish). Approximately 50% of these cells are viable as determined by the Trypan blue exclusion test (20).

In these experiments, it was desirable to culture the whole population of brain cells in order to study interactions between cells, various types of differentiation markers, and the selection of preneoplastic cells from a carcinogen-treated brain. In the following descriptions, this method is used as the basis for various applications. For the more specific studies of cerebellar neurons in monolayer culture, the procedure is as follows. The cerebella from four to eight 7-day-old BD-IX rats are cut into small tissue cubes and trypsinized for 15 min as described above. The cell suspension is seeded in poly(L-lysine)-coated culture wells or flasks. An initial growth inhibition of nonneuronal cells is obtained by a short addition of cytosine arabinoside to the cultures. The culture conditions, otherwise, are presented elsewhere (21).

Although the standard method is based on the use of plastic dishes, preparation of cells for scanning electron microscopy or for immunofluorescence/ immunohistochemistry can be done by placing ethanol-rinsed glass coverslips into the plastic dishes at seeding. When a monolayer is formed, the coverslips are fixed and prepared for ultrastructural analysis according to standard procedures. For immunohistochemical analysis the coverslips are carefully washed in phosphate-buffered saline (PBS) at 37°C for 5 min and then fixed in a freshly prepared 4% (v/v) paraformaldehyde solution for 20 min at 4°C. This procedure is followed by an incubation for 30 min in 5% dimethyl sulfoxide (DMSO) (for studies of glial fibrillary acidic protein or neuron-specific enolase). For detection of S-100 protein, the coverslips are fixed in cold acetone for 1 min and then washed in PBS (19). Apart from this, standard methods for immunofluorescence and immunohistochemistry are used.

Applications and General Experiences

On normal fetal brain cells in monolayer culture we have investigated the ultrastructural characteristics during exposure of epithelioid glioblasts to semipurified glial maturation factor (22). The morphological characteristics of the various stages of astrocytic differentiation could thus be characterized, which enabled comparisons to be made between premalignant and fully malignant cells during transformation in culture. Development of malignancy implied the acquisition of a more stable phenotype which was less responsive to the maturation factor (23). Concomitantly, there was a decreased morphological response to cyclic AMP, although cAMP-dependent protein kinase was expressed to a similar degree as in normal cells. There was, however, a different distribution between protein kinases I and II when cells became malignant (24). We have also employed the culture methods for studying direct effects of high hydrostatic pressure on fetal rat brain cells (25). One surprising finding was that malignant glioma cells are far more resistant to high hydrostatic pressure than normal brain cells.

The study of malignant transformation of fetal rat brain cells has been our main application of monolayer culture. In these experiments, a single pulse of the carcinogen ethylnitrosourea was given transplacentally to BD-IX rats at the eighteenth day of gestation. After 1–4 days, the brains were explanted to monolayer culture and studied in order to see if the same malignant transformation would take place *in vitro* as would otherwise occur in the brains of the offspring. Through a series of publications we could show that the brain cells underwent stepwise alterations, gradually acquiring properties of a neoplastic phenotype (20, 23; for review, see Ref. 26). During the first weeks, there was an increased outgrowth of differentiated cell types, including astrocytes, oligodendrocytes, and neurons in the brain cells that had been exposed to ethylnitrosourea, whereas control cultures gradually reverted to an epithelioid population of immature glioblasts (27, 28), with the development of nodules consisting of tightly entangled neurons and glial cells, occasionally with the formation of myelin and even neurites. Thus, mutagenic and carcinogenic effects *in vivo* may alter the differentiation pattern in subsequent cell culture development. In the early phases, preneoplastic cells may have normal morphology, although their differentiation pattern is more independent than in untreated control cultures.

After this initial phase the cells gradually changed morphology. Atypical morphology and rapid growth occurred several months before the cells were able to form tumors by reimplantation on isogeneic hosts (20). The neoplastic phenotype of these tumors corresponded to astrocytoma, neurinoma, and glioblastoma (29). More recently, other workers have been able to induce oligodendrogliomas from fetal rat brain cells as well as neoplastic transformation of newborn rat astrocytes in culture (30, 31).

The process of malignant transformation can also be accelerated by exposing the transforming cells to phorbol esters *in vitro* (32). This malignant transformation *in vitro* is also accompanied by the expression of the *cis*-oncogen and platelet-derived growth factor (33). Thus, malignant transformation which otherwise is hidden in the brain *in vivo* can be studied directly as a stepwise process in monolayer cell culture where the phenotypic properties and differentiation patterns of the various classes of neural cells have been well characterized.

Malignant Cells

On this basis, some comments will be made on the extensive literature on the culture of malignant cells from the CNS *in vitro*. Malignant glioma cells of both animal and human origin can be propagated in monolayer culture as continuous cell lines (29, 34). Their ultrastructure and cytoplasmic characteristics, including cytoskeleton and surface microstructure, are well described (35–37). The gliomas are known to be heterogeneous tumors, showing a wide range of different phenotypic properties within the same primary tumor or continuous cell line (34, 35, 38). This also applies to their chromosome and DNA pattern, which can vary widely in cultured lines (39, 40). Interestingly, it has been found that aneuploid brain tumors are more easily cultured and developed into continuous cell lines than diploid tumors (41). Furthermore, their repair capacity after alkylating damage, induced, for example, by ethylnitrosourea, shows wide variations, although some cell lines are able to remove alkylated products from DNA rapidly (42).

The preparation techniques for electron microscopical studies of glioma cells *in vitro* are well standardized. It has been shown that tumor cell attachment, as well as formation of ruffling membranes and migration, follows a characteristic pattern (43). This also applies to the motility and contractility of primary brain tumor cells, which can be directly quantitated by use of the Rose perfusion chamber (44).

Recently, genomic alterations in glioma cells have been characterized. This applies to clonal alterations (45), gene amplifications (46), and to the subsequent overexpression of different gene products, such as the EGF receptor gene (47, 48). The release of different growth factors,* such as interleukin 1 (49), PDGF (50, 51), and a T-cell suppressor factor related to TGF-β (52), can be of importance both for their interactions with other cells in culture, and as paraneoplastic phenomena in patients. It has also been shown that neuroblastoma and glioma cells might produce angiotensinogen and different enzymes that can be related to tumor cell invasiveness (53–55). In addition, the tumor cells may show an altered expression of different growth factor receptors, such as insulinlike growth factor and EGF (56, 57). The cells may therefore show an increased response to a growth stimulatory signal.

Another important practical approach to the study of cultured human glioma cells in the antigenic heterogeneity that has been described by panels of monoclonal antibodies (58–61). Furthermore, monoclonal antibodies provide a unique possibility for studying specific cell surface proteins and sphingolipids on human glioma cells (62–64).

The differentiation pattern of the glioma cells evidenced by the presence of glial fibrillary acidic protein (GFAP) and uptake of different transmitter substances also provides information on their malignancy potential (65). Surprisingly, striated muscle differentiation is not an uncommon finding in human malignant glioma cells in culture, which further points at their genetic heterogeneity (66). The differentiation pattern of glioma cells can also be

---

* PDGF, Platelet-derived growth factor; EGF, epidermal growth factor; TGF-B, transforming growth factor B.

influenced by external factors (67). Interestingly, their growth can be suppressed or strongly modulated by both glia maturation factor and nerve growth factor (68, 69).

The development of stem cell assays for human malignant brain tumors may be of considerable value for characterizing their potential malignancy and response to chemotherapeutic agents (70).

In conclusion, the monolayer culture of neoplastic glial cells from both humans and experimental animals offers unique possibilities for neurobiological and neurochemical research. In addition, different genomic alterations may provide new information on normal neural cell functions.

Nonadherent Organ Culture

At present, several methods are available for maintaining brain tissue in organ culture. (1) The tissue can be kept in a gyratory shaker apparatus which keeps the tissue in suspension and moving continuously for the whole culture period. (2) The tissue can be kept in a stationary culture, either in a clot or on a plastic surface. Such cultures will attach to the underlayer and grow out, gradually forming a monolayer. (3) The tissue can be kept as spheroids in a stationary suspension culture on a nonadherent substratum. A more specialized type of stationary culture is to embed the tissue in a semisolid medium. This technique is mainly used for the cloning of tumor cells. Our own approach has been to keep the organ fragments or cell aggregates as stationary cultures on a nonadherent substrate such that neither the substrate nor movement would interfere with the growth and differentiation of the tissue.

Solid Hemisphere Tissue Fragments in Stationary Organ Culture

Brains from fetuses of the inbred BD-IX rat strain are taken at the eighteenth day of gestation, dissected out, and placed in sterile petri dishes containing PBS at pH 7.4. Under a stereomicroscope the brain lobes are dissected free, the meninges carefully removed, and the lobe tissue cut into approximately 800-μm-sized cubes. Multiwell dishes of 16 mm diameter (Nunc, Denmark) are base coated with 0.5 ml of 0.75% (w/v) semisolid agar (Agar Noble; Difco Laboratories, Detroit, MI). One fragment is transferred to each well and 1 ml of growth medium is added. The medium consists of Dulbecco's modification of Eagle's medium (Flow Laboratories, Glasgow, Scotland) supplemented with 10% heat-inactivated newborn calf serum, four times the prescribed concentration of nonessential amino acids, L-glutamine, penicillin (100 IU/ml), and streptomycin (100 μg/ml). The cultures are maintained at 37°C in 5% CO_2 in air with 100% relative humidity. They are observed daily under a phase-contrast microscope. The medium is changed every second day. The culture period is up to 50 days. For size measurements, the diameter of the fragments is measured every second day, from the start of the culture period until day 50 in a phase-contrast microscope with a calibrated grid in one of the oculars. The size is expressed as half the sum of two diameters at right angles to each other. Viability of the tissue is checked by the transfer of fragments to ordinary tissue culture vessels. Observation of the attachment of fragments and cellular outgrowths to the bottom of the wells within 48 hr is regarded as an expression of viability of the tissue.

For morphological studies, fragments are fixed and processed according to standard procedures for light and transmission electron microscopy. Immunohistochemistry is done using different markers on 10-μm frozen sections or on 6-μm-thick paraffin-embedded sections following standard methods (for further details, see Ref. 71).

During the first 5 days of culture, the fragments will obtain a spherical morphology. This shape is retained during the rest of the culture period. There is also a considerable decrease in the size of the fragments during the first 20 days of culture. The diameter is reduced by 65% during this period, followed by an only 2.5% decrease between days 20 and 50. Regardless of the initial size of the fragments, all fragments reach a steady state of about 300 μm in diameter (Fig. 1).

The five different cell layers in the fetal hemisphere usually disappear within the first 2 days of culture, although a high rate of mitotic activity is seen. From day 5 until day 10 it is not possible to see separate layers, although signs of cellular organization can be observed. Macroglia and some microglia appear and numerous necrotic cells are observed, usually randomly distributed throughout the fragments. Between 15 and 20 days in culture a three-layered structure appears. In the center, neurons and astrocytes predominate and there are a few oligodendrocytes present.

The midlayer consists mainly of a prominent neuropil of variable thickness with cellular outgrowths from both the central and peripheral layers. In the peripheral layer, oligodendrocytes dominate and some scattered neurons are observed. This three-layered structure does not change between day 20 and day 40 and mitotic activity persists. From day 40 to day 50 the layered structure disappears, neuropil becomes the main constituent, and neurons and astrocytes are seen throughout the fragments, while in the periphery, there are many astrocytes, and mitotic activity ceases.

After a few days of culture, different types of junctions between cells are

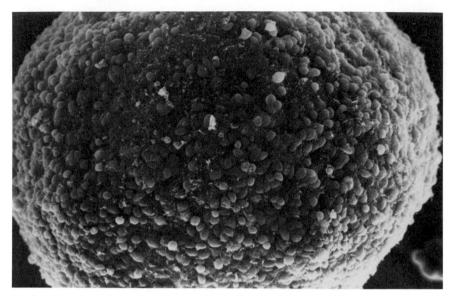

FIG. 1 Scanning electron micrograph of 300-μm-diameter brain fragment after 20 days in culture. ×290.

present. Such cell contacts include intermediate junctions, tight junctions, gap junctions, and synapses. Myelinization of axons is observed after 10 days in culture. After 30 days, cilia are seen in small central cavities in the fragments. Subependymal basement membrane labyrinths are also present after 10 days of culture (72).

This system with a preserved tissue matrix provides a differentiation of the cells which is roughly similar to the development in the corresponding newborn rat brain. Another advantage is that no shaking procedure is required. The fragments are directly observable on a day to day basis and a high number of parallel cultures can be kept in microwell chambers using a minimum of incubator space. The culture period is equal to or even longer than that reported for primary brain cell monolayer cultures.

The disadvantage of this method is the initial size reduction and high rate of cell death which occur in the fragments. The volume of the fragments after 20 days is several times smaller than the initial explant size. With this reservation, the method can be considered as a simple organotypic brain culture model. Some applications of this method will be mentioned below.

Aggregates of Brain Cells in Stationary Culture

In addition to the above-mentioned stationary culture system, we have slightly modified the commonly used reaggregation method for organ culture of fetal rat brain. The modified method is as follows. Brains of 18-day-old rat fetuses are dissected out as described above. They are then cut into small pieces (0.5 × 0.5 mm), washed four times in PBS, and serially trypsinized (3 × 5 min) with 0.025% trypsin in PBS at pH 7.4. Further action of trypsin is stopped by transferring the cell suspension into growth medium at 4°C. The medium consists of Dulbecco's modified Eagle's medium as described above. The cell suspensions are counted and the numbers of viable cells are determined by the Trypan blue exclusion test.

The cells are seeded at a concentration of 3×10^6 cells into each well of 16-mm multiwell dishes (Nunc, Denmark). Each well is first coated with 0.5 ml of 0.75% agar in medium, upon which the cell suspension in 0.8 ml of medium is pipetted. The cultures are kept in an incubator at 100% relative humidity, 95% air and 5% CO_2 at 37°C, and studied daily under a phase-contrast microscope. After 48 hr the cells have assembled into aggregates of various sizes. Single aggregates can then be transferred into new agar-coated wells and are maintained there for up to 40 days. The medium is changed once a week.

The initial size of the aggregate depends on the number of cells seeded into the wells, the range being between 400 and 700 μm in diameter. For the next 20 days the diameter of the aggregates gradually reduces, reaching a constant size of approximately 300 μm, irrespective of their initial size.

During the first 20 days, the cells gradually differentiate into morphologically mature neurons, astrocytes, and oligodendrocytes. A tightly packed neuropil is also present that is most prominent in a cell-sparse outer layer of the aggregates. The central core consists of neurons, astrocytes, and oligodendrocytes. Between 12 and 20 days of culture, differentiation of neurons, myelinization, and formation of synapses take place (Fig. 2). This occurs in parallel with biochemical maturation, where the expression of neuron-specific enolase (NSE), glial fibrillary acidic protein (GFAP), and S-100 protein gradually appears from 1 to 3 weeks of culture. Macrophages are also present, situated randomly both inside and at the surface of the aggregates. Ependymal cells with cilia are also present as well as subependymal basement membrane labyrinths. The aggregates can be cultured for up to 40 days before the viability declines (73–75).

When compared to other methods of aggregating cultures, the present version is simple to perform, and can be kept with many parallel cultures in a small space. No shaking procedures are necessary. Apart from this, the

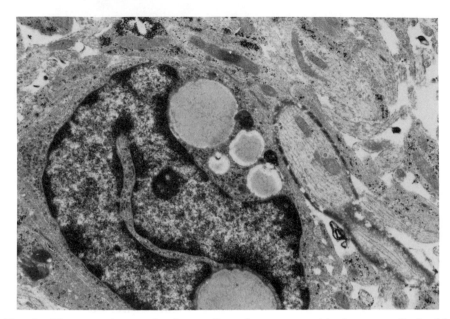

FIG. 2   Electron micrograph of a myelinated axon present in the neuropil of a 25-day-old brain aggregate. An astrocyte is also present, with an invaginated nucleolus and clumped chromatin adjacent to the nuclear membrane. ×12,500.

presence of macrophages offers an interesting possibility for studying the local immune response in the developing brain.

Malignant Cell and Tissue Cultures

Malignant growth takes place in a three-dimensional fashion, forming solid tumor tissue and spreading as single cells in the surrounding normal tissue matrix. In tumors there is a complex architecture of tumor cells, an extracellular matrix, and vessels, together with a variable number of inflammatory cells.

For tumors of the CNS, several types of organ culture have been used. These include the maintenance of solid pieces in ordinary organ culture for limited periods (76), maintenance of solid tissue spheroids either in gyratory shakers or stationary on a nonadherent substrate, as well as the formation of reaggregated tissue from tumor cell suspensions. In particular, the latter type of culture has been extensively used for the study of human gliomas (77–79). In spheroids of this type the formation of an extracellular matrix has been demonstrated (80). In addition, the *in vitro* biological properties and growth capacity of the glioma cells have been well characterized (81). Spheroid cultures of gliomas have already been employed for combination chemotherapy studies and compared to the *in vivo* growth of the same tumors (82). We have employed the following method, originally described by Yuhas *et al.* (83), for obtaining multicellular spheroids from both rat and human glioma cells.

Single-cell suspensions of glioma cells are obtained from monolayers by trypsinization. The cells are then resuspended in fresh growth medium (Eagle's medium with Dulbecco's modification as described above). Ten milliliters of the suspension containing 3×10^6 cells is seeded into a 10-cm plastic culture dish (Nunc) base-coated with 10 ml of 0.75% semisolid agar in medium. The cultures are then grown under standard tissue culture conditions (37°C in 5% CO_2 in air with 100% relative humidity). After 4 days numerous spheroids of different sizes appear. Spheroids measuring approximately 300 μm in diameter are selected for further experiments (84). The spheroids can be maintained in culture for prolonged periods, where for instance, they can be used for confrontation experiments (see below), and for transplantation studies.

We have also developed a modified organ culture method for glioma tissue obtained both from surgical specimens as well as from stereotactic biopsies of brain tumors (85). The method is as follows. Brain tumor tissue is obtained from patients either as stereotactic biopsies with a diameter of approximately 0.5 mm, or as tumor pieces (maximum size 0.5 cm). The tissue is immediately transferred aseptically to a test tube containing Dulbecco's modification of Eagle's medium (Flow Laboratories) supplemented with 10% heat-inactivated newborn calf serum, four times the prescribed concentration of nonessential amino acids, and 2% L-glutamine, 100 IU/ml penicillin, and 100 μg/streptomycin.

The biopsy material is cut into ~0.5-mm-sized pieces and incubated in 80-cm^2 tissue culture flasks (Nunc). The flasks are base-coated with 10 ml of 0.75% agar (Agar Noble; Difco Laboratories) in medium. The volume of the overlay suspension containing the tumor pieces is 12 ml. The medium is changed every week. The spheroids are cultured for up to 70 days in 5% CO_2 in air at 37°C and at 100% relative humidity and studied daily with a phase-contrast microscope. Between 5 and 10 days, tumor spheroids are selected with a Pasteur pipette using a stereomicroscope and placed in 16-mm-diameter multiwell dishes base-coated with 0.5 ml of agar. One spheroid is placed together with 0.8 ml of medium in each well. These single fragment cultures can be followed for up to 80 days.

We have found that, of 21 different gliomas, including grade 1–3 astrocytomas and glioblastomas, 17 were able to form spheroids. They maintained a close similarity to the histology of the original tumor for the whole culture period. This includes the morphology of the tumor cells and matrix as well as preservation of small vessels (Fig. 3).

A limitation of the method is the large areas of necrosis that are characteristic of glioblastomas *in vivo*. In the spheroids, necrotic areas may occasionally be seen, as well as small areas of degenerated tumor tissue. However, when appropriate dissection is performed at explantation, it is possible to achieve viable tumor material for culture. By using the bromodeoxyuridine labeling technique and mitotic counts, active proliferation in the spheroids is seen throughout the culture period, with a mean labeling index of approximately 9%.

Cells are also shed from the spheroids, which may explain why the cell proliferation often does not lead to spheroid growth. Different protein markers of brain tumors (GFAP, S-100, and NSE) are retained. Such spheroid cultures can also be used in confrontations with normal brain tissue for invasiveness studies as shown below.

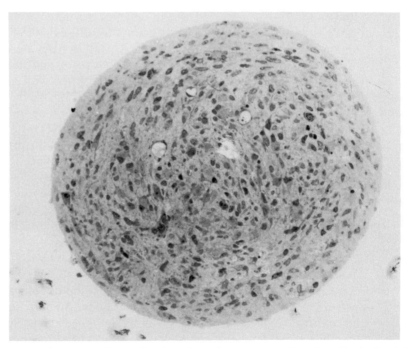

FIG. 3   Semithin toluidine-stained section of an organotypic spheroid obtained from an astrocytoma. The brain tumor biopsy has been in culture for 20 days. Note the vessels present inside the spheroid. ×310.

Confrontation Cultures

Several modifications of confrontation cultures are available for studies of interactions between different tissue types. Such cultures have mainly been applied to the study of the invasive properties of malignant gliomas. The basis for this is that when two normal brain aggregates are put together, they rapidly fuse into one large aggregate. The same occurs with two tumor spheroids. However, when a tumor spheroid is confronted with a normal brain cell aggregate, the former will progressively invade the normal tissue. The original method was devised by Mareel *et al.* (86), and first used for brain tumors by de Ridder and Laerum (87).

The technique involves the incubation of 0.3- to 0.5-mm-diameter fragments of 9-day-old embryonic chick heart in a gyratory shaker for 72 hr. The fragments will then form a spheroid consisting of a core of muscle cells surrounded by a few layers of fibroblastoid cells. The precultured heart fragments are put together with tumor spheroids on semisolid bactoagar in Tyrode's solution, 2 ml each in 35-mm plastic culture dishes (Falcon Plastics, Oxnard, CA). After 2 hr in close contact, the spheroids and heart fragments are firmly attached to each other. They are then carefully washed by pipetting Tyrode's solution onto the surface, and therefore removed with a spatula using a stereomicroscope. The confrontations are then transferred to 50-ml Erlenmeyer flasks and incubated at 37°C on a gyratory shaker at 70 rpm. Cultures are observed or photographed daily with a stereomicroscope and usually fixed at 1, 4, 6, and 7 days in either Bouin's fixative for paraffin embedding or glutaraldehyde for epoxy resin.

Malignant glioma cells will first migrate on the surface of the fragments and thereafter progressively invade, until the heart tissue is destroyed, usually after 7 days of coculture (88). The invasion is carried out in part by single cells, in part by groups of malignant cells, and occasionally the invasion involves a solid tissue mass (89). The histological pattern of the tumor spheroid during invasive growth closely reflects the *in vivo* growth pattern (88). Transmission electron micrographs show how cytoplasmic extensions of the glioma cells protrude between the heart muscle cells, gradually destroying the heart cell junctions. This process is followed by lysis of the normal tissue (89). Later, the system was extended to the study of invasive human glioma cells, where a pattern of invasiveness similar to that observed in malignant rat glioma cell lines may be seen (90).

The advantage offered by this system is that it is highly standardized and has been employed for a multitude of different types of invasive tumor cells. In addition, the structures of heart muscle tissue and glioma tissue are so different that they are easily distinguishable, particularly at the ultrastructural level.

Local invasiveness is considered to be the most critical property of malignant brain tumors, giving such tumors bad prognosis (for a review, see Ref. 91). One of the main goals has, therefore, been to develop methods where invasive glioma cells could be confronted with their "natural" target tissue, which is the normal brain. Our strategy has followed two main lines. The first was the development of an organ culture system for solid brain tissue which could be confronted with glioma spheroids. This would give the advantage of resembling the local conditions in the brain as far as possible, apart from the lack of blood circulation and local inflammatory reaction. However, such a system would give the glioma cells an advantage, since they can rapidly detach from the tumor spheroid. In contrast, the solid tissue matrix will not allow the brain cells to do the same. Therefore, we also developed a modified aggregate culture of normal brain cells where glioma and normal brain cell aggregates had been formed in the same manner. Thereby, the normal cells would be able to reform the architecture in the same way as the tumor cells, although they would not be expected to have invasive properties. We describe here applications of the above-mentioned organ culture methods in confrontation cultures.

Precultured Brain Fragments as Target Tissue

Precultured brain fragments are, after 20 days, confronted with tumor spheroids on the surface of 0.5 ml of 0.75% semisolid agar medium in 16-mm multiwell dishes. The two tissue pieces are placed in close contact by means of a sterile syringe. After 2 hr at 37°C, the two structures have attached firmly to each other, and 1 ml of growth medium (Dulbecco's modified Eagle's medium as described above) is carefully added. It is important to ensure that the cocultures do not adhere to the agar. If they do adhere, they must be carefully detached. The cocultures are observed daily in a phase-contrast microscope and usually fixed and prepared for light microscopy every second day during a 19-day culture period. The sections are serially mounted on slides. In addition, the sizes of the tumor spheroids and the normal brain fragments in the sections are measured.

After 24 hr the cocultures are seen as two spherical structures attached to each other (Fig. 4). Thereafter, the tumor cells with progressively invade and gradually destroy the normal brain tissue layers, one after the other. Due to the layered structure of the brain tissue, it is easy to see what has been replaced by the tumor tissue, and the extent of invasion. Usually, a complete destruction of the normal tissue is observed after 19 days of coculture, and after 30 days more than 90% of the brain fragments are found in the central necrotic part of the tumor spheroid. However, a small part of the brain tissue will sometimes persist (92).

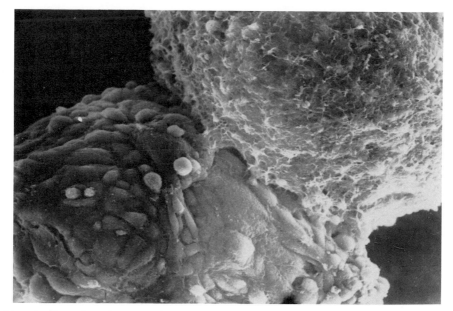

FIG. 4 Scanning electron micrograph of a confrontation between a brain fragment and a brain tumor spheroid after 24 hr of culture. Note the firm attachment between the two structures. ×400.

Using scanning electron microscopy, it has been observed that the malignant cells in the initial phase of confrontation culture will extend small cytoplasmic processes and ruffling membranes toward the normal brain cells, while the opposite never occurs (93). Thereafter, long cytoplasmic processes will penetrate in between the normal brain cells. Transmission electron microscopy shows that rat glioma cells will invade and replace the peripheral parts of the brain fragments, followed by degeneration of brain tissue. Surprisingly, specialized junctional structures between normal and malignant cells can be observed. Furthermore, the invading glioma cell exhibit a high level of phagocytic activity (92).

Fetal Rat Brain Aggregates as Target Tissue

When the reaggregated fetal rat brain cell cultures are used as targets, the invasion by malignant brain tumor cells occur in a similar manner to that seen in solid brain tissue (94). For tumor cell lines that will not form multicellular tumor spheroids, another procedure for confrontation cultures is followed. Tumor cells taken from confluent monolayer cultures are added to each 16-mm well of multiwell dishes (5×10^5 cells in each well). Each well already contains a precultured normal fetal brain cell aggregate that has been kept for 20 days. After 24 hr of coculture between the normal aggregate and the tumor cell suspension, the aggregates with adhered tumor cells are taken out with a pipette, washed twice in medium, and placed in agar-coated microwells containing medium. The medium is changed every third day. After 1, 4, 6, and 12 days of coculture, the specimens are fixed and prepared for light and transmission electron microscopy. As in the previous case, malignant rat glioma cells progressively invade the normal brain aggregate. This usually occurs as a progressive destruction of the outer neuropil layer after 3 days (Fig. 5). After 12 days of coculture, the tumor cells have in most cases replaced the normal tissue. This invasive pattern is similar to that observed when the same tumor cells are transplanted to the brains of isogeneic hosts (94). Both normal brain cells and glioma cells show considerable phagocytic capacity in culture. However, there are great variations between different glioma cell lines, where those with high phagocytic capacity also show high destructive ability on the normal tissue (95). There is possibly some relation between the excretion of proteolytic enzymes by invasive cells and their ability to invade and destroy normal tissue.

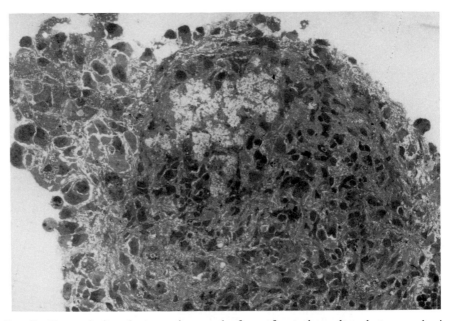

FIG. 5   Transmission electron micrograph of a confrontation culture between a brain aggregate and a brain tumor spheroid after 72 hr of culture. Note the replacement of normal tissue by tumor cells, and the cystic areas present in the normal tissue. ×270.

Semisolid Agar Culture of Glioma Cells

The cloning of glioma cells in semisolid agar medium usually follows the pattern seen with other types of tumor cells, both explanted as suspensions of primary tumors, as well as from monolayer cultures of continuous cell lines. We have used the following procedure. After trypsinization, aliquots of cultured glioma cells are suspended in medium at a concentration of 100 single cells per 25-cm² culture flask (Nunc). The medium consists of 0.15% bactoagar (Difco Laboratories) and 10% inactivated bovine serum in Dulbecco's modification of Eagle's medium as described above. In each test, 4–6 flasks are incubated (100% relative humidity, in air with 5% CO_2 at 37°C) and monitored for colony formation after 16 days of incubation.

This procedure can also be used for cloning of cultured cell lines by aspirating single colonies with a Pasteur pipette, trypsinization for 1–2 min, and transfer to plastic dishes for further monolayer culture. This agar culture procedure seems to select for subpopulations of tumor cells with phenotypic properties other than those of the parent line and sometimes with higher malignant potential (96).

General

The three-dimensional culture systems for both normal and malignant neural cell populations offer a wide variety of research possibilities. However, the opportunities offered by clot cultures and slice cultures as well as related modifications that have not been dealt with in this review should also be taken into consideration (for details, see Refs. 97–99). In addition, neural cell aggregates cultured *in vitro* can be transplanted as intracerebral, identifiable grafts and further studied in their natural habitat (100). Apparently, there are no appreciable species differences with respect to possibilities for the different types of culture applications. Mouse, rat, and human brain cells (see below) as well cells from other species can be used. However, the critical factor seems to be the period of explantation, where fetal or newborn brain cells display the best propagation ability.

There are some differences between spheroids of solid brain tissue and reaggregated brain cell cultures, although an organotypic pattern is reformed in both cases. For choice of method, the necessity of having a preformed tissue matrix is an important consideration. In addition, the selection of subpopulations is slightly different with the two methods, the aggregate cultures seeming to favor growth of macrophages. Whether these are preformed in the explanted tissue or are grown *de novo* from multipotent hematopoietic stem cells present in the brain is not known. In our experience, an advantage is offered by the stationary nonadherent cultures, since neither a shaking procedure nor the substratum will interfere with the growth of the tissue.

Special attention should be paid to the potential offered by confrontation culture procedures, where, for example, interactions between normal, preneoplastic, and malignant cells can be studied with high magnification and at the membrane level.

The disadvantage with the three-dimensional systems is that relatively small tissue amounts are obtained, and this may limit the possibilities for biochemical analysis. One is, therefore, dependent on micromethods, including immunohistochemical and similar methods.

In Vivo Culture

The diffusion chamber culture method was devised by E. Metchnikoff in the nineteenth century, and has been extensively used since the 1950s. At that time, the method was mainly used for culturing tumor types which were subject to histological examination. Later, the cell clot within the chambers could be dissolved by proteolytic enzymes and the cell numbers accurately quantitated. Since early in the 1970s, the method has been extensively used for culture of hematopoietic cells, both from animals and humans. We have used it as an alternative method for studying the kinetics of glioma cells under standardized conditions *in vivo*. The background for this is that cell culture often means selection of subpopulations of the tumor cells which can be very different from those that are the actual malignant population *in vivo* (101).

The method is as follows. The chambers are made of Perspex rings, 3 mm thick, internal diameter 10 mm, covered with Millipore filters on each side (pore size: 0.22 μm). A slightly conical hole in the Perspex ring is used for pipetting the cell suspension into the chambers. They are then sealed with a plastic stopper and a drop of Tensol cement no. 6 (ICI, Wellwyn Garden City, Herts, England). The chambers are previously sterilized overnight at 80°C. One hundred microliters of cell suspension is pipetted into each chamber with a constrictor pipette, and the sealed chambers are stored in petri dishes containing culture medium at room temperature until implantation.

Under general anesthesia, the chambers are implanted in the peritoneal cavity of the animals. This can be done in mice, one chamber into each, or in rats, with two chambers on either side. The abdominal wall and skin wound are thereafter closed with metal suture clips.

Depending on the cell type, $1-5 \times 10^5$ cells are implanted per chamber. At different times after implantation (4 hr to 2 weeks), the chambers are removed and the cells harvested. To dissolve the cell clots, the chambers are shaken, four together, in 5 ml of a solution of 0.5% (w/v) pronase P (Serva Finbiochemica, Heidelberg, FRG) and 5% (w/v) Ficoll (Pharmacia, Uppsala, Sweden) in 0.9% (w/v) aqueous NaCl solution for 1 hr at room temperature. The chambers are then washed in saline, blotted, punctured to aspirate content, and washed twice with 100 μl of saline to remove all the cells. Cells can then be counted, or further propagated in other types of culture (102).

Under these conditions, both glioma and neurinoma cells will grow exponentially, but usually more slowly than in monolayer cell culture. Furthermore, primary eighteenth-day fetal rat brain cells can also be cultured, forming organoid structures in the chambers (unpublished observations). For purposes where monolayer culture *in vivo* is desirable, a small glass coverslip can be inserted centrally in the chamber. A monolayer will then be formed by glioma cells on the glass surface. After 1–4 days the coverslips can be removed and used for different types of studies (103).

Miscellaneous

Human Cultures

From the preceding sections and from other chapters in this volume, it will be evident that human neural cells can be studied in culture for various purposes and with several different techniques. In the same way as for rat brains, fetal tissue seems, with some exceptions, to be necessary for the propagation of normal brain cells (104). Usually, the tissue is obtained from abortions, meaning that the available tissue comes from a few months of embryonic development. Human fetal brain cells have also been established as continuous cell lines following transfection with plasmids (105). Recently, spheroid cultures of human embryonic brain tissue have been reported (106). These cultures have also been used as targets for invasive human glioma cells. A limitation with these systems is that the differentiation of the brain cells does not correspond to the mature or early maturing brain. However, monolayer cultures of adult human glial cells obtained from neurosurgical operations can easily be obtained (107). In addition, the development of antigenic phenotype and functions of human glial cells have also been studied in 16- to 18-week-old fetuses (108).

Serum-Free Cultures

For several years, various subclasses of neural cells have been cultured in chemically defined media (see, e.g., Ref. 5). During recent years, more data have accumulated on nutritional factors which influence the growth and development in defined media of neural cells, such as astrocytes (109), oligo-dendrocytes (110, 111), and rat neocortex explants (112). Similarly, primary cultures of rat ependymal cells can now be grown in serum-free medium (113).

We have employed a chemically defined medium for growth of both human and rat glioma cells (114). Although the cells grew more slowly than in serum-containing medium, they could be propagated both in monolayers and as spheroids in the chemically defined medium. We are now employing the method for studying confrontation cultures between human gliomas and normal rat brain aggregates (114a). This has the advantage of permitting studies of cell properties related to invasiveness under strictly controlled conditions, as well as enabling enzymatic studies on invasive cells to be performed.

General Comments and Conclusions

Although the basic methods for cell and tissue culture of the central nervous system are not new, we are now faced with a new situation concerning their potential as research tools. This is mediated by rapid new developments related to direct neural cell interactions as well as messenger-type activities associated with distant interactions. This, combined with refined culture methods and chemically defined media, gives new opportunities for further research in this field.

It is known that astrocytes can protect cultured neurons from degeneration induced by anoxia in culture; this is one of several examples of astroglial–neuronal interactions that can be studied in cocultures (115, 116). Another example is the finding that the extracellular matrix of rat brain microvessels can modulate the phenotype of astroglial cells (117).

Present data indicate that a multitude of signal substances and growth factors strongly influence the different classes of brain cells in cultures. Both somatomedin C (118) and interleukin 2 (119, 120) are potent modifiers of oligodendrocyte development and proliferation.

Platelet-derived growth factor is a potent stimulator of both oligodendrocyte and bipotential progenitor cells. This effect seems to be mediated through astrocyte secretion (121–123). Astroglial and fibroblast growth factors have important neurotropic functions and support survival of neurons in primary culture (124–126). Both astroglial growth factor and inducers of protein kinase C stimulate differentiation of astrocytes in aggregating cultures (127, 128). In addition, α_2-tocopherol seems to be of importance for decreasing neuronal necrosis and reactive gliosis in such aggregate cultures (129); different brain-derived peptides may act as regulators of glia proliferation (130–132), and epidermal growth factor and growth hormones are known to stimulate differentiation and myelinization in brain cell aggregates (133). Furthermore, cell-derived proteases and protease inhibitors appear to act as regulators of neurite outgrowth (134).

Although long-term cultures of nontransformed brain cells are still limited to a few months of growth, the new knowledge of growth and differentiation-inducing factors as well as promoters of cell survival gives a potential for considerably increasing this period (135). Basic and simple monolayer as well as organ culture methods for cells of the CNS therefore will become even more important research tools in the near future.

Acknowledgments

All of our work cited in this review has been supported by the Norwegian Cancer Society. We thank Mrs. Lynn Kløve and Dr. Sverre Mørk for valuable advice and Mrs. Aud Isaksen for typing the manuscript.

References

1. R. G. Harrison, *Proc. Soc. Exp. Biol. Med.* **241,** 140 (1907).
2. J. C. Kawamoto and J. N. Barrett, *Brain Res.* **348,** 84 (1986).
3. S. Fedoroff and L. Hertz (ed.), *Adv. Cell. Neurobiol.* **1,** (1980).
4. S. E. Pfeiffer (ed.), "Neuroscience Approached through Cell Culture," p. 385. CRC Press, Boca Raton, Florida, 1984.
5. O. D. Laerum, S. Steinvåg, and R. Bjerkvig, *Acta Neurol. Scand.* **72,** 529 (1985).
6. J. E. Bottenstein (ed.), "Cell Culture in the Neurosciences." Plenum, New York, 1980.
7. P. E. Spoerri, H. C. Ludwig, and Y. Ogawa, *Acta Anat.* **123,** 64 (1985).
8. C. M. Regan, *Experientia* **44,** 695 (1988).
9. E. Hansson, L. Rönnbäck, A. Lowenthal, and M. Noppe, *Dev. Brain Res.* **21,** 175 (1985).
10. P. G. E. Kennedy, *J. Neurol., Neurosurg. Psychiatry* **50,** 798 (1987).
11. R. W. Oppenheim, *Trends NeuroSci. (Pers. Ed.)* **8,** 487 (1985).
12. R. Lim and K. Mitsunobu, *Science* **185,** 63 (1974).
13. R. Lim, S. Troy, and E. Turriff, *Exp. Cell Res.* **106,** 375 (1977).
14. P. L. Mobley, *Brain Res.* **398,** 366 (1986).
15. A. Peterson, L. Odland, M. Sensenbrenner, and M. Walum, *Int. J. Dev. Neurosci.* **4,** 35 (1986).
16. S. Temple and M. C. Raff, *Nature (London)* **313,** 223 (1983).
17. E. Barbaresa, S. E. Peiffer, and J. H. Carson, *Dev. Biol.* **96,** 84 (1983).
18. E. Hansson, *Neurobiology* **30,** 369 (1988).

19. O. D. Laerum, S. J. Mørk, Å. Haugen, E. Bock, L. Rosengren, and K. Haglid, *J. Neuro-Oncol.* **3,** 137 (1985).
20. O. D. Laerum and M. F. Rajewsky, *JNCI, J. Natl. Cancer Inst.* **55,** 1177 (1975).
21. B. Engelsen and R. Bjerkvig, in "Culture of Animal Cells" (I. Freshney, ed.), 2nd ed., p. 227. Liss, New York, 1987.
22. Å. Haugen and O. D. Laerum, *Brain Res.* **150,** 225 (1978).
23. Å. Haugen, O. D. Laerum, and E. Bock, *Acta Pathol. Microbiol. Scand., Sect. A* **89,** 393 (1981).
24. R. Ekanger, D. Øgreid, O. Evjen, O. Vintermyr, O. D. Laerum, and S. O. Døskeland, *Cancer Res.* **45,** 2578 (1985).
25. W. Dibb, E. Morild, and O. D. Laerum, *Virchows Arch. Cell Pathol.* **38,** 169 (1981).
26. O. D. Laerum, S. J. Mørk, and L. De Ridder, *Prog. Exp. Tumor Res.* **27,** 17 (1984).
27. Å. Haugen and O. D. Laerum, *JNCI, J. Natl. Cancer Inst.* **61,** 1415 (1978).
28. Å. Haugen and O. D. Laerum, *JNCI, J. Natl. Cancer Inst.* **63,** 455 (1979).
29. O. D. Laerum, M. F. Rajewsky, and M. Schachner, *Z. Krebsforsch.* **89,** 273 (1977).
30. J. P. Bressler, R. Cole, and J. de Vellis, *Cancer Res.* **43,** 709 (1983).
31. J. P. Bressler and J. de Vellis, *Brain Res.* **348,** 21 (1985).
32. T. Kokunai, K. Korosue, N. Tamaki, and S. Matsumoto, *Cancer Res.* **46,** 1377 (1986).
33. P. F. Lens, B. Altena, and R. Nusse, *Mol. Cell. Biol.* **6,** 3537 (1987).
34. S. H. Bigner, R. Bjerkvig, O. D. Laerum, L. H. Muhlbaier, and D. D. Bigner, *Anal. Quant. Cytol. Histol.* **9,** 435 (1987).
35. J. R. Shapiro, *Semin. Oncol.* **13,** 4 (1986).
36. Å. Haugen and O. D. Laerum, *Acta Pathol. Microbiol. Scand., Sect. A* **86,** 415 (1978).
37. Å. Haugen and O. D. Laerum, *Acta Pathol Microbiol. Scand., Sect. A* **86,** 101 (1978).
38. D. D. Bigner, C. Schold, S. H. Bigner, D. E. Bullard, and C. J. Wikstrand, *Cancer Treat. Rep.* **65,** 45 (1981).
39. D. D. Bigner, S. H. Bigner, J. Ponten, B. Westermark, M. S. Mahaley, E. Ruoslahti, H. Hernschman, L. F. Eng, and C. J. Wikstrand, *J. Neuropathol. Exp. Neurol.* **3,** 201 (1981).
40. S. J. Mørk and O. D. Laerum, *Acta Pathol. Microbiol. Scand., Sect. A* **274,** 403 (1981).
41. K. Onda, R. Tanaka, K. Washiyama, N. Takeda, and T. Kumanishi, *Acta Neuropathol.* **76,** 433 (1988).
42. N. H. Huh and M. F. Rajewsky, *Carcinogenesis* **7,** 435 (1986).
43. V. P. Collins and U. T. Brunk, *Ultrastruct. Pathol.* **7,** 321 (1984).
44. H. Koga, *J. Neurosurg.* **62,** 906 (1985).
45. C. D. James, E. Carlbom, J. P. Dumanski, M. Hansen, M. Nordenskjold, V. P. Collins, and W. K. Cavenee, *Cancer Res.* **48,** 5546 (1988).

46. S. H. Bigner, P. C. Burger, J. A. Wong, M. H. Werner, R. Stanley, M. D. Hamilton, H. L. Muhlbaier, B. Vogelstein, and D. B. Bigner, *J. Neuropathol. Exp. Neurol.* **47**, 191 (1988).

47. T. A. Libermann, *J. Cell Sci., Suppl.* **3**, 161 (1985).

48. L. T. Malden, *Cancer Res.* **48**, 2711 (1988).

49. A. Fontana, H. Hengartner, N. De Tribolet, and E. Weber, *J. Immunol.* **132**, 1837 (1984).

50. C. Betsholtz, C. H. Heldin, M. Nister, B. Ek, A. Wasteson, and B. Wester-mark, *Biochem. Biophys. Res. Commun.* **117**, 176 (1983).

51. M. Nister, C. H. Heldin, A. Wasteson, and B. Westermark, *Proc. Natl. Acad. Sci. U.S.A.* **81**, 926 (1984).

52. R. de Martin, B. Haendler, R. Hofer-Warbinek, H. Gaugitsch, M. Wrann, H. Schlusener, J. M. Seifert, S. Bodmer, A. Fontana, and E. Hofer, *EMBO J.* **6**, 3673 (1987).

53. D. L. Clemens, E. Clauser, M. R. Celio, and T. Inagam, *Brain Res.* **364**, 205 (1986).

54. K. Danø, E. Dabeltsteen, L. S. Nielsen, K. Kaltoft, E. L. Wilson, and J. Zeuthen, *J. Histochem. Cytochem.* **30**, 1165 (1982).

55. J. L. Gross, D. L. Behrens, D. E. Mullins, P. L. Kornblith, and D. L. Dexter, *Cancer Res.* **48**, 292 (1988).

56. S. Gammeltoft, R. Ballotti, A. Kowalski, B. Westermark, and E. van Ob-berghen, *Cancer Res.* **48**, 1233 (1988).

57. P. A. Steck, P. Lee, M.-C. Hung, and W. K. A. Yung, *Cancer Res.* **48**, 5433 (1988).

58. C. J. Wikstrand, F. C. Grahmann, R. D. McComb, and D. D. Bigner, *J. Neuropathol. Exp. Neurol.* **44**, 229 (1985).

59. B. De Muralt, N. De Tribolet, and A. C. Diserens, *Eur. J. Cancer Clin. Oncol.* **21**, 207 (1985).

60. P. G. E. Kennedy, B. A. Watkins, D. G. T. Thomas, and M. D. Noble, *Neuropathol. Appl. Neurobiol.* **13**, 327 (1987).

61. D. Stavrou, E. Keiditsch, F. Schmidberger, K. Bise, I. Funke, W. Eisen-menger, R. Kurrle, B. Martin, and U. Stocker, *J. Neurol. Sci.* **80**, 205 (1987).

62. G. V. Sherbet, R. M. Kalbag, M. S. Lakshmi, M. E. Tindle, and M. Wildridge, *Invasion Metastasis* **3**, 98 (1983).

63. B. Berra, S. M. Gaini, and L. Riboni, *Int. J. Cancer* **36**, 363 (1985).

64. S. Hakomori and R. Kannagi, *JNCI, J. Natl. Cancer. Inst.* **71**, 231 (1983).

65. M. C. Frame, R. I. Freshney, and P. F. T. Vaughan, *Br. J. Cancer* **49**, 269 (1984).

66. P. F. Jacobsen, D. J. Jenkyn, and J. M. Papadimitriou, *J. Neuropathol. Exp. Neurol.* **46**, 431 (1987).

67. R. I. Freshney, *Anticancer Res.* **5**, 111 (1985).

68. R. Lim, D. J. Hicklin, T. C. Ryken, X.-M. Han, K.-N. Liu, J. F. Miller, and B. A. Baggentoss, *Cancer Res.* **46**, 5241 (1986).

69. Y. Marushige, N. R. Raju, K. Marushige, and A. Koestner, *Cancer Res.* **47**, 4109 (1987).

70. M. L. Rosenblum, M. A. Gerosa, and C. B. Wilson, *J. Neurosurg.* **58**, 710 (1983).
71. S. K. Steinsvåg and O. D. Laerum, *Experientia* **41**, 1517 (1985).
72. S. K. Steinsvåg, *Experientia* **42**, 798 (1986).
73. R. Bjerkvig, S. K. Steinsvåg, and O. D. Laerum, *In Vitro Cell. Dev. Biol.* **22**, 180 (1986).
74. R. Bjerkvig, *In Vitro Cell. Dev. Biol.* **22**, 193 (1986).
75. R. Bjerkvig, *in* "Culture of Animal Cells" (I. Freshney, ed.), 2nd ed., p. 278. Liss, New York, 1987.
76. J. R. Hess, J. Michaud, R. A. Sobel, M. M. Herman, and L. J. Rubinstein, *Acta Neuropathol.* **61**, 1 (1983).
77. J. L. Darling, N. Oktar, and D. G. T. Thomas, *Cell Biol. Int. Rep.* **7**, 23 (1983).
78. J. Carlsson, K. Nilsson, B. Westermark, J. Ponten, C. Sundstrøm, E. Larsson, J. Bergh, S. Påhlman, C. Busch, and V. P. Collins, *Int. J. Cancer* **31**, 523 (1983).
79. H. Acker, J. Carlsson, E. Durard, and E. M. Sutherland (eds.), *in* "Spheroids in Cancer Research." Springer-Verlag, Berlin and New York, 1984.
80. T. Nederman, B. Norling, B. Glimelius, J. Carlsson, and B. Brunk, *Cancer Res.* **44**, 3090 (1984).
81. G. Bendiktsson, J. Carlsson, and S. Nilsson, *Acta Pathol. Microbiol. Scand., Sect. A* **91**, 291 (1983).
82. M. Kitahara, R. Katakura, J. Suzuki, and T. Sasaki, *Int. J. Cancer* **40**, 557 (1987).
83. J. M. Yuhas, A. P. Lie, A. O. Martinez, and A. J. Ladman, *Cancer Res.* **37**, 3639 (1977).
84. S. K. Steinsvåg, *JNCI, J. Natl. Cancer Inst.* **74**, 1095 (1985).
85. R. Bjerkvig, A. Tønnesen, O. D. Laerum, and E. O. Backlund, *J. Neurosurg.*, in press (1990).
86. M. Mareel, J. Kint, and C. Meyvisch, *Virchow's Arch. Cell Pathol.* **30**, 95 (1979).
87. L. de Ridder and O. D. Laerum, *JNCI, J. Natl. Cancer Inst.* **66**, 723 (1981).
88. S. Mørk, L. de Ridder, and O. D. Laerum, *Anticancer Res.* **2**, 1 (1982).
89. S. J. Mørk, O. D. Laerum, and L. de Ridder, *Anticancer Res.* **3**, 373 (1983).
90. L. I. de Ridder, O. D. Laerum, S. J. Mørk, and D. D. Bigner, *Acta Neuropathol.* **72**, 207 (1987).
91. O. D. Laerum, R. Bjerkvig, S. K. Steinsvåg, and L. de Ridder, *Cancer Metastasis Rev.* **3**, 223 (1984).
92. S. K. Steinsvåg and O. D. Laerum, *Anticancer Res.* **5**, 137 (1985).
93. S. K. Steinsvåg, *Invasion Metastasis* **5**, 255 (1985).
94. R. Bjerkvig, O. D. Laerum, and O. Mella, *Cancer Res.* **46**, 4071 (1986).
95. R. Bjerknes, R. Bjerkvig, and O. D. Laerum, *JNCI, J. Natl. Cancer Inst.* **78**, 279 (1987).
96. K. Hanke (ed.), Ph.D., dissertation. Fakultät für Biologie, Eberhard-Karls-Universität Tübingen, Federal Republic of Germany, 1979.
97. B. H. Gähwiler, *Experientia* **40**, 235 (1984).
98. M. M. Bird, *J. Anat.* **136**, 293 (1983).
99. D. Munoz-Garcia and S. K. Ludwin, *J. Neuroimmunol.* **8**, 237 (1985).

100. J. A. Colombo, J. I. Almeida, and S. Molina, *Exp. Neurol.* **98,** 606 (1987).
101. O. D. Laerum, S. Mørk, M. F. Rajewsky, I. L. Hansteen, and Å. Haugen, *Anticancer Res.* **3,** 187 (1983).
102. O. D. Laerum, A. Grüneisen, and M. F. Rajewsky, *Eur. J. Cancer* **9,** 533 (1973).
103. O. D. Laerum, D. F. Hülser, and M. F. Rajewsky, *Cancer Res.* **36,** 2153 (1976).
104. J. T. Rutka, J. R. Riblin, R. Balkissoon, D. Wen, C. A. Myatt, J. R. McCulloch, and M. L. Rosenblum, *Dev. Neurosci.* **9,** 154 (1987).
105. E. O. Major, A. E. Miller, P. Mourrain, R. G. Traub, and E. de Widt, *Proc. Natl. Acad. Sci. U.S.A.* **82,** 1257 (1985).
106. L. Pulliam, M. E. Berens, and M. L. Rosenblum, *J. Neurosci. Res.* **21,** 521 (1988).
107. N. Forsby, *Acta Pathol. Microbiol. Immunol. Scand., Sect. A* **93,** 235 (1985).
108. P. G. E. Kennedy and J. Fok-Seang, *Brain* **109,** 1261 (1986).
109. A. Michler-Stuke, J. R. Wolff, and J. E. Bottenstein, *Int. J. Dev. Neurosci.* **2,** 575 (1984).
110. R. P. Saneto and J. de Vellis, *Proc. Natl. Acad. Sci. U.S.A.* **82,** 3509 (1985).
111. A. E. de los Monteros, G. Roussel, N. M. Neskovic, and J. L. Nussbaum, *J. Neurosci. Res.* **19,** 202 (1988).
112. H. J. Romijn, B. M. de Jang, and J. M. Ruijter, *J. Neurosci. Methods* **23,** 75 (1988).
113. M. Weibel, B. Pettmann, J.-C. Artault, M. Sensenbrenner, and G. Labourdette, *Dev. Brain Res.* **25,** 199 (1986).
114. L. A. Akslen, K. J. Andersen, and R. Bjerkvig, *Anticancer Res.* **8,** 797 (1988).
114a. M. Lund-Johansen, *Invasion Metastasis,* in press (1990).
115. S. Vibulsreth, F. Hefti, M. D. Ginsberg, W. D. Dietrich, and R. Busto, *Brain Res.* **422,** 303 (1987).
116. E. Hansson, *Life Sci.* **39,** 269 (1986).
117. J. B. Grinspan, M. Lieb, J. Stern, M. Rupnick, S. Williams, and D. Pleasure, *Dev. Brain Res.* **33,** 291 (1987).
118. F. A. McMorris, T. M. Smith, S. DeSalvo, and R. W. Furlanetto, **83,** 822 (1986).
119. E. N. Benveniste and J. E. Merrill, *Nature (London)* **321,** 610 (1986).
120. R. P. Saneto, A. Altman, R. L. Knobler, H. M. Johnson, and J. de Vellis, *Neurology* **83,** 9221 (1986).
121. F. Besnard, F. Perraud, M. Sensenbrenner, and G. Labourdette, *Neurosci. Lett.* **73,** 287 (1987).
122. W. D. Richardson, N. Pringle, M. J. Mosley, B. Westermark, and M. Dubois-Dalcq, *Cell* **53,** 309 (1988).
123. M. C. Raff, L. E. Lillien, W. D. Richardson, J. F. Burne, and M. D. Noble, *Nature (London)* **333,** 562 (1988).
124. B. Pettmann, G. Labourdette, M. Weibel, and M. Sensenbrenner, *Funkt. Biol. Med.* **243,** 243 (1985).
125. R. S. Morrison, A. Sharma, J. de Vellis, and R. A. Bradshaw, *Proc. Natl. Acad. Sci. U.S.A.* **83,** 7537 (1986).
126. K. Unsicker, H. Reichert-Preibsch, R. Schmidt, B. Pettmann, G. Labourdette, and M. Sensenbrenner, *Proc. Natl. Acad. U.S.A.* **84,** 5459 (1987).

127. M. Weibel, B. Pettmann, G. Labourdette, M. Miehe, E. Bock, and M. Sensenbrenner, *Int. J. Dev. Neurosci.* **3,** 617 (1985).
128. P. Honegger, *J. Neurochem.* **46,** 1561 (1986).
129. M. Halks-Miller, M. Henderson, and L. F. Eng, *J. Neuropathol. Exp. Neurol.* **45,** 471 (1986).
130. D. Guilian and T. J. Baker, *J. Cell Biol.* **101,** 2411 (1985).
131. D. Giulian and T. J. Baker, *J. Cell Biol.* **102,** 803 (1986).
132. D. Giulian and D. G. Young, *J. Cell Biol.* **102,** 812 (1986).
133. G. Almazan, P. Honegger, J.-M. Matthieu, and B. Guentert-Lauber, *Dev. Brain Res.* **21,** 257 (1985).
134. D. Monard, *Trends NeuroSci. (Pers. Ed.)* **11,** 541 (1988).
135. K. Meller and M. Waelsch, *J. Neurocytol.* **13,** 29 (1984).

[16]   Brain Cell Culture in Rotation-Mediated Aggregates

Paul C. Goldsmith and Michael E. Berens

Introduction

A reliable *in vitro* method to study cell–cell interactions in the central nervous system (CNS) is detailed in this chapter. The primary advantage of brain cell culture using rotation-mediated three-dimensional aggregates (RMAs) is the establishment and maintenance of a near *in situ* environment. Cultured brain RMAs demonstrate the presence of diverse cell types, including neurons, astrocytes, oligodendrocytes, ependymal cells, macrophages, endothelial cells, and fibroblasts (1). These components may generate an extracellular matrix which mimics the *in vivo* milieu, and therefore the intact brain itself.

Rotation-mediated aggregate (RMA) culture of dissociated tissue was first described by Moscona (2). Since then, RMAs have been used to study various heterogeneous tissues such as the anterior pituitary (3, 4) and sev-

Methods in Neurosciences, Volume 2

eral regions of the brain (5). Aggregate culture of fetal brain was successfully employed by Seeds (6) to study differentiation of neuronal elements. Brain cells adopted mature biochemical properties after 1 month in RMA culture (7). Cytological assembly into characteristic histological structures also occurred in murine fetal brain in aggregate culture (8). Since RMA assembly begins from single-cell suspensions of brain tissue, there apparently are specific surface markers which promote an orderly reassociation of fetal brain cells. These RMA properties and functional relationships may change with gestational age. More recently, specific innervation of particular neurons and analysis of synapses produced *in vitro* have been studied in RMA cultures (9).

Development of stromal elements in the brain has also been successfully investigated using aggregate cultures. Purified astrocytes and oligodendrocytes are capable of aggregate formation and subsequent synthesis of myelin (10). Maturation of astrocytes has been followed in RMA culture by Monnet-Tschudi *et al.* (11). RMA systems provide the opportunity to clarify the importance of various cell–cell interactions in directing immature precursors to fully differentiated progeny (12). Successful RMA culture of brain tissue in serum-free, defined medium may further promote clarification of the role of soluble factors in glial cell differentiation (13).

The RMA model of the CNS has been employed for neurotropic viral infections (14), for mechanisms of malignant glioblastoma invasion (15–18), and presently for investigations of hypothalamic neuron maturation and synapse formation. Additional applications may emerge in disciplines of developmental neurobiology, neurophysiology, and neuroanatomy, the pathology of myelination and demyelination, axonal migration and regeneration, and determination of CNS toxicity to various cancer chemotherapeutic agents.

Materials and Methods

Preparation of Equipment

Successful initiation of brain aggregate culture has been found to be dependent on well-siliconized glass culture vessels, and accurate speed of rotation. Culture glassware (25- and 50-ml DeLong flasks; Bellco Biotechnology, Vineland, NJ) is cleaned by overnight soaking in Contra D-70 (Curtis Matheson Scientific, Inc., Houston, TX) made as a 5% (v/v) solution. After thorough rinsing in distilled deionized water, the dried glassware is placed in an enclosed chamber and exposed to dimethyldichlorosilane (D-3879; Sigma Chemical Co., St. Louis, MO) vapor under reduced pressure for 2 hr. After thorough rinsing in water, the glassware is sterilized by autoclaving.

Careful attention to calibrate the horizontal rotation of orbital shaker platforms to a speed of 72 rpm in a controlled CO_2 incubator is necessary. Faster and slower speeds have proved less successful in generating RMAs of consistent size. A stroke length of rotation of approximately 2 cm has proved to be adequate to maintain the cells in a suspended condition in the flasks. Adhesion of the cells or aggregates to the walls of the flasks can be a progressive problem and indicates poor silanization of the glassware. Occurrence of even minimal attachment to the walls of the vessel warrants transfer of the aggregates to another flask. Also, during the initial days of culture, removal of large clumps of debris by gentle aspiration with a Pasteur pipette promotes more consistent RMA formation.

Tissue Collection and Dissociation

Fresh human fetal brain tissue is collected and placed in test tubes containing minimal essential medium (MEM) with antibiotics. The tissue is kept cold by standing the tube in wet ice. Dissociation of the brain is achieved by gently expressing the tissue through sterile mesh. Serial passage through 200- and 100-μm mesh Nitex (Tetko Inc., Elmsford, NY) is adequate to generate a single-cell suspension. Sieves of the mesh are prepared by boring a large opening in the screw-on lids of specimen cups. The mesh is held in place by the installed lid, and the cup resterilized by ethylene oxide. Brain tissue is pressed through the mesh using the plunger of a syringe. Performing as much of the procedure as possible at 4°C enhances yield of viable cells. Cells are collected, then transferred to centrifuge tubes, and washed twice using buffered saline. The final cell preparation is resuspended in MEM containing nonessential amino acids, dextrose (6 mg/ml), insulin (20 μg/ml; Sigma), gentamicin, and 10% (v/v) fetal calf serum. Viable cell counts are determined using Trypan blue exclusion. The cells are adjusted to a concentration of 1.0×10^7 viable cells per milliliter. Viability is typically between 20 and 40% of the collected human fetal cells, but may exceed 90% for fresh murine specimens. Four-milliliter aliquots are added to each 25-ml DeLong flask. The flasks are incubated on the rotating platforms kept at 37°C, 7.5% CO_2, humidified air. Other investigators have used CO_2 levels of 10%, but we found this to be without merit.

Aggregate Maintenance

After 2 days, half the medium is replaced with fresh medium. The flasks are placed at an angle of approximately 45° on a bed of ice, which allows the aggregating cells to sediment to the perimeter of the flask without risking adhesion to the glass. Two milliliters is easily removed from the flask using a pipette. This is replaced with an equal volume of fresh medium supplemented as above. The contents of the flask are resuspended by gentle swirling. After 2 additional days on the platform rotator in the incubator, the contents of each 25-ml DeLong flask are transferred to a 50-ml DeLong flask with the addition of 5 ml of fresh medium containing the same additives but with 15% fetal calf serum. The aggregates are replenished with 50% fresh medium every 2–3 days. The time to aggregate formation for individual specimens is somewhat variable. Daily observation during the initial week of culture is imperative to monitor aggregate generation and stability. During the latter phases of RMA culture, the color of the culture medium is the principal determinant for medium renewal; this typically is done on alternate days.

Tissue Collection and Survival of RMAs in Culture

Predetermination of Cell Populations

A minimum of 10–12 samples of murine forebrain tissue measuring 4 mm^3 makes a worthwhile dispersion and provides enough cells to create 200–400 RMAs in 4 ml in a 25-ml DeLong flask. About 20 such tissue samples will similarly yield two DeLong flasks. One human fetal brain specimen measuring 9 mm^3 will usually produce enough cells for a single flask, so that additional specimens can be maintained separately if desired. It is better to increase the amount of starting material by increasing the number of discrete tissue samples rather than increasing their size. Otherwise, the regional specificity of the desired cell types may be lost.

Selection of Species and Brain Area

Murine CNS is especially suited for these studies. Required numbers of staged fetal brains can be collected from one or more litters. Dissection of the desired brain region is facilitated by using two 18-mm microdissecting knives (Cat. No. RS-6250; Roboz Surgical Instrument Co., Inc., Washington, D.C.) in scissors fashion under the dissecting microscope. Human fetal brain regions are usually selected without microdissection, but specific boundaries should still be observed. Areas of the CNS which will differentiate into the desired cell types should be selected. These fetal neurons will probably not display the desired phenotype spontaneously in culture. However, after establishing the experimental system with the appropriate cells, survival and neurite outgrowth can be promoted by controlling the culture conditions (6, 19).

Age of Fetal Brain

We have had particular success with 14-day gestational age (dga) fetal mouse hypothalami. Less viable and less hearty RMAs were obtained with 15-dga dispersions, although cerebral cortex from 16-dga mice can do very well (L. Pulliam, personal communication). Poor cell viability and very heterogenous aggregates resulted from 0 day (birth) and 1 day postnatal preparations. Human brain specimens from 12- to 20-weeks gestational age have also been successfully cultured with this same system.

Time RMAs Are in Culture

RMAs show distinct changes over time *in vitro*. Without alteration of standard rotating-culture conditions, murine RMAs evolve through (1) a dynamic developmental phase for 2–6 days; (2) a stable, phenotypically mature phase from about day 7 to day 28; and (3) a phase of accelerating degeneration during weeks 4–6 (see below). Human aggregates go through a similar phase of dynamic remodeling early after formation, with expulsion or degradation of dead cells, and substantial remodeling by cell migration and proliferation. In contrast, however, human aggregates demonstrate a markedly prolonged culture survival, sometimes in excess of 8 weeks. The length of phases and velocity of these changes will vary with culture conditions, including speed of rotation, volume of medium, and contamination. Therefore, the experimental paradigm should dictate the appropriate time of RMA selection and the incubation conditions. The availability of different stages of aggregate maturity with characteristic cell populations, stability, and differentiation makes this system applicable to several kinds of studies.

Techniques for Microscopy

Fixation

All basic light microscopic (LM) and electron microscopic (EM) methods can be performed on lightly pelleted aggregates. Fortunately, RMAs in static medium always sink to the bottom of their container. The geometry of a tilted 50-ml DeLong flask allows introduction of a sterile, disposable 5-ml pipette and retrival of accumulated RMAs in a small volume of medium. Collections of 10–50 RMAs can thus be transferred to 1.5-ml minicentrifuge tubes which are placed in a standard tabletop centrifuge and gently packed at 200 g for 30 sec at 23°C. Remove the tubes carefully, and take off the medium with a micropipette without disturbing the pellet. With the tubes in a rack, slowly pipette 1 ml of fixative down the side. For routine LM and EM studies, fixation with 1% (w/v) paraformaldehyde, 1% (v/v) glutaraldehyde, in 0.15 M sodium cacodylate buffer, pH 7.4 (CB), containing 0.02% (w/v) $MgCl_2$ gives good pellets and excellent structural preservation. [We do not routinely add 0.02 mM $CaCl_2$ because high Ca^{2+} has been reported to stimulate transmitter release (20).] Continue fixation undisturbed for 30 min at 4°C. The fixative may then be removed, replaced with 0.1 M CB or with 0.1 M Tris-HCl buffer, pH 7.4, containing 0.9% (w/v) NaCl (TBS), and the pellet stored at 4°C until further processed. We have found that TBS is most convenient because of its suitability for both LM and EM techniques, lower background with preembedding immunoperoxidase staining methods, and compatibility (without precipitation) with most EM *en bloc* heavy metal stains.

Light Microscopy

For LM examination, coherent fixed pellets may be treated as if they were small pieces of tissue, and embedded without regard to sample orientation. However, unstained pellets are difficult to follow through dehydration and infiltration procedures. Therefore, after sufficient washing in buffer, pellets can be lightly stained with toluidine blue (partially removed by subsequent alcohols) or eosin (once in 70% ethanol) to help visualize them. Since both these stains fluoresce, they should not be used prior to fluorescence immunostaining. For paraffin embedding, encase pellets in warm 4% (w/v) agar in TBS to create a larger sample for casette-type processing. RMAs in two-dimensional lattices are also easily handled by wrapping them in lens tissue (e.g., Ross Optical Lens Tissue; A. Rosmarin, Metuchen, NJ) at the buffer stage for subsequent dehydration and embedding in paraffin. The choice of either paraffin or plastic embedding will of course be dictated by plans for subsequent immunostaining, and section thicknesses of 8–10 μm (paraffin) or 0.5–1 μm (plastic) for best microscopic resolution. General embedding techniques for paraffin and plastic are suitable for RMAs, and likewise, general histological stains are applicable to the LM tissue sections (Fig. 1).

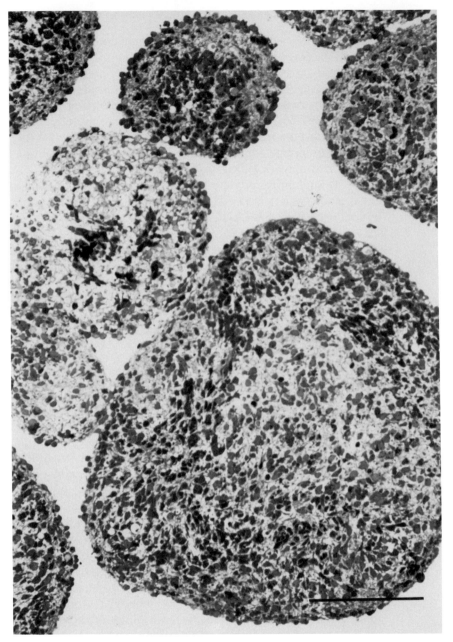

Fig. 1   Light micrograph (LM) of aggregates from 13-dga mouse hypothalami after only 1 day in rotation-mediated culture. Note differences in size and component elements, the regionalized distribution of cells, and the surface blebbing of surface glial nuclei. Epon section (1.0 μm) stained with toluidine blue. Bar, 100 μm.

Electron Microscopy

Pellets designated for EM are conveniently left in 1.5-ml microcentrifuge tubes for processing. After washing in CB (4 × 10 min), postfix pellets in 2% (w/v) osmium tetroxide in the same buffer for 30 min. Following several washes, add a filtered solution of 0.5% (w/v) tannic acid in CB for 10 min at 23°C. Wash them immediately in 1% (w/v) Na_2SO_4 in CB (4 × 10 min), and then dehydrate them for 10 min in 50% (v/v) ethanol. Stain the pellets *en bloc* with 5% (w/v) uranyl acetate in 50% ethanol for 30 min at 23°C, and continue dehydration in a series of graded ethanols for 10 min each. Following absolute ethanol (4 × 10 min), infiltrate pellets overnight in 1 : 1 mixture of propylene oxide : Epon 812. Following two changes of Epon (4 hr each), transfer them to polyethylene embedding capsules and cure the plastic at 60°C for 48–72 hr. Thick sections (1 μm) are mounted on glass slides, stained with toluidine blue, and examined in the LM. Silver to gold thin sections (60–90 nm) are retrieved on uncoated, 200-mesh copper grids, and stained with uranyl acetate and lead citrate. It is helpful to examine the sections in the EM at several magnifications to observe cell arrangements, surface specializations, and organelles.

Characteristics of RMAs

Dispersed hypothalamic neurons and glia from mice 13 dga to 1 day postnatal age have been successfully incorporated into RMAs within 48 hr *in vitro*. Under identical conditions and speed of rotation, their shapes vary from spheroidal to oblate and irregular, with diameters mostly in the range of 150–400 μm. The arrangement of their cellular constituents is remarkably consistent, even though the relative proportions of their cell types may differ (as determined from immunostaining). The life cycle of RMAs in continuous rotating culture is quite reproducible from one dispersion to the next. Therefore, features and changes that murine RMAs exhibit over time can conveniently be discussed in three periods of growth and development.

Dynamic Phase (Days 2–6)

From days 2–6 of rotation, RMAs from fetal murine CNS dispersions remain composed of basically undifferentiated cells. Soon after the formation of the spheroids, one or two layers of surface glia create a limiting envelope and join together at their apical borders with tight junctions (macula adherens). In the LM, these glial nuclei sometimes appear rounded up and bulging outward into the medium (Fig. 1). In the EM, they appear less regular, more often flattened and polymorphic, and filled with fine particulate, and some densely clumped chromatin. The darkened cytoplasm is generally unspecialized, and contains many free polyribosomes, a few flattened rough endoplasmic reticulum (RER) cisternae, very little Golgi apparatus, a limited number of dense mitochondria, and occasional lysosomes.

Just beneath these glia, a zone rich in neuroblasts and their neurites is present after only 1 or 2 days of rotation. These neuroblasts appear undifferentiated, with larger, rounded nuclei containing granular chromatin and a few peripherally located nucleoli. Their small amounts of paler, perikaryal cytoplasm are often juxtaposed, and contain more numerous RER cisternae, larger mitochondria, and a few Golgi elements. These cells do not contact the medium, but extend their processes inward into a loose network composed of primitive neurons, thin processes, and smaller glia. Even at the beginning of this stage, neurites can be identified as axons or dendrites according to the usual morphological criteria. Sometimes they form well-developed synapses amid neuronal networks. These synapses are usually axodendritic, as judged by accumulations of presynaptic vesicles, occasional dense-core granules, and pre- and postsynaptic thickenings flanking a classical synaptic cleft (Fig. 2A).

Vital staining with Trypan blue reveals that early RMAs slough most dead cells from their outer surface, while nonviable internal cells seem to be retained and cannibalized by phagocytic cells. These phagocytes contain a variety of clear vacuoles and active phagosomes, and occasionally are seen dividing. Larger clumps of pycnotic cells and debris, however, are usually conveyed to the surface and extruded. Due to the removal of nonliving material and the sorting of certain viable cells, considerable reorganization takes place during this dynamic phase.

Stable Phase (Days 7–28)

After 7 days of rotation–incubation, the processes of cell movement, reorganization, and debris ejection are noticeably reduced. RMAs retain their configuration, including internal cavities if already present, and enter a 21-day period of relative structural stability. Although major cell populations also maintain their number and ratio, they are by no means quiescent. During this time, neurons and glia continue to grow and differentiate, expressing their distinct phenotypes and hallmark substances, until about 28 days of incubation.

By the beginning of this stable phase, glia covering the RMA surface have acquired the appearance of mature ependymal astrocytes. Their specializations include (1) multiple tight junctions (macula adherentes) tacking them laterally to neighboring glia; (2) a few short microvilli on their external surface; (3) groups of clear and coated vesicles beneath their outer plasmalemma (suggesting a role in transport or fluid homeostasis); (4) a single, outwardly directed cilium on some of the cells; and (5) variable amounts of bundles of intermediate filaments. These filaments are glial fibrillary acidic protein (GFAP)-immunoreactive with both the A15K and anti-GFAP antisera, thus confirming their astrocytic nature (Fig. 3). The same type of cell and specializations delimit internal cavities within RMAs, and similarly prohibit entry of underlying axons and other processes. Their structural role, taken together with morphological characteristics, suggests that these astrocytes are analogous to the ependymal cells lining the mammalian cerebroventricular system.

Within the confines of limiting astrocytes, neurons and neuronal processes continue to grow and develop for at least 3 more weeks of rotation–incubation. Proliferation and developmental processes are so great that all open spaces formerly present within murine RMAs become completely filled with tightly packed dendrites and axons. In fact, by day 22 the density and complexity of RMA parenchyma mimics that of the mature, adult brain (Fig. 2B). This consolidation leads to a greater number of morphologically identified synapses, particularly in the outer zone of the RMA where neurons predominate. Within the interior, the incidence of synapses is less frequent, perhaps due to the larger number of intervening glial elements. Here, many macrophages become completely engorged with large, lipoid-filled phagosomes and lamellated myelin figures. Bundles of intact, myelinated axons surrounded by 10–12 myelin lamellae occur sporadically within murine RMAs after 22 days of incubation. Toward the center, however, electrolucent areas containing diluted cytoplasm and fragments of membranous organelles are early evidence of isolated cell demise at this time.

Degenerative Phase (4–6 Weeks)

From 4–6 weeks there is an accelerating decline in the status of the murine RMAs. In several older cultures, we have noted that some RMAs lose their spheroidal form and may take on bizarre, bilobed shapes. Although we have not examined these RMAs ultrastructurally, these changes are probably due to central necrosis and eccentric cavitation. In addition, aging RMAs sometimes enlarge to perhaps 2 or 3 times their previous diameter, even though more nonviable cells continue to be sloughed. In static incubations of similar age, we have also noted certain RMAs displaying various dumbbell shapes, conceivably the result of RMAs either pulling apart or sticking together.

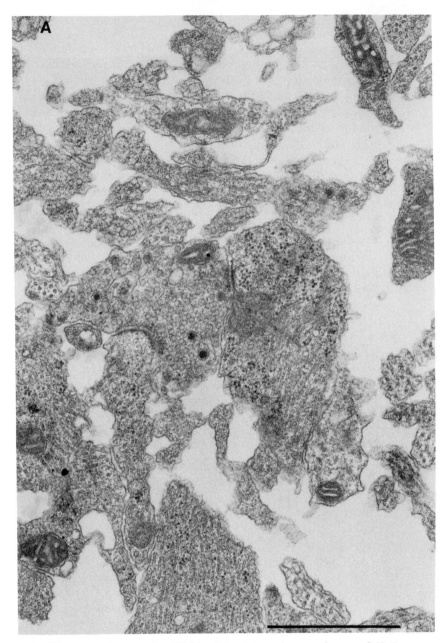

FIG. 2 Electron micrographs (EMs) of the internal parenchyma of 13-dga mouse RMAs after (A) 1 day and (B) 22 days of rotation culture. (A) After 1 day of culture, the RMA matrix consists of loosely arranged glial elements (here with enlarged mitochondria) and neuronal processes which occupy only about half the available space. Sections through axonal neurotubules, clear vesicles, and dense-cored granules are apparent. In murine RMAs, presynaptic vesicles and synaptic specializa-

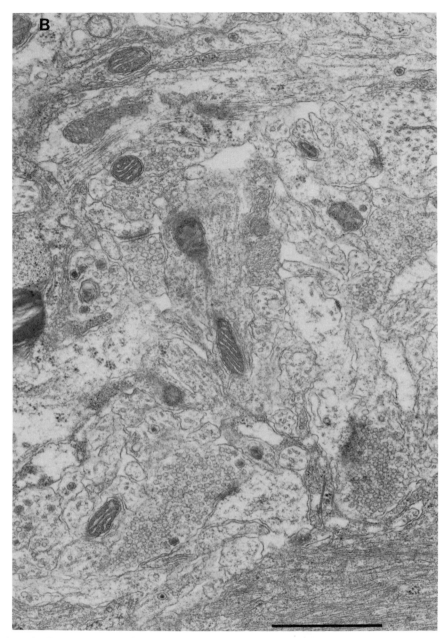

tions indicate axon terminals and synapses at this early stage of culture. Bar, 1 μm. (B) After 22 days in culture, the proliferation of axons and glia (bottom) nearly fills the RMA interior. Increased numbers of synapses occur at this time, except in the center, where glial processes predominate. Phagocytes containing myelin-filled inclusions (at left) increase with time in culture. Bar, 1 μm.

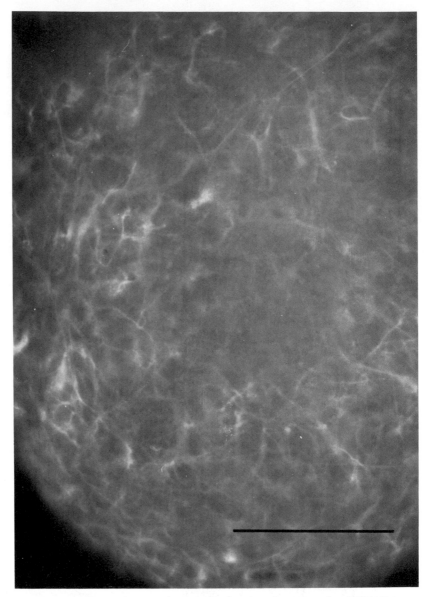

FIG. 3   Immunofluorescence micrograph showing the network of GFAP-immuno-positive astrocytic processes in a 13-dga murine RMA in the stable phase of aggregate development. Bar, 50 μm.

Taken together with the increased diameter of some RMAs and the adhesiveness of DNA from sloughed or damaged cells, we feel that older RMAs probably cohere. This impression is supported by our observation on several occasions of formation of two-dimensional square or rhombic lattices or "sheets" of 10–15 tightly packed RMAs in some chronic incubations in static tissue culture. Furthermore, in some long-term human RMAs, especially if conditions of rotation–incubation have not been optimal, all the RMAs in a flask may combine into a single, spheroidal mass perhaps 5 mm in diameter. Therefore, it appears that RMA adhesion is part of the degenerative process shown by both human and murine aggregates. Although we have not examined enough older RMAs to determine the mechanisms of their decline, it is apparent that their organization, differentiation, and viability decrease throughout the degenerative phase.

Immunostaining to Determine Cell Types

In order to identify the cellular constituents of RMAs, immunocytochemistry (ICC) with specific antisera should be performed. If the experimental protocol allows, change RMAs to serum-free medium for the last 24 hr before immunostaining. This will reduce and may eliminate unpredictable cross-reactivity between the serum (e.g., fetal bovine serum) and the immunoreagents. Addition of serum supplements to all diluted immunoreagents (1–10%) is also advised. Possible nonspecific cross-reactivity between the serum and the immunoreagents should be tested using appropriate controls.

Since antigenicity and adequate penetration of immunoreagents are important considerations, reduce the concentration of glutaraldehyde in the fixative to 0.1%, but leave other components unchanged. For both LM and EM ICC studies, fixation with 1% paraformaldehyde, 0.1% glutaraldehyde, in 0.15 M sodium cacodylate buffer, pH 7.4, containing 0.02% $MgCl_2$ gives adequate morphology and pellet formation. With low concentrations of glutaraldehyde, it is often worthwhile to recentrifuge the pellets while in fixative to ensure that the RMAs are closely packed and thus cross-linked together.

Pellets can be left in this fixative with or without glutaraldehyde at 4°C to protect against leaching out of antigens. Postfixation with 1 : 1 methanol : ethanol for 5 min at 23°C shortly before immunostaining improves antigenicity, especially of structural proteins. Of course, this treatment can only be used for LM samples due to its deleterious effects on ultrastructure. However, it also permeabilizes the pellet, and thus eliminates the need for detergent or graded alcohol pretreatment for LM immunostaining.

Preembedding Immunostaining of RMA Pellets

Pretreatments are all performed at 23°C.

1. Place pellets in 20 mM lysine-HCl in 0.1 M TBS for 15 min to inactivate aldehyde groups. This treatment is preferable to 1% (w/v) sodium borohydride in TBS since it is less reversible and gentler to ultrastructure.
2. Transfer to 0.1% (v/v) saponin in TBS for 10 min to permeabilize cell membranes. This concentration for LM ICC is reduced to 0.01% saponin for EM ICC. However, saponin can promote loss of some membrane-bound antigens. Alternatively, a series of graded enthanols (10, 15, and 40% in TBS) for 10 min each followed by rehydration to TBS can be used. However, this too has drawbacks of being considerably more time consuming and sometimes less effective at improving penetration. Of course, if 1:1 methanol:ethanol postfixation has been employed for LM ICC, this permeabilization step may be omitted.
3. Placing the pellets in 0.5% (v/v) hydrogen peroxide + 0.01% (w/v) sodium azide in TBS for 10 min successfully eliminates endogenous peroxidase activity.
4. Addition of 3% (v/v) normal goat serum (NGS) + 1% (w/v) bovine serum albumin (BSA) in TBS blocks nonspecific staining.

Immunostaining

Appropriate concentrations of primary antisera must be determined from previous experience and from dilution experiments performed on this system. The most successful working dilutions of several antisera along with the preferred immunolabels we have used to characterize murine RMAs are given in Table I. We generally incubate RMAs in diluted primary antisera overnight at 4°C to ensure binding equilibrium. Attention must be given to the primary antiserum host so that appropriate linking immunoglobulins (IgGs) are used. Of course, specificity controls for antigen recognition must be run for all immunostaining techniques and their modifications. These generally involve preincubation of the diluted primary antiserum with a saturating (equivalence) concentration of the respective immunogen to block specific staining. If the immunogen consists of a hapten plus carrier, the carrier protein is added to the primary antiserum diluent at a standard concentration of 3% (w/v). The technical reliability of each staining method is tested by substitution of normal rabbit serum or TBS for the primary antiserum or subsequent immunoreagents and confirmed by the absence of immunostaining.

TABLE I Primary Antisera Used to Characterize Murine RMAs

Antigen	Antiserum	Host	Dilution	Source	Labeling[a]
Structural proteins					
Glial fibrillary acidic protein (GFAP)	anti-GFAP	Mouse	1 : 250	Labsystems Oy, Helsinki, Finland	IGS
GFAP and neurofilament	A15K	Rabbit	1 : 250	Larry Eng, VA, Palo Alto, CA	IGS/PAP
Neurofilament	anti-α-MSH[a,b]	Rabbit	1 : 250	Incstar Corp, Stillwater, MN	IGS/PAP
Secreted proteins					
Adrenocorticotropic hormone (ACTH) (34–39)	Kathy	Rabbit	1 : 300	Richard Mains, Johns Hopkins, Baltimore, MD	IGS
Corticotropin-releasing hormone (CRF)	anti-oCRF oC30	Rabbit	1 : 300	Wylie Vale, Salk Institute, La Jolla, CA	PAP
Luteinizing hormone-releasing hormone (LHRH)	LR1 20-6-79	Rabbit	1 : 5000	Robert Benoit, Montreal General Hospital, Canada	PAP
Enzymes					
Choline acetyltransferase (ChAT)	anti-ChAT #AB8	Rat	1 : 50	William Mobley, UCSF School of Medicine, CA	PAP
Dopamine β-monooxygenase (DBH)	anti-DBH #6	Rabbit	1 : 1000	Donna Wong, Stanford Univ. School of Medicine, CA	PAP
Glutamate decarboxylase (GAD)	anti-rGAD #1440-4	Sheep	1 : 1000	Virginia Weise, NIMH, Bethesda, MD	PAP
Neuron-specific enolase (NSE)	anti-NSE #AB951	Rabbit	1 : 250	Chemicon Intern Inc., El Segundo, CA	PAP
Phenylethanolamine N-methyltransferase (PNMT)	anti-PNMT #21	Rabbit	1 : 250	Donna Wong, Stanford Univ. School of Medicine, CA	PAP
Tyrosine monooxygenase (TH)	anti-TH #TE 101	Rabbit	1 : 400	Eugene Tech Intern, Allendale, NJ	PAP

[a] IGS, Immunogold staining; PAP, peroxidase–antiperoxidase technique; α-MSH, α-melanocyte-stimulating hormone.
[b] From U. C. Drager, D. L. Edwards, and J. Kleinschmidt, *Proc. Natl. Acad. Sci. U.S.A.* **80**, 6408 (1983).

Peroxidase–Antiperoxidase (PAP) Technique

Following incubation in the primary antiserum, rinse pellets well (3 × 10 min) in 0.1 M TBS. If complex experiments entail primary antisera from various species (e.g., antigen screening), we often insert rabbit anti-mouse, anti-rat, or anti-sheep IgG as the second immunoreagent to simplify and synchronize subsequent protocols. The pellets are rinsed well again, and then incubated in 1 : 100 goat anti-rabbit IgG (GaRbIgG; ICN Biomedicals, Lisle, IL), rinsed well in TBS (3 × 10 min), and incubated in 1 : 100 rabbit PAP (Organon Teknika Corp., West Chester, PA), both made up in 0.1 M TBS + 3% NGS, for 30 min each at 23°C. After thorough washing, pellets are exposed to the chromogenic mixture of 0.03% (w/v) 3,3′-diaminobenzidine tetrahydrochloride (DAB; Sigma Chemical Corp., St. Louis, MO) and 0.001% hydrogen peroxide in 20 mM Tris-HCl buffer, pH 7.6, for 6 min at 23°C. The appropriate time of DAB exposure can be determined independently by observing the reaction on a few test RMAs on a glass microscope slide under the LM. The nickel–cobalt-intensified DAB reaction (21) also gives excellent results (see Fig. 4C). The reaction is terminated by removal of DAB and thorough washing (4 × 10 min) with TBS.

At this point, depending on design, pellets can be prepared for LM by embedding in plastic or enveloped in agar for embedding in paraffin. For EM, postfix in 2% osmium tetroxide in 0.1 M CB or other compatable buffer, treat with tannic acid, stain with uranyl acetate, and then process the pellets for EM as described above. If processing is delayed, PAP-stained pellets should be fixed in buffered 0.5% glutaraldehyde for 10 min to inhibit further peroxidative activity. This is also recommended if pellets are to be subjected to double-label immunostaining.

Immunogold Staining

As a second marker, we have used immunogold staining (IGS) which makes use of goat anti-rabbit IgG (or goat anti-mouse IgG) coupled to 5- to 15-nm colloidal gold. Choice of gold particle size involves consideration of (1) the limited permeability of RMAs, since penetration varys inversely with particle size; (2) nature of the protein to be labeled, since structural proteins (e.g., GFAP) and certain secreted proteins (e.g., proopiomelanocortin peptides) are particularly well-labeled with IGS as opposed to PAP; (3) LM or EM IGS, since only 15-nm gold is visible at the LM level; and (4) use of IGS with silver intensification (IGSS), since this makes both sizes of gold visible at the LM level. We make our own IGS reagents in order to achieve a high protein concentration (250 μg/ml), similar to that in the PAP complex (22). However, several reliable IGS reagents are commercially available, and may be used instead.

For IGS, wash pellets well in TBS (3 × 10 min), and then incubate them in a 1 : 4 dilution of IgG-coupled colloidal gold (250 μg protein/ml) for 0.5–1 hr at 23°C. Longer incubation times may be necessary with more dilute, commercially available gold preparations. Wash pellets very thoroughly in 20 mM TBS, pH 8.2 (4 × 10 min or longer, to overnight) to remove nonspecifically adherent gold particles, and then evaluate them in the LM. If IGS with 15-nm colloidal gold is not visible, the PAP complex may be used as a linking reagent (1 : 100 in 20 mM TBS, pH 8.2, + 1% BSA for 30 min) without DAB, prior to reincubation in the IGS immunoreagent. If specific IGS is visible, it may be enhanced for photomicrography by silver intensification (IGSS) with commercial kits such as IntenseM (Janssen Pharmaceuticals, Beerse, Belgium). It is convenient to dilute the final IntenseM solution 1 : 1 with TBS in order to slow down and control the reaction. Monitoring this process by LM reveals a gradual color change from red to orange to brown, and finally to black over the course of 10 min. Very satisfying IGSS with no background precipitation of silver can be obtained by early removal of the reagent and washing the pellet in buffer.

Pellets can then be prepared for LM by embedding in plastic or enveloped in agar for embedding in paraffin. For EM, they should be postfixed in 2% osmium tetroxide in 0.1 M CB treated with tannic acid, stained en bloc with uranyl acetate, and then processed as described above for EM. Although osmium will oxidize and remove reduced silver, 5-nm gold is clearly visible in the EM without the silver enhancement.

Double-Label Preembedding Immunostaining

It is sometimes necessary to perform double-label immunostaining to investigate colocalization of two substances in the same RMA or cell type. Consistent use of only two immunostaining methods (and likewise only two immunolabeling reagents) is helpful in reducing variables, standardizing procedures, and comparing and evaluating results. It is preferable to use primary antisera from separate species to avoid cross-reactivity of immunoreagents and markers. However, it is not always feasible to obtain two good primary antisera from different species. If they are from the same species, use the higher avidity primary antiserum first at higher dilution with the PAP technique and DAB, since this reaction product inactivates the first series of immunoreagents (23). Follow this with the IGS-working dilution of the second primary antiserum (usually twice the concentration used with PAP) and gold immunostaining. As long as the second primary antiserum concentration is at least 10 times that of the first, even if it is from the same species, we have not observed any cross-reactivity between these two sequences, even at the ultrastructural level. Technical controls for the double-labeling procedure involve replacement of either primary antiserum with TBS. The absence of cross (double)-labeling of antigenic tissue sites indicates the integrity of each immunostaining method in the PAP–IGS technique.

Two-Dimensional Plating of Rotation-Mediated Aggregates

The solid geometry of intact RMAs presents a physical barrier to the penetration of immunoreagents and a complex matrix of interacting cells. Immunostaining and analysis of cell–cell relationships can be much more revealing with two-dimensional (2-D) material. Therefore, we developed a method of converting essentially spherical RMAs into 2-D cultures at any stage of development. In brief, we remove RMAs from suspension on the rotating orbital shaker, and allow them to settle, attach, and grow out on a static substrate. Although cell–cell relationships and interactions may be altered, 2-D RMAs are far easier to manipulate, examine, and record. We have not yet determined how the change to 2-D culture alters cell populations, specialization, or gene expression. However, we have observed that neurons and glia maintain their association and differentiated state for up to 14 days in 2-D culture.

Two-Dimensional Culture Technique

Culture RMAs on 15-mm-diameter round, plastic coverslips (Thermanox, No. 5414, Lux Scientific, Inc, from E&K Scientific Products, Inc., Saratoga, CA) to facilitate subsequent treatment and processing of 2-D cultures. Coat sterile coverslips with a substrate such as extracellular matrix (ECM) produced from confluent cultures of bovine corneal endothelial cells (24). Other substrates which favor cell attachment, growth, or differentiation can also be used. Place one coated coverslip in each well of a 24-well tissue culture plate (#3047, Falcon Plastics, Oxnard, CA). With a 5-ml disposable plastic pipette, draw up 2 ml of medium and 3 ml (about 200 RMAs) from the DeLong flask. (Replace 3 ml of medium in the DeLong flask and return it to the incubator.) Pipette about 200 μl into each well, and, with a sterilized, flame-polished Pasteur pipette, distribute 5–10 RMAs near the center of each well (average 8 RMAs/coverslip or about 200 RMAs total). Place the culture plate in an incubator, and within hours the RMAs are firmly attached to the coated coverslips.

After 24 hr, glia have migrated outward in all directions from the perimeter of the RMA on the substrate surface. After 48–72 hr, the central RMA has begun to collapse into an erect dome of mixed cell types, but mainly neurons. By 5 days, the original RMA attachment site is occupied by large masses (>100) and smaller groups of about 20 neurons nestled in the angles between diverging glial septa (Fig. 4A and B). Neuronal clusters radiate neurites in all directions, while the glial septa continue outward to join the surrounding circular mat of flattened glial cells. Individual stellate glia migrate beyond this nearly confluent glial monolayer, and assume more elongated shapes as they migrate further away. When RMAs are plated close together such that perimeter glia collide, their glial distributions merge into expected patterns which display phenotypes typical of their location relative to both RMAs. These glial arrangements appear basically unchanged after 2-D culture for 8 days and probably longer.

Although most neurons remain associated with the central mass, under normal conditions about 10% of the total leave and move outward. After 7 days in culture, individual and small groups of neurons reach the perimeter of the glial outgrowth. A few small, bipolar neurons occur sporadically on the substrate, but many more prefer to cling to the flattened glia. Their somatas, which have only a thin rim of peripheral neuroplasm, sometimes seem arranged around the nucleus, on top of these astrocytes (Fig. 4C). These neurons direct their axons outward, toward other neurons and processes, interacting and sometimes forming dense and intricate networks. Axonal networks can interconnect RMAs and also form axon bundles which can course for large distances (Fig. 4D).

Microscopy

Thermanox coverslips refract transmitted light and thus give a poor image in an inverted phase microscope. Therefore, it is best to observe 2-D RMA cultures directly in the LM by placing moist coverslips cell-side up on a glass microscope slide. Coverslips are easily freed from the bottom of culture plate wells with the aid of a simple lifting tool, made from an 18-gauge needle, with the bevelled tip bent backward 90° to the shaft. A pair of fine forceps (Dumont 3C) used in conjunction with the lifter enables removal and manipulation of the coverslips.

The greatest advantage of Thermanox coverslips is that they are unaffected by volatile solvents (including propylene oxide) normally used in

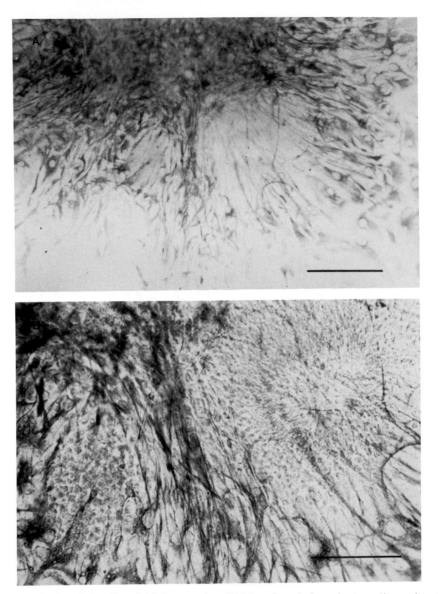

FIG. 4   LMs of details of 16-dga murine RMAs after 5 days in two-dimensional culture (A and B) and 14-dga murine RMAs after 7 days in two-dimensional culture (C and D). (A) Antiserum A15K IGS to show processes and septa formed by migrating astrocytes. Clearer areas between glial partitions contain the neuroblasts shown in B. Bar, 100 μm. (B) Portion of A at higher magnification focused on groups of A15K-negative neuroblasts between glial septa. Bar, 50 μm. (C) Immunostaining for

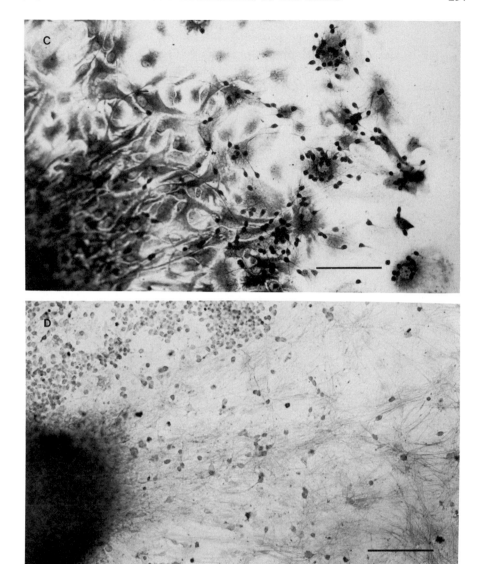

GFAP and NSE with IGS–PAP (nickel–cobalt intensified) reveals both stellate, flattened astrocytes with large, rounded nuclei, and smaller, dark neuronal perikarya with extended processes. Note how neurons preferentially attach to glial surfaces, and their neurites communicate with one another. Bar, 100 μm. (D) Immunostaining for ChAT (IGS–PAP) shows the elaborate network of neural processes extending from one RMA to another neighboring RMA (to the right). Bar, 100 μm.

dehydration, infiltration, and plastic embedding. For LM, therefore, coverslips with stained 2-D RMAs are simply dehydrated, cleared in xylene, and placed RMA-side up on top of a large drop of Pro-Texx (American Scientific Products, McGaw Park, IL) or similar mounting medium on a glass microscope slide. Another large drop of Pro-Texx is put on top of the RMAs, and a glass coverslip placed over them to complete the "coverslip sandwich." The resulting preparation permits transmitted LM photomicrography through glass at higher magnification with crisp detail.

For EM, stained 2-D RMAs on coverslips are postfixed with 2% osmium tetroxide in CB for 1 hr, rinsed well in CB, treated with 0.5% tannic acid in CB for 20 min, and partially dehydrated to 50% ethanol for block staining with uranyl acetate for 30 min at 23°C. Following dehydration through absolute ethanol and propylene oxide, RMAs are flat embedded against another Thermanox coverslip in Epon 812 cured at 60°C. Areas of interest are selected by LM, cut out with a pair of scissors, and the fragments then reembedded flat in the cap of polyethylene capsules. They can be thick sectioned or serially sectioned on an ultramicrotome and viewed in an EM without counterstain.

Immunocytochemical Staining

The procedures for the PAP technique or IGS 2-D RMAs on coverslips in 24-well culture plates are performed as described above. We have used all of the antisera listed in Table I for LM immunostaining with good results (e.g., see Fig. 4C). Preparation of coverslips for LM or EM observation is exactly as described above.

Model for Glioma Invasion of the Central Nervous System

Human fetal RMAs were cultured for 10 days to establish the stationary phase of the brain model. Aggregates of 600 to 900 μm were dominant in this system from a 19-week gestational brain. Coculture with cells from the human malignant glioma cell line U251-MG (25) was initiated by seeding 1000 glioma cells with approximately 200 aggregates in agarose-coated multiwell plates. Plates were prepared by mixing molten agarose (Type VII, Sigma) with RMA culture medium to achieve a 0.5% final agarose concentration. Aliquots of 0.5 ml were placed in each well, and the plates chilled at 4°C for 30 min to ensure the formation of a gel. The coculture was incubated in standard brain aggregate medium for 7 days, then rinsed in buffer, and processed for light microscopy as described above. The invasion of the model brain tissue by this malignant neoplasia occurs without apparent necrosis or mechanical disruption of the brain aggregate (Fig. 5). Glioma proliferation at the site of apparent initial tumor cell attachment produces a region of near-total RMA brain cell displacement by larger tumor cells. In addition, some solitary tumor cells appear located within the parenchyma of the RMA distant from the compact tumor mass. This is in contrast to the generalized demise of rat fetal brain aggregates when invaded by glioma cells (16).

Further Applications

The association of neurons and supportive glia in RMAs presents unique opportunities for manipulation and investigation of experimental models of the CNS. RMA methodology may also be applied to well-defined cell populations, following separation and purification of individual cell types or acquisition of various neuronal and glial cell lines now available. Homogeneous RMAs may be formed from these pure cell populations for studies of paracrine and other phenomena. Heterogeneous RMAs may also be created to investigate desired intercellular relationships and dependencies. Immediate access of RMA components to test substances and reagents suggests numerous approaches to studies on development, differentiation, and functional interaction.

The convenient size of RMAs not only makes them visible with the unaided eye, but also facilitates examination of cellular events using various LM techniques. Colorimetric or fluorescent Ca^{2+} probes (e.g., fura-2, indo-1), pH fluorochromes (e.g., seminaphthorhodafluors), or other ion-specific dyes can be used to assess ionic flux or cell activity. Certain cells can be vitally labeled before or after formation of RMAs using various microspheres (Polysciences, Inc., Warrington, PA) or perhaps colloidal gold-filled Sendai virus (26). The nuclei of selected cells or merely a transfected portion of their DNA can also be labeled with ethidium bromide or Hoechst 33258 in advance, so that their behavior in aggregates can be observed. The growth and movement of the labeled cells can then be followed with still photomicroscopy, with cinematography, or with videomicroscopy using long-depth-of-field objectives.

Because of their size, RMAs can also be held with a suction pipette, and individual cells microinjected with various tracers (e.g., horseradish peroxidase) and identified. Similarly, if low-molecular-weight vital dyes (e.g., Lucifer Yellow, LY) are microinjected, experimental manipulation of cell connectivity (e.g., by gap junctions) can be assessed, as has been demonstrated

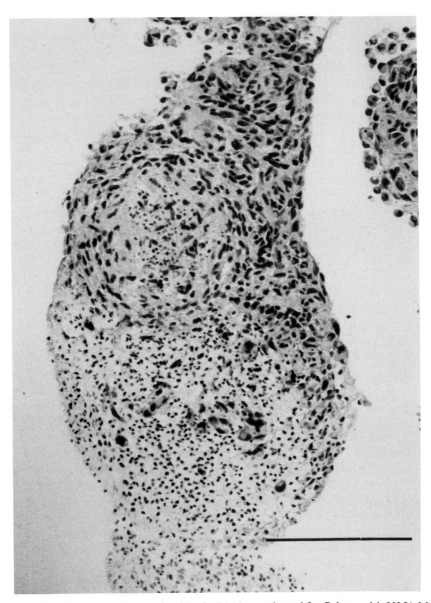

FIG. 5   Nineteen-week human fetal brain RMA cocultured for 7 days with U251-MG glioma cells. Large, oval nuclei characterize glioma cells invading the RMA from above. In addition to the large tumor mass which has replaced approximately half the RMA, isolated single glioma cells have migrated into the normal RMA tissue. Bar, 500 μm.

with isolated pancreatic islets (27). In addition, after immobilization with a suction pipette, electrophysiological recording and patch clamping can be used to analyze membrane polarization, permeability, and receptor activity.

In preliminary studies, we have examined the effects of added nerve growth factor β (NGF-β) on the survival of RMAs. The diencephalic regions of 16 neonatal BALB/c mouse brains were collected, dispersed, and the cells equally divided between two flasks within 3 hr. After 6 days of rotation incubation, one of the flasks received 50 ng/ml NGF-β ($\times 9$ ml) in fresh serum-containing medium, while the other flask received fresh medium alone. This protocol was repeated on days 2, 4, 7, 9, 11, and 14, at which times 10–30 RMAs were removed from each flask (+NGF and −NGF), pelleted, and fixed for EM as described above.

On day 2, some cell death was noted in the center of most RMAs, and central necrosis continued on day 4, with or without NGF. By day 7, however, the +NGF RMAs had improved, and were better than those −NGF. Mature neurons were first noted in +NGF RMAs on day 9, while the status of −NGF RMAs was unchanged. Healthy, differentiated neurons, fibers, and myelin profiles were obvious on day 11 and 14 in +NGF RMAs, but those −NGF continued to do poorly. The nature of the neurons in NGF-β-treated RMAs could not be determined without immunostaining, but the benefits of NGF treatment were obvious. These results suggest that further experiments with RMAs and growth factors might provide valuable information on the maintenance and survival *in vitro* of selected neuronal populations.

Attachment of RMAs to coverslips and subsequent 2-D culture also present many unique experimental opportunities. In addition to their suitability for morphological examination, 2-D RMA cultures can also be conveniently used for physiological studies. A small Sykes–Moore superfusion chamber (200 μl) created between the RMA-adherent surfaces of two separated coverslips (28) permits discrete time-course analysis of glial or neuronal secretion under control or stimulated conditions. If applied to neuroendocrine components, this system allows sensitive measurement of pulsatile hormone secretion from cells and/or neurons which show inherent oscillatory activity.

Whether one choses to utilize RMAs in suspension or 2-D culture, they clearly present a model system limited only by the imagination. The effects of almost any biological substance can be tested (e.g., peptides, transmitter agonists and antagonists, second messengers, steroids and other hormones, ions and channel blockers, toxins, viruses, and microbes) as well as physical variables, such as heat, radiation, and electrical fields. Since RMAs can be created from diverse natural, enriched, or clonal cell components and be made homogeneous or heterogeneous by design, no biologist should dismiss an idea before considering this versatile system.

Acknowledgments

We would especially like to thank Cheryl A. Padula for producing excellent immunostaining and electron microscopic data. We would also like to thank Paola Villar for performing cell dispersions and aggregations, and Dr. Eun Jung Kim for his help with murine brain dissection. Special thanks to Dr. Lynn Pulliam for guidance in the initial phases in this work. This work was supported by HD10907, the Andrew W. Mellon Foundation, and the MSC-07 Simon Fund.

References

1. R. Bjerkvig, S. K. Steinsvag, and O. D. Laerum, *In Vitro Cell. Dev. Biol.* **22,** 180 (1986).
2. A. A. Moscona, *Exp. Cell Res.* **22,** 455 (1961).
3. B. van der Schueren, C. Denef, and J.-J. Cassiman, *Endocrinology (Baltimore)* **110,** 513 (1982).
4. C. Denef and M. Andries, *Endocrinology (Baltimore)* **112,** 813 (1983).
5. F. Monnet-Tschudi, A. N. Eberle, and P. Honnegger, *Dev. Brain Res.* **26,** 125 (1986).
6. N. W. Seeds, *Proc. Natl. Acad. Sci. U.S.A.* **68,** 1858 (1971).
7. P. Honegger and E. Richelson, *Brain Res.* **109,** 335 (1976).
8. G. R. DeLong, *Dev. Biol.* **22,** 563 (1970).
9. L. Won, A. Heller, P. C. Hoffman, B. H. Wainer, S. Price, and P. Greengard, *Soc. Neurosci. Abstr.* **13,** 1180 (Abstr. 322.9) (1987).
10. F. Guentert-Lauber, F. Monet-Tschudi, F. X. Omlin, P. Favrod, and P. Honegger, *Dev. Neurosci.* **7,** 33 (1985).
11. F. Monnet-Tschudi, L. F. Eng, J. M. Matthieu, and P. Honegger, *Dev. Neurosci.* **10,** 165 (1988).
12. F. Aliosi, C. Agresti, D. D'Urso, and G. Levi, *Proc. Natl. Acad. Sci. U.S.A.* **85,** 6167 (1988).
13. L. Bologa, R. Cole, F. Chiappeli, R. P. Saneto, and J. de Vellis, *Brain Res.* **457,** 295 (1988).
14. L. Pulliam, R. D. Dix, H. S. Panitch, and J. R. Baringer, *J. Virol. Methods* **9,** 301 (1984).
15. S. K. Steinsvag, O. D. Laerum, and R. Bjerkvig. *JNCI, J. Natl. Cancer Inst.* **74,** 1095 (1985).
16. R. Bjerkvig, O. D. Laerum, and O. Mella, *Cancer Res.* **46,** 4071 (1986).
17. L. I. de Ridder, O. D. Laerum, S. J. Mørk, and D. D. Bigner, *Acta Neuropathol.* **72,** 207 (1987).

18. L. Pulliam, M. E. Berens, and M. L. Rosenblum, *J. Neurosci. Res.* **21,** 521 (1988).
19. R. S. Morrison, H. I. Kornblum, F. M. Leslie, and R. A. Bradshaw, *Science* **238,** 72 (1987).
20. J. A. Drewe, G. V. Childs, and D. L. Kunze, *Science* **241,** 1810 (1988).
21. J. C. Adams, *J. Histochem. Cytochem.* **29,** 775 (1981).
22. R. Lamberts and P. C. Goldsmith, *J. Histochem. Cytochem.* **33,** 499 (1985).
23. L. A. Sternberger and S. A. Joseph, *J. Histochem. Cytochem.* **27,** 1424 (1979).
24. N. Ferrara, P. Goldsmith, D. Fujii, and R. Weiner, *in* "Methods in Enzymology" (P. M. Conn, ed.), Vol. 124, p. 245. Academic Press, Orlando, Florida, 1986.
25. J. Ponten and B. Westermark, *Med. Biol.* **56,** 184 (1978).
26. S. C. Ardizzoni, A. Michaels, and G. W. Arendash, *Science* **239,** 635 (1988).
27. L. Orci, *Proc. Int. Congr. Endocrinol., 8th* p. 6 (Plenary Lecture-7) (1988).
28. G. Martinez de Escalera, K. C. Swearingen, and R. I. Weiner, *in* "Methods in Enzymology" (P. M. Conn, ed.), Vol. 168, p. 254. Academic Press, San Diego, California, 1989.

[17] Microcultures of Dissociated Primary Central Nervous System Neurons

Efrain C. Azmitia

Introduction

The growth of neurons in culture was first demonstrated in 1907 by Ross Harrison (1). The procedure has been adapted to permit morphological observations of cluster neurons in a controlled environment. The technique has been extremely valuable for studying cell attachment, survival, growth cone function, and neurite extension, and this mainly morphological approach continues to be extremely useful for both anatomical and electrophysiological studies. Biochemical and pharmacological analysis has been largely confined to the study of cell lines or nonneuronal mitotic cells since large numbers of cells from a homogeneous preparation are required.

The development of a microculture system has been aimed at establishing a large number of separate cultures of primary central nervous system (CNS) neurons. The procedure of cell dissociation of fetal brain cells was first described by Varon and Raiborn (2). My contribution has been to prepare a solution of dissociated primary cells from brain regions rich in neurons of a known neurotransmitter content and to plate these cells onto 96-well plates treated with an artificial positively charged substratum. The neurons are grown under standard tissue culture techniques and biochemical procedures adapted for rapid and sensitive measurements of chemically identified neurons. The ability to utilize 96-well plates has made available all the recent technology designed for analysis of monoclonal antibody production, for use in the large-scale analysis of neurochemical indicators of specific neurotransmitter neurons. This microculture approach utilizes multitipped pipetters, small 96-well plate incubators, multiwell plate centrifuges, a Titertek multiskan spectrophotometer, automatic injector systems for high-performance liquid chromatography (HPLC), computer-assisted scintillation counting, and statistical and graphic software analysis. The ability to grow and analyze the maturation of chemically identified primary neurons in microcultures permits routine study of up to 1000 cultures a week by a single research team.

The tremendous generation of data provides a means of reliable screening for neuronotrophic and neurotoxic effects of drugs, hormones, and brain extracts (3). The verification that a biochemical change reflects an alteration in neuronal survival and maturation must be obtained by morphological criteria. To this end, the 8-well chamber slides are utilized in conjunction with immunocytochemistry and/or autoradiography.

The precise method used in preparing these microcultures is given in the following sections. Basic method and theory of tissue culture are available from a volume of *Methods in Enzymology* (4) or from a number of books devoted specifically to neuronal cultures (5–9).

Cell Preparation

Maximum-barrier (pathogen-free) timed pregnant rats are obtained from Taconic Farms (Germantown, NY) to arrive for use at 14-days gestation (dg). The monoaminergic neurons of the brain stem (serotonergic, dopaminergic, and noradrenergic) have completed their final mitosis by this time (10) and we can focus on survival and maturational events. The animals are maintained in a pathogen-free environment if necessary before their use. The rats are anesthetized with ether, swabbed with 70% (v/v) ethanol, and the fetuses removed by cesarean section using antiseptic procedures. The entire placenta is transferred to a 150-mm sterile petri dish (Lab-Tek Division, Miles Lab, Inc., Naperville, IL) containing ice-cold D-1 solution [contains (w/v) 0.8% NaCl; 0.04% KCl; 0.006% $Na_2HPO_4 \cdot 12H_2O$; 0.003% KH_2PO_4; 0.5% glucose; 0.00012% phenol red; 0.0125 penicillin G, and 0.02% streptomycin, pH 7.4] (Sigma Chemical Co., St. Louis, MO).

The fetuses are removed from the placenta in a laminar flow hood (Model EG-4320, Edge Gard Hood, Baker Co., Inc., Sanford, ME) and transferred to fresh D-1 solution. All dissections of fetal tissue are performed using a binocular dissecting microscope (Bausch & Lomb Stereo Zoom 7 with increased working distance supplementary lens, Cat. # BL 31-27-01-17; Bausch & Lomb Union, NJ) located in the laminar flow hood. Surgical mask and cap are routinely used when operating the dissecting microscope. The brains are removed from the skull using two pairs of straight-edged watchmaker's forceps and placed in a 60-mm petri dish (Corning Glass Works, Corning, NY) with fresh D-1 solution (5°C).

Two straight-edged #11 scalpels (Propper Manufacturing Co., Inc., Long Island City, NY—a number of #11 scalpels do not come to a sharp point and are therefore not preferred) are used to make a coronal cut at the apex of the mesencephalic flexure and at the pontine flexure (Fig. 1). The tegmentum is exposed by cutting dorsally from the cerebral aqueduct and separating the corpus quadrigemina. Two sagittal cuts are made approximately 0.5–1.0 mm lateral to the midline. Immunocytochemical studies have shown that the majority of the ascending serotonin (5-HT)-immunoreactive neurons lie within this mesencephalic raphe strip (11–13). The majority of the ventral tegmental dopaminergic neurons lie just rostral to the first mesencephalic flexure cut, with the lateral cuts extending about 1.5 mm (14). The majority of the noradrenergic neurons lie in the lateral strips in the caudal half of the mesencephalic pontine strip.

The raphe pieces from all the fetuses are collected in fresh D-1 solution in a 35-mm petri dish (Corning) and then transferred to a 20-ml conical tube (Corning) in about 0.5 ml D-1 solution/10 fetuses. The strips are gently agitated by repeated trituration using a Pasteur pipette with a fire-polished tip. First a large-bore (=1 mm) and then a small-bore (<0.5 mm) pipette is used. The use of trypsin is avoided since it results in a significantly lower yield of viable serotonergic neurons, in agreement with the studies by Varon and Saier (15), who reported a lower yield of large neurons following trypsin dissociation.

The cell suspension is brought up to 1.5 ml/fetus with room-temperature (19°C) complete neuronal media [(CNM): 91.5% Eagle's minimum essential medium (MEM; Cat. # M-0268, Sigma), 0.029% nonessential amino acids (Cat. # 320-1140AG, GIBCO, Life Technologies, Inc., Grand Island, NY), and 7.5% (w/v) fetal bovine serum (FBS; Sigma Cat. # F6761)]. All solutions

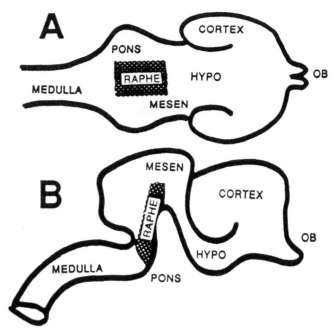

Fig. 1   A schematic representation of a fetal rat brain (E 14, 12 mm CRL) shown from a ventral (A) and lateral (B) view. The rostral brain stem raphe nuclei shown in the shaded area contain the majority of the ascending serotonergic neurons. HYPO, Hypothalamus; MESEN, mesencephalon; OB, olfactory bulb.

except FBS are prepared weekly from powdered reagents and sterilized by filtration (Nalgene Sterile Disposable TC Filter Unit, 150-ml capacity, 0.2-μm pore size; Cat. # 155-0020, Fisher Scientific Co., Fairlawn, NJ). The MEMs obtained from GIBCO and Sigma contain 1.8 mM Ca^{2+}, which is more than is optimal for serotonergic neurons (0.5 mM). For experiments where we need to have precise Ca^{2+} concentrations, a Ca^{2+}/Mg^{2+}-free solution is used (Sigma Cat. # M-4767) and supplemented with calcium chloride (Sigma). Fetal bovine serum is bought from Sigma and tested to obtain the minimum necessary concentration [between 5 and 7.5% (w/v)]. The FBS is aliquoted into sterile vials stored at $-70°C$ and thawed immediately before use. The final cell preparation in CNM is allowed to settle for 10 min to precipitate large tissue debris and the clear supernatant is used without centrifugation to avoid damage to the large neurons. The completeness of the dissociation is checked under a microscope before proceeding, and the cell density is determined using a hemocytometer (Levy and Levy-Hausser corpuscle counting chamber; Fisher Scientific Co.). A vital stain (trypan blue, Aldrich Chemical Co., Inc., Milwaukee, WI) is used periodically to establish the percentage of viable cells after dissociation (usually greater than 90%).

Preparation of Plates

The 96-well plates (Nunc, Denmark; Becton Dickinson and Company, Lincoln Park, NJ) are used for biochemical and low-power morphological studies, while 8-well glass slides (Lab-Tek tissue culture chamber/slides; Miles Scientific, Miles Lab, Inc., Naperville, IL) are used for high-power morphometric analysis. The two are prepared similarly with a solution of poly(D-lysine) (15 μg/ml, 70,000–150,000 MW; Sigma) applied to cover the bottom of the wells the night before (shorter times have been used successfully). The poly(D-lysine) solution is removed, and the wells rinsed once with MEM and filled with CNM before use.

The mesencephalic raphe cells are plated at an initial plating density (IPD) of approximately 1.0×10^6 cells/cm^2 (the area of the wells is 0.28 cm^2) by the addition of 180 μl of the cell suspension to the empty wells (CNM is removed from the wells immediately before use), using a 1-ml Rainin pipetter with sterile plastic tips (Rainin Co., Woburn, MA). Use of a smaller volume pipetter increases the risk of contamination. The solution is briefly agitated before each application. All the trays and slides are filled as quickly as possible without a time break. The trays and slides are covered and kept at room temperature before further solutions are added. Cell attachment is around 90% (15a). The plates are transferred to a CO_2 incubator (Napco Incubator, Model 6300) maintained at 37°C with 95% humidity and 5% CO_2–95% air.

It should be stressed that the "normal" conditions routinely used in tissue culture might not be ideally suited for each particular neurotransmitter system being studied. For example, external glucose concentrations are normally supplemented to 0.5% (w/v) in CNM for neurons (16). However, we have recently seen that a concentration of 0.15% is best for short-term serotonergic cultures (see Fig. 2). The reader is thus alerted to the fact that detailed studies are required for establishing optimal concentrations of glucose, calcium, FBS, and other major components found in culture media. This should also apply to use of the main "serum-free" formulas available commercially for neuronal cultures (17).

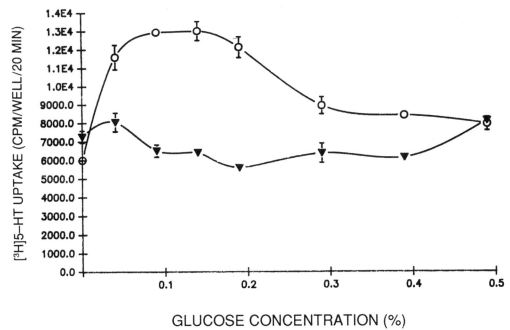

FIG. 2   Effects of glucose at 2 and 4 days. A glucose-free medium is made by combining amino acids (GIBCO, Cat. No. 320-1135 AG) and a vitamin mixture (GIBCO, Cat. No. 320-1120 AG) and adding the following: 6.7 g/liter NaCl, 0.265 g/liter $CaCl_2 \cdot 2H_2O$, 0.1 g/liter $MgSO_4$, 0.4 g/liter sodium phosphate monobasic, 2.2 g/liter sodium bicarbonate, and 0.011 g/liter phenol red. The solution is then adjusted to pH 7.4 and is filtered. Glucose is added at various concentrations. The values shown are the average ± SEM ($n = 4$). Microcultures are grown for either 2 (▼) or 4 (○) days, and initial plating density is 1.0×10^6 cells/cm^2.

Cocultures

The effects of the presence of target neurons on the behavior of the mesencephalic raphe cells are tested in a coculture preparation (3, 18). The fetal target cells are dissected as described for the raphe cells. In general, cortical, striatal, olfactory bulb, and spinal cord cells can be easily collected from the 14-day-old fetuses. Hippocampus and cerebellum are removed from 16- to 18-day-old fetuses because of the problems of removing the meninges from younger tissue (19, 20). The target area is dissected, dissociated, and cell density is determined as described. The mixture of raphe and target cells is suspended prior to plating in 20-ml sterile scintillation vials (Fisher Scientific, Cat. # 03-337-4). The cells are then transferred to the wells as a mixture.

Antimitotic Drugs

The fetal CNS cell mixtures contain both postmitotic neurons and a variety of dividing neurons, and glial, ependymal, and endothelial cells. In short-term cultures (1–5 days), the influence of the dividing cells does not appear to be a problem. In long-term cultures, 5-fluoro-2-deoxyuridine (20 μg/ml; Sigma, F-0503) and uridine (50 μg/ml; Sigma U-3750) are added either at time zero or at the first medium change after 3 days incubation. The antimitotic drug in the CNM is kept for 36–48 hr and then fresh CNM is added to the cultures after a single rinse to remove all the 5-fluoro-2-deoxyuridine and the cellular debris. Cultures can now be maintained for longer than 2 weeks. Certain researchers advocate using horse serum in these long-term cultures (20), but better growth of serotonergic neurons with only FBS has been observed.

Uptake Analysis of Identified Neurons

The measurement of the high-affinity uptake of a tritiated neurotransmitter (or substrate, in the case of cholinergic neurons) provides one of the most reliable biochemical estimates of the surface area (soma and neurite) of a specific neurotransmitter cell (21–24). The uptake is a more reliable indicator of cell number and size than measurements of transmitter or enzyme content present in the cells or released into the medium. In our microcultures of mesencephalic raphe, the amount of [^{3}H]5-HT high-affinity uptake is linearly related to the number of plated 5-HT-immunoreactive neurons and to the days in culture as shown in Table I. For other neurotransmitter systems, the uptake of [^{3}H]norepinephrine, [^{3}H]dopamine, [^{3}H]choline, [^{3}H]glutamate, or [^{3}H]GABA can be used (25, 26).

The cultures are taken from the incubator and the medium is removed. Fresh MEM with 0.5% glucose (37°C) is used to very gently rinse the cells two times. The reaction solution (200 μl) contains 50 nM [^{3}H]5-HT (19–27 Ci/mmol; New England Nuclear, Du Pont Co., Boston, MA), 0.5% glucose, and 10^{-5} M pargyline in MEM. The reaction is allowed to proceed for 20 min at 37°C. The concentration of [^{3}H]5-HT used has been shown to be selectively retained by serotonergic neurons, as demonstrated by autoradiographic pharmacology (21, 27), and is five times lower than the concentra-

TABLE I   Serotonin (5-HT) Accumulation Expressed per Cell[a]

Number of cells/cm^2	5-HT-immuno-reactive cells/cm^2	Counts per minute[b]		5-HT pmol/cm^2	5-HT fmol/cell
		Total[c]	Nonspecific[d]		
1,964,286	10,996	44,563 + 1,529 (4)*	880 + 169 (4)*	10.40	0.95
982,143	4,443	16,099 + 2,390 (4)****	404 + 80 (4)*	3.73	0.84
736,607	1,998	7,679 + 1,145 (3)**	233 + 13 (2)**	1.77	0.89
491,071	1,111	1,082 + 247 (4)****	229 + 94 (3)****	0.20	0.18
98,214	—	310 + 46 (3)	246 + 79 (2)	0.01	—

[a] Immunocytochemistry with 5-HT antibody at a dilution of 1/2000. Pretreatment with 10^{-5} M pargyline and 1-tryptophan (50 and 80 min, respectively) before fixation in 4% paraformaldehyde (5°C) in 0.1 M phosphate buffer (pH 7.2) with 0.05% MgCl$_2$ and 5% sucrose. [^{3}H]5-HT = 6 × 10^{-8} M, 20 min, 37°C; Hanks' balanced salt solution containing 0.5% glucose; fluoxetine = 10^{-5} M. Well area = 0.28 cm^2. [From Azmitia et al. (3).]

[b] t-Statistical test: * $p < 0.001$, ** $p < 0.01$, *** $p < 0.02$, **** $p < 0.05$.

[c] Statistical values in total counts per minute are compared to the next lowest number in column.

[d] Statistical values for nonspecific counts per minute are expressed against the total counts per minute.

tion needed to detect uptake of 5-HT by astrocytes in culture (28). Nonspecific accumulation and retention of [^{3}H]5-HT are calculated by incubating the cultures as described but in the presence of 10^{-5} M fluoxetine (gift of Eli Lilly Co., Indianapolis, IN), which is a recognized specific uptake blocker for serotonergic neurons (29).

After the 20-min incubation period, the medium is very carefully and quickly removed and the cultures are washed twice with 0.1 M phosphate buffer (pH 7.4) in a saline solution (0.85%). The cells are air-dried before 200 µl of absolute ethanol is added to each culture for 1 hr at room temperature (RT). From each well, 150 µl is removed and placed in 5 ml of Liquiscint (National Diagnostics, Manville, NJ) and counted for at least 1 min in a Beckman liquid scintillation counter (Model LS 1801, Beckman Instruments, Inc., Somerset, NJ; counting efficiency is 58%). The specific uptake of [^{3}H]5-HT is calculated as the difference between the total and nonspecific accumulation. The nonspecific uptake is usually between 1 and 10% of the total uptake, as shown in Table I. Protein determination is performed using the Lowry method and a Titertek Multiskan spectrophotometer (Flow Laboratories, Inc., McLean, VA).

Analysis of Media

At the end of the culture period, the medium can be collected and analyzed. Typically, 100 µl of medium is added to 50 µl of a 0.3 M perchloric acid and

EDTA solution. The solution can be frozen or immediately analyzed by direct injection into an HPLC column for determination of transmitters, their metabolites, or drug residues. Due to the small volume of the wells, a sensitive HPLC protocol must be followed.

Immunocytochemical Analysis of Serotonergic Neurons

Cultures grown on the 8-well slides (can also be performed on 96-well plates) are washed after 24–96 hr (longer times are hard to analyze because of fiber outgrowth) with MEM two times. The cells are then fixed with ice-cold 4% (w/v) paraformaldehyde (EM Sciences Cat. # 19200, Ft. Washington, PA) and 0.05% $MgCl_2$ in 0.1 M phosphate buffer, pH 7.4. The cells are fixed for at least 2 hr at 5°C. The cultures are carefully washed three times with 0.1 M phosphate buffer with 0.85% saline, pH 7.4, and three times with 0.1 M Tris buffer with 0.85% saline, pH 7.4 (TBS). The primary antibody raised against serotonin (Incstar Cat. # 20080, Stillwater, MI) is prepared at 1:8000 dilution in 0.3% Triton X-100 and 1% normal goat serum in TBS (the antibody may give high background staining when first used unless preincubated on slides containing non-5-HT cells). Routinely, the primary antibody solution is reused five or six times and discarded when specific staining begins to decrease in intensity.

A volume of 100 μl is added to each well and the plates incubated overnight at 4°C (shorter times can be used if solution is at RT). The slides are gently washed three times with TBS and incubated at RT in biotinylated antibody against rabbit (Elite ABC Vector Stains Kit, Vector Labs, Inc., Burlingame, CA) for 1 hr and washed twice with TBS. The slides are incubated in a freshly prepared solution of 0.05% (w/v) 3,3'-diaminobenzidine (Sigma) and 0.003% (v/v) H_2O_2 in TBS for 4–8 min (monitor staining intensity with inverted microscope). The slides are washed three times with TBS and given a final quick rinse in distilled H_2O before being dried. The plastic chambers and gaskets are removed, the slides rehydrated and then dehydrated, cleared with xylene, and mounted. Morphometric analysis of the 5-HT-IR neurons is performed on a Leitz Orthoplan (Kramer Scientific, Yonkers, NY) with a 40× planapo objective using a Bioquant computer-assisted program (R&M Biometric, Inc., Nashville, TN). The cell density is calculated from counts of 5-HT-IR somas in 15 selected areas (0.19 mm^2) and expressed as cells per square centimeter. The soma area and neurite length are calculated from 50 randomly selected 5-HT-IR neurons. The values are expressed as average with SEM or as a histogram. Descriptive and comparative statistics are determined with the Bioquant program and the graphs drawn with the Sigma Plot software program.

Drug Application

The drugs used are freshly made up in MEM, and the stock solution filtered (Uniflo, pore size 0.2 μm; Schleicher and Schuell, Inc., Keene, NH). The drug concentrations are made between 1 mM and 1 pM in serial dilutions in quadruple. The drugs are heated to 37°C in a Hotpack Incubator room (Model UWP 105601, Hotpack Corp., Philadelphia, PA) and applied from least to greatest concentration in 20-μl aliquots using a 200-μl Rainin pipetter in a Sterile Gard Hood (Model SG-400, Barker Co. Inc.). Controls are placed at the beginning and end, and occasionally in the middle of our 96-well plates. Drugs can be applied at any time and new drugs are applied singularly after plating or repeatedly once a day for 3–5 days of culture. In the repeated application protocol, a 20-μl aliquot is removed before each application, but the CNM is not changed, to avoid disturbing the cultures. A graph of the effects of the $S(+)$- and $R(-)$-MDMA (ecstasy, 3, 4-methylenedioxymethamphetamine) enantiomers is shown in Fig. 3 (30). It can be seen that the procedure is able to detect the greater toxicity shown *in vivo* for the $S(+)$ compared to the $R(-)$ enantiomers of MDMA.

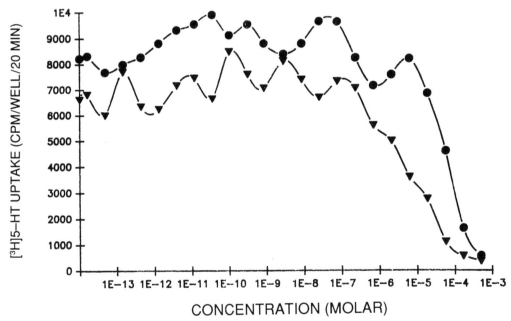

FIG. 3   The effects of a single application of either $S(+)$-MDMA (▼) or $R(-)$-MDMA (●) at the time of plating. The values are the averages ($n = 4$) after 4 days in culture of 1.2×10^6 cells/cm^2. [From Azmitia *et al.* (30).]

Extract Application

The application of tissue extracts from adult or aged animals is essentially described by Azmitia *et al.* (3) and by Varon *et al.* (31). Briefly, the tissue is homogenized in a 50% MEM solution (5°C) at 10 volume/wt using 10 passes from a loose-fitting Teflon pestle homogenizer. The homogenate is spun at 10,000 *g* for 20 min at 5°C, and the supernatant collected, filtered, and applied to the cultures at the time of plating in serial dilution in quadruple. Characterization of the extracts can be monitored with the microcultures, but care should be taken to select buffers and treatments which are not directly toxic to the cultured neurons.

Statistical and Graphic Analysis

The use of microcultures provides values for a large number of individual wells. Given that the wells contain an equal number of cells from a homogeneous suspension of dissociated cells, then each well is a unit of a normal population and can be treated as such statistically. The counts per minute obtained for each well from the scintillation counter are recorded directly onto a floppy disk of an IBM PS/2, Model 50 computer for descriptive and comparative statistics using a Systat (Systat, Inc., Evanston, IL) software program. The averages, SD, and SEM are obtained for each condition. Values more than three SD from the mean with the exclusion of the value are dropped. Analysis of variance is run for each plate separately and a Tukey posthoc analysis of statistics is determined. Individual *t*-test comparisons for all groups are also generated.

Graphical analysis of the data is produced using the mean and SEM generated on a Sigma Plot (Jandel Scientific, Sausalito, CA) software program. Linear regression and higher order regressions with confidence values are recorded with a hard copy of the graph produced on a plotter (Hewlett-Packard, Model 7475A). Examples of the graphs generated are shown in the figures presented in this chapter.

Acknowledgment

The able assistance of Tajrena Alexi and Xiao Ping Hou in the preparation of this chapter and in ensuring smooth operation of the tissue culture operation is gratefully recognized.

References

1. R. Harrison, *Anat. Rec.* **1,** 116 (1907).
2. S. Varon and C. W. Raiborn, *Brain Res.* **12,** 180 (1969).
3. E. C. Azmitia, P. M. Whitaker-Azmitia, and R. Bartus, *Neurobiol. Aging* **9,** 743 (1988).
4. W. B. Jakoby and I. H. Pastan, *in* "Methods in Enzymology" (W. B. Jakoby and I. Pastan, eds.), Vol. 58. Academic Press, New York, (1979).
5. J. E. Bottenstein and G. Sato, "Cell Culture in the Neuroscience." Plenum, New York, 1985.
6. S. Federoff and L. Hertz, "Cell, Tissue, and Organ Culture in Neurobiology." Academic Press, New York, 1977.
7. E. Giacobini, A. Vernadakis, and A. Shahar, "Tissue Culture in Neurobiology." Raven, New York, 1980.
8. P. G. Nelson and M. Lieberman, "Excitable Cells in Tissue Culture." Plenum, New York, 1981.
9. G. Sato, "Tissue Culture of the Nervous System." Plenum, New York, 1973.
10. J. M. Lauder and F. Bloom, *J. Comp. Neurol.* **155,** 469 (1974).
11. E. C. Azmitia, M. J. Perlow, M. J. Brennan, and J. M. Lauder, *Brain Res. Bull.* **7,** 703 (1981).
12. H. G. H. Lidov and M. E. Molliver, *Brain Res. Bull.* **9,** 559 (1982).
13. J. M. Lauder, J. A. Wallace, H. Krebs, P. Petruz, and K. McCarthy, *Brain Res. Bull.* **9,** 605 (1982).
14. C. Kotake, P. C. Hoffman, and A. Heller, *J. Neurosci.* **2,** 1307 (1982).
15. S. Varon and Saier, *Exp. Neurol.* **48,** 135 (1975).
15a. E. Yavin and Z. Yavin, *Cell Biol.* **62,** 540 (1974).
16. P. Benda, F. De Vitry, R. Picart, and A. Tixier-Vidal, *Exp. Brain Res.* **23,** 29 (1975).
17. J. E. Bottenstein, S. D. Skaper, S. S. Varon, and G. H. Sato, *Exp. Cell Res.* **125,** 183 (1980).
18. A. Prochiantz, M. C. Daguet, A. Herbert, and J. Glowinski, *Nature (London)* **293,** 570 (1981).
19. G. A. Banker and W. M. Cowan, *Brain Res.* **126,** 397 (1977).
20. M. Segal, *J. Neurophysiol.* **50,** 1249 (1982).
21. E. G. Azmitia and W. F. Marovitz, *J. Histochem. Cytochem.* **28,** 636 (1980).
22. E. C. Azmitia, M. J. Brennan, and D. Quartermain, *Int. J. Neurochem.* **5,** 39 (1983).
23. D. F. Kirskey and T. A. Slotkin, *Br. J. Pharmacol.* **67,** 387 (1979).
24. Y. Nomura, F. Maitoh, and T. Segawa, *Brain Res.* **101,** 305 (1976).
25. A. Schousboe, *in* "Neuroscience Approached through Cell Culture" (S. Pfeiffer, ed.), Vol. 1, pp. 107–142. CRC Press, Boca Raton, Florida, 1982.
26. J. R. Cooper, F. E. Bloom, and R. I. Roth, "Biochemical Basis for Neuropharmacology," 5th ed. Oxford Univ. Press, London and New York, 1986.

27. G. Doucet, L. Descarries, M. A. Audet, S. Garcia, and B. Berger, *Brain Res.* **441,** 233 (1988).
28. H. K. Kimelberg and D. M. Katz, *Science* **228,** 889 (1985).
29. R. W. Fuller, K. W. Perry, and B. B. Molloy, *Life Sci.* **15,** 1161 (1974).
30. E. C. Azmitia, R. B. Murphy, and P. M. Whitaker-Azmitia, *Brain Res.,* in press (1990).
31. S. Varon, R. Adler, M. Manthorpe, and S. D. Skaper, *in* "Neuroscience Approached through Cell Culture" (S. Pfeiffer, ed.), Vol. 2, pp. 53–79. CRC Press, Boca Raton, Florida, 1983.

[18] Long-Term Organotypic Culture of Central Nervous System in Maximow Assemblies

C. Dominique Toran-Allerand

Introduction

Organotypic Culture

Long-term, organotypic culture of the central nervous system (CNS) is one of several tissue culture techniques available for studying cellular, metabolic, and molecular aspects pertaining to the development and function of nervous tissue. The raison d'être of the organotypic method, which was introduced by Maximow (1) in 1925, lies in its unique ability to promote the highly organized growth and progressive cytological and histological differentiation of specific, anatomically identifiable, CNS regions over weeks and months in ontogenetic patterns characteristic of such regions *in vivo*. Its underlying philosophy is based on the premise that the cellular interactions between neurons themselves and between neurons and the supporting cells of a region, as well as the complex, three-dimensional intercellular organization itself, are all fundamental to developmental processes and to normal neural function. This technique thus attempts to preserve as many cells of as heterogeneous a population as possible, so as to avoid introducing the inevitable bias of selection inherent in dissociated cell culture methods. This specific aspect is particularly apt for most brain regions, since they usually exhibit considerable developmental, phenotypic, and functional heterogeneity. Specific neuronal subsets therein may be either few in number, randomly distributed, or regionally localized, and thus may be very susceptible to loss following mechanical and/or enzymatic dissociation.

Maximow Method

Long-term, organotypic culture of the CNS, using Maximow double-coverslip assemblies (Fig. 1), evolved from the classical studies of Murray and Peterson and their colleagues, starting in the early 1950s (see Refs. 2–4 for review). Ironically, however, while antedating by decades dissociated cell and aggregate neural culture methods, the Maximow method remains little known and little used.

Maximow cultures are prepared from relatively thick (~350–400 μm) anatomically defined, sections (slices), termed explants, of undifferentiated or poorly differentiated fetal, newborn, or early postnatal tissues of various vertebrate species, but most frequently the rat and mouse. Such cultures can be maintained for extended periods of time *in vitro* as single explants or cocultures that are juxtaposed or several millimeters apart, for the purpose of studying a broad range of morphogenetic parameters of neuronal development. These cultures have been used to study developmental aspects, such as cell migration, neuronal survival, axon and dendrite differentiation, myelinogenesis, and synaptogenesis. The maturation of functional or bioelectric properties has also been studied in a correlative fashion.

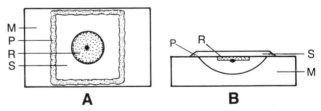

A   **B**

FIG. 1 The Maximow double-coverslip assembly. (A) View from above and (B) view from the side. M, Maximow slides; S, square coverslips; R, collagen-coated round coverslip with explant; P, paraffin/petroleum jelly seal. The assembly is depicted in the "hanging drop" position which is used for viewing with an upright microscope. The cultures are incubated in the inverted or "lying drop" position. The double-coverslip unit is affixed to the Maximow slide by a paraffin/petroleum jelly seal (see the text).

The apparent lack of popularity of the Maximow method is probably due to the fact that, while the culture techniques themselves are not at all difficult, precise dissection of anatomically discrete regions of, for example, the living fetal and neonatal brain are very difficult because of the paucity of landmarks (and of atlases). Moreover, both the high water content of fetal and neonatal brains and their unmyelinated state give the tissue a consistency which, even when thoroughly chilled, is extremely difficult to section precisely. Culture in Maximow assemblies, in addition, is both labor- and time-intensive, because of the demands of the technique itself and the need for frequent feeding schedules. Despite retention of much of the *in vivo* organizational complexity achieved by the Maximow method, there are both structural and functional abnormalities relative to the *in vivo* condition which are produced by the deafferented and/or nonafferented *in vitro* state. Extensive topographical shifts may also occur when the three-dimensional explants spread on the flat surface of the substratum—a phenomenon dramatically exaggerated in another organotypic culture method: roller tube cultures placed in a rotating drum (5).

Although Maximow cultures remain many layers thick, unlike roller tube cultures which spread to quasi-monolayers, the Maximow assembly permits long-term, undisturbed, serial observations of the living explant by direct viewing under high-power light microscopy, using long-working-distance (1-mm) microscope lenses. Even within the relatively thick explant, the progressive differentiation and development of living neurons and myelinated processes can be clearly delineated (Fig. 2), and any changes thereof can be evaluated on a daily basis—adding another dimension to any developmental analyses. In contrast, such analyses are more difficult to carry out with roller tube cultures without transfer of the coverslip to another container for each viewing, with the inherent risk of contamination. Although the viewing of living explants in Maximow assemblies, because of their very thickness, is limited to high-power, bright-field microscopy, the surrounding zone of outgrowth, which consists essentially of single cells and their processes (neurons and neuroglia), can also be readily studied with phase or differential interference contrast methods. Moreover, individual cultures can also be subsequently studied by the same wide range of histological, biochemical, and electrophysiological techniques applied to nervous tissue *in vivo*. While cultures maintained in Maximow assemblies have been extensively studied by classical bioelectric techniques (see Ref. 3, for review), it would appear that, with some additional experimental manipulations, such as acute cleaning of the culture surface with low-enzyme saline (6), they also offer unique opportunities for intracellular electrophysiological recordings and the use of patch–clamp and fluorescent imaging (7) techniques. Maximow cultures used in this way are particularly valuable in view of the recent interest in and

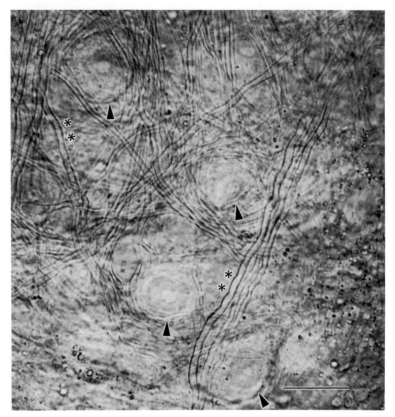

FIG. 2   Cluster of living Purkinje cell neurons and their myelinated axons in a 21-day-old culture of the newborn mouse cerebellum. Neuronal cell bodies (arrowheads), seen at various planes of focus in the explant, are interspersed among the myelinated fibers, which appear as parallel, birefringent lines (asterisks). Bright-field microscopy. Bar, 30 μm.

our lack of understanding of neuronal population interaction in relatively intact brain circuits (8).

At present, the Maximow method is the procedure of choice for long-term *in vitro* developmental studies that require optimal neural differentiation and anatomic fidelity in ontogenetic and cytoarchitectonic patterns most closely resembling those of comparable fetal and neonatal CNS regions *in situ*. Moreover, for certain situations where the expression of developmental parameters such as central myelinogenesis is dependent on the retention of the three-dimensional architecture of both neurons and of their cellular interactions (9), or for studies where the topographical distribution of neuronal subsets such as the estrogen receptor-containing cells in specific brain regions is critical (10), Maximow cultures have no peer. This chapter focuses in in detail on those methodological aspects of organotypic culture of the CNS that are specific to the Maximow double-coverslip assembly technique.

Special Techniques

Water for Tissue Culture

The water used for the final soaking of the glassware as well as for nutrient media and balanced salt solutions must be of the highest purity possible. High levels of endotoxins, organics, and heavy metals, trivial to acute experiments, remain despite redistillation and adhere to glassware, producing disastrous effects on cultured neural tissue. Wherever possible, we have used Milli-Q (Millipore, Ridgefield, NJ) processed water, sterilized (if necessary) just before use, through a 0.22-μm filter (Millex-GV; Millipore, Bedford, MA).

Packaging and Sterilization Procedures

All cleaned glassware is packaged in tins (Thomas Scientific, Swedesboro, NJ), glass pipette cannisters (Bellco, Vineland, NJ), or wrapped in heat-resistant paper (Steriroll; A. J. Buck and Sons, Cockeysville, MD) and sterilized either at 170°C for 2 hr (paper, cannisters) or 200°C for 3 hr (tins). Plastic screw caps and rubber stoppers are stored in petri dishes and sterilized by autoclaving at 121–123°C, 15 lbs psi for 25 min.

Cleaning Procedures

The cleaning procedures for the various items used in the Maximow method are the most demanding of all the tissue culture methods currently in use, since most of the items needed are not available as disposable plasticware. Thus, the cleaning procedures are very varied, time-consuming, and often complicated, as each category of glassware may have its own special cleaning requirements. The cleaning of the glassware and instruments, however, is a very important aspect of this tissue culture method, as the cultures are extraordinarily sensitive to the noxious effects of traces of chemical contaminants (unpublished observations).

Cleaning by Specific Categories

Maximow depression slides (75 mm × 45 mm, 7–8 mm thick; Roboz Surgical Instrument Co., Washington, D.C.) are boiled in two changes of 2% (v/v) Isoclean (Markson, Phoenix, AZ), rinsed sequentially in running hot tap water and deionized water, boiled once in distilled water, soaked in three changes of high-purity water for 24 hr each, drained, air dried, and sterilized in cans by dry heat.

Petri dishes, test tubes, bottles, washing dishes, volumetric flasks, centrifuge tubes, stender dishes, and crystalizing dishes are boiled for 20 min first in 2% Isoclean, then in sodium metasilicate (11) [40 ml of a 20% (w/v) stock solution for each 2 liters of deionized water], and rinsed sequentially under running hot tap water and running deionized water. The glassware is then soaked overnight in 1% (v/v) hydrochloric acid, rinsed extensively and sequentially under cold tap water and deionized water, and then soaked in three changes of high-purity water for 24 hr. The glassware is then drained, dried, packed in tins or wrapped in paper, and sterilized.

Coverslips [22 mm round, No. 1 thickness (Corning Glassware, Corning, NY); 40 × 40 mm square, No. 3 thickness (Clay Adams, Parsippany, NJ)] are arranged in small staining racks (Chen; Thomas), boiled in two changes of 2% Isoclean, rinsed sequentially in running hot tap water and deionized water, boiled once in distilled water, and air dried. The coverslip-containing racks are then placed for 24 hr in a mixture of concentrated sulfuric acid and No-Chromix, a nondichromate-oxidizing agent (Godax Labs, New York, NY). (Dichromate ions stick to glass and are toxic.) The coverslips are subsequently rinsed sequentially in running deionized water, soaked in three changes of high-purity water for 24 hr each, dried, stored in petri dishes (100 × 15 mm, Pyrex), placed in cans, and sterilized.

"Dissecting" Maximow slides, embryological watch glasses, and Kline concavity slides are processed like the coverslips with Isoclean and sulfuric acid/No-Chromix, as described above.

Pipettes are collected in jars containing 2% Isoclean, soaked therein for 24 hr, rinsed thoroughly for 30 min in a pipette washer, dried at 80°C, and soaked in concentrated sulfuric acid/No-Chromix overnight. They are rinsed extensively in a pipette washer with running tap water and deionized water and soaked in three changes of high-purity water for 24 hr each, drained, dried, plugged with cotton, and sterilized in glass cannisters.

Instruments are boiled once in 2% Isoclean, rinsed extensively in deionized water and distilled water, boiled once in distilled water, air dried, packed in stainless steel instrument boxes (Moria, Paris, France), and sterilized by dry heat (170°C) or by autoclaving.

Balanced Salt Solutions

The more commonly used nutrient media, which generally contain 20–40% serum and glucose levels of 6.0–6.5 mg/ml, are hypertonic for the CNS (C. D. Toran-Allerand, unpublished observation). We have found that reducing the tonicity enhances neurite outgrowth, cellular migration, and spreading of the explants, resulting in an optimal thickness for gaseous exchange and diffusion of nutrients. Any of the several available balanced salt solution (BSS) formulations (Hanks', Earle's) may be used for preparing collagen-coated coverslips and as a component of nutrient media. We, however, prefer to use hypotonic Simms' BSS, as originally modified by Murray by a 15% (v/v) dilution with water (personal communication). It is prepared according to the following formula in g/liter final concentration: NaCl (6.400), KCl (0.320), $CaCl_2$ (0.089), $MgCl_2 \cdot 6H_2O$ (0.163), $NaH_2PO_4 \cdot H_2O$ (0.017), $Na_2HPO_4 \cdot 12H_2O$ (0.385), $NaHCO_3$ (0.400), glucose (0.800). The components are added to water of the highest purity and sterilized by filtration (0.22 μm). If desired, sterile 0.05% (w/v) phenol red (GIBCO, Grand Island, NY) (0.5 ml/liter) may be added as an indicator, and the BSS gassed with 5% CO_2–95% air (sterile) to achieve a final pH of 7.4. Gey's BSS (for slides) (GIBCO), supplemented with 6.5 mg/ml glucose and 10% horse serum, is used during the dissection, because of its ability to maintain pH ~7, despite prolonged exposure to air under laminar flow.

Culture Substratum (Collagen)

Since CNS explants do not develop on glass or plastic surfaces alone, a variety of substrata, such as polyamines (polylysine; polyornithine), collagen, and plasma clots, have become available for use. Only rat tail (type I) collagen, however, has proved consistently to be the specific substratum of choice for the Maximow method. Collagen gels are very supportive of the outgrowth of cell processes and of cellular migration as well as resistant enough to withstand the inevitable trauma that accompanies the daily handling of the cultures and the bi- or triweekly feedings, during their prolonged maintenance *in vitro*. Highly purified bovine dermis (type II) collagen (Vitrogen; Collagen Corp., Palo Alto, CA), in contrast, has proved unsatisfactory in our hands for long-term organotypic culture of brain regions. Such cultures have rarely survived more than 10 days *in vitro,* despite an initial luxuriant, albeit totally disorganized, pattern of outgrowth of individual neurites without evidence of fascicle formation. This pattern of growth may be related to the apparent removal of the proteo- and glycosaminoglycans consequent to the purification procedures, which allegedly include unwinding of the helical structure of the collagen (Collagen Corp., personal communication). Spinal cord and cord–ganglia cultures, in contrast, do develop quite well, presumably because of Schwann cell conditioning of the Vitrogen surface by the laying down of basement membrane material which is more supportive of peripheral neurite outgrowth.

While rat tail collagen is available commercially as a sterile liquid or lyophilisate (Collaborative Research, Bedford, MA; Boehringer-Mannheim, Indianapolis, IN; Biomedical Technology, Stoughton, MA; Sigma, St. Louis, MO), we prefer the quality of that made in the laboratory (~5.5–6.5 mg/ml protein). In addition, the protein concentration of the liquid form of the commercial product is too low (0.16–3.6 mg/ml) to produce a substratum suitable for long-term culture of explants with respect to its durability as well as its ability to promote optimal outgrowth. Moreover, unlike the crystal clarity of the laboratory-made product, the commercial preparations are generally opalescent, and the gelled collagen is filled with debris. Collagen-coated coverslips are prepared by ammoniating (8) or air drying (9) a dialyzed rat tail collagen solution obtained by dilute acetic acid (0.01 M) extraction from the tail of a 9-month to 1-year-old male rat, as modified from Ehrmann and Gey (12), Bornstein (13), Roufa *et al.* (14), and protocols from the laboratories of Margaret R. Murray and of Richard P. Bunge.

Collagen Extraction

Preparative Steps

The following instruments are sterilized in advance: (2) large hemostats, (4) small hemostats (mosquito forceps), (2) large bone (Liston) forceps, (2) 4½-in. straight scissors, (2) 4½-in. straight forceps, and (2) #5 watchmaker's forceps.

For each tail, 150 ml of the highest purity water is sterilized by filtration (0.22 μm) and placed in a 150-ml centrifuge bottle (Corning). An additional 15 ml of sterile water per tail is placed in a sterile 15 × 60 mm petri dish (Pyrex) and weighed on a balance in order to determine subsequently the weight of the tendons.

A 0.01 M (0.1%) acetic acid solution is prepared from a 1 M (10%) stock solution of glacial acetic acid sterilized by filtration (pore size: 0.22 μm). Stronger concentrations will damage the filter.

Pulling of Rat Tails

The tails from 9-month-old (350–400 g) male rats are cut off after euthanasia and scrubbed thoroughly three times with soap and water, rinsed in deionized water and 80% (v/v) ethanol, and stored in a sterile petri dish for a minimum of 24 hr at −80°C. All subsequent steps, as well as all sterile procedures in general, are carried out under rigidly aseptic conditions in a horizontal laminar flow hood (Edgegard; Baker Co., Sanford, ME) by personnel wearing caps, gowns, and facial masks. On the day of collagen extraction, the tail is thawed and sterilized in 80% ethanol for 20 min, then set to dry in a sterile, large petri dish (20 × 150 mm; Pyrex). The tail is clamped at its base near the hairline with the large hemostat. The skin is removed by cutting fully around the hemostat *through the skin* completely but *not* through the tendons. Two mosquito forceps are clamped in parallel on the cut edges of the skin on both sides of the tail, and the two forceps are pulled distally. The skin should invert readily and slide off like a glove. Care must be taken to prevent the denuded tail from touching the surface of the laminar flow hood, as the skin is removed. Collagen obtained from skin-free tails is crystal clear and totally devoid of the scales and other debris that may be otherwise present and are virtually impossible to remove.

The large hemostat is placed near the tip of the tail, and the tail is successively fractured, but *not* cut through, into $\frac{1}{4}$- to $\frac{1}{2}$-in. pieces, using the bone forceps. Each fractured distal piece is drawn out from the remainder of the tail, and the resulting long, white, tendon strands are cut free from the bone fragments and collected in the 15 × 100 mm petri dish that contains sterile water. After the tail has been pulled completely, the tendons are transferred through five successive rinses of sterile water, swirling thoroughly to remove any blood, fat, or other debris.

With the two pairs of watchmaker's forceps, the tendons are teased apart into fine filaments—the finer the filament, the more complete the acetic acid extraction—and any additional debris is removed. The dish containing the tendons and water is weighed, and the weight of the dish with water alone is subtracted to obtain the total weight of the tendons. The tendon filaments are transferred *in toto* to a 150-ml centrifuge bottle (Corning), containing a sterile solution of 0.01 M acetic acid. The actual volume of the acetic acid is determined by the weight of the tendons, based on the ratio of 150 ml of 0.01 M acetic acid per gram of tendon. The yield of tendon/tail may vary considerably. The centrifuge bottles are stoppered and stored in the refrigerator at 4°C for 5 days with daily swirling to expose all the tendon filaments to the acetic acid in order to optimize the collagen extraction. The translucent mixture is centrifuged at 10,000 rpm for 2 hr at 4°C, and the clear supernatant is transferred with a Pasteur pipette to sterile test tubes, stoppered, and stored at 4°C until needed. A sample is checked for sterility in trypticase soy broth. Two tails are generally pulled each time, with an average yield of 300 ml of collagen solution after centrifugation.

Dialyzing the Collagen

Collagen must be dialyzed extensively against either high-purity water (pH 7.4) or culture medium (15) [Eagle's basal medium (BME) at one-tenth normal strength (16) before its use: 20 ml of 10× BME, 4.5 ml of 7.5% (w/v) NaHCO$_3$, 2 ml of 200 mM L-glutamine, plus sterile H$_2$O to 2 liters]. For 200 ml of collagen, 2 liters of sterile water or BME is added to a dialysis bottle (Dialyzer, Bellco). The pH of the BME is adjusted to 6.5 with 1 M HAc prior to use. Four 10-in. pieces of dialysis tubing (Spectra/Por; 12,000–14,000 MW cutoff are boiled for 15 min in 25 mM EDTA, rinsed for 3 hr under running deionized water, followed by 10 rinses with highest purity water. (The tubing is handled with gloves throughout.) One end of each tubing is sealed with a Spectra/Por closure and weighted with 50 3-mm glass beads before attaching the open end of the dialysis tubing to the glass holder of the dialyzer, using 4-0 surgical silk. The glass holder opening is closed by a screw cap, and the unit is hung on a stainless steel holder. The bags are autoclaved in 2 liters of highest purity water which may be replaced with the same volume of 0.1× BME before use. After autoclaving, the bottle must be allowed to cool to 4°C before use (usually overnight). Fifty milliliters of collagen is added to each of four dialysis bags through the screw-cap opening, and the solution is then dialyzed three times for 18–24 hr each at 4°C. At the end of the dialysis period, each dialysis bag is removed and slit with a sterile scalpel blade (#11; Bard-Parker), allowing the moderately viscous collagen solution to flow into a sterile crystallizing dish (Pyrex; Fisher Scientific, Fairlawn, NJ). The collagen is then ready for use or can be stored indefinitely at 4°C. A sample is checked for sterility in trypticase soy broth.

Preparation of Collagen Gels

The collagenized coverslips are prepared either by spreading two drops (100 μl) of collagen over a 22-mm round coverslip and allowing it to air dry in the laminar flow hood or gelling the collagen by exposure to ammonia vapor (from concentrated NH$_4$OH on sterile filter paper) for 2–3 min. The pH of collagen dialyzed against 0.1× BME is adjusted to ~6.8 with sterile 1 N NaOH before use. The bottom of an inverted Maximow slide, placed in a large (150 × 20 mm) petri dish, is useful for supporting 6–8 overhanging round coverslips (held in place by a small drop of sterile water to allow spreading of the collagen). Coverslips are handled at their overhanging edge with flat forceps. Air-dried collagen-coated coverslips are prepared just before use and are rehydrated in BSS before storing in nutrient medium in Columbia staining jars with ground-glass tops (Thomas). Ammoniated coverslips must be extensively washed free of ammonia in high-purity water (pH 7.4). To encourage the completeness of the biphasic polymerization of the ammoniated gels, the collagen-coated coverslips are allowed to sit undisturbed in ~10 ml of high-purity water (pH 7.4) in the Columbia staining jar for 24 hr (S. Varon, personal communication), followed by three changes in high-purity water of 15 min each. The need to adjust the pH of the high-purity water to 7.4 is critical, as prolonged soaking of collagenized coverslips in water at its usual acid pH (5.5–5.7) has led to a significant loss of collagen through gradual dissolution of the gel. The coverslips are then placed in 8.5 ml of BSS containing three Pasteur pipette drops (150 μl) of serum for a minimum of 12–24 hr at room temperature. They are generally transferred to nutrient medium on the day of use, but can be stored in BSS or nutrient medium for up to 2 weeks at 4°C.

For collagen gels strong enough to withstand the repeated stresses produced by muscle contractions in long-term organotypic cocultures of fetal spinal cord–ganglion complex with skeletal muscle, gelling of the collagen by photoreconstitution, as described by Masurovsky and Peterson (17) [9 parts collagen and 1 part 0.2% (w/v) riboflavin 5'-phosphate], may also be used. Hydrated collagen matrices (15, 16), on the other hand, do not appear strong enough to withstand repeated, daily inversions of the nutrient medium in the Maximow assembly (see below) over long periods of time and tend to work themselves loose from the coverslips and float.

Nutrient Medium

The complex, biological nutrient media used for equilibrating the coverslips and for feeding the cultures are serum-containing and tend to be individualized by each investigator. *De novo* myelinogenesis in CNS cultures, for example, will not occur with less than 15–20% serum (unpublished observations). Our basic nutrient medium consists of heat-inactivated (56°C, 30 min) horse serum (25%, v/v) [gelding serum is used for gonadal steroid-deficient conditions (18) (Hazleton Biologics, Lenexa, KS)]; Eagle's minimal essential medium, Earle's base, supplemented with nonessential amino acids (50%); linoleic acid/bovine serum albumin complex (1.025 μg/ml); sodium pyruvate (1 mM); L-glutamine (2 mM); selenium (5 ng/ml); transferrin (5 μg/ml); 3,3',5-triiodothyronine (T_3) (10^{-12}–10^9 M); Simms' BSS [12% (v/v)]. The medium is supplemented with 9% (w/v) glucose (361 μl) to achieve a final concentration of 6.5 mg/ml. *Antibiotics are never used.* For our studies of gonadal steroid effects *in vitro,* phenol red has been omitted from the nutrient media and BSS, since recent observations (19) have shown that the phenol red concentration (10 μM) of media obtained commercially is definitely, albeit weakly, estrogenic. Whether this effect is due to the fact that phenol red is related structurally to the nonsteroidal estrogen diethylstilbesterol (DES) or to an estrogenic contaminant of the phenol red is not entirely clear. At this concentration, however, the binding affinity of phenol red for the estrogen receptor (K_D 10^{-5} M) while only one-thousandth that of estradiol, would represent a 10% receptor occupancy, which in itself is sufficient for some of the effects of estradiol in the CNS *in vivo*.

Dissection Procedures

Organotypic explants may be derived from virtually any region of the variously aged fetal and newborn mouse and rat CNS. In our laboratory, as in others, the hypothalamus, preoptic area, septum, hippocampus, cerebral cortex, striatum, locus coeruleus, midbrain, cerebellum, and spinal cord, for example, have lent themselves readily to long-term culture. The nature of the study to be performed dictates the age of the tissue and choice of the region to be used, based on its developmental history. The degree of anatomic fidelity ultimately achieved, however, is determined to a considerable extent by the developmental stage at explantation, which is a function not only of the regional patterns of neurogenesis but of the ongoing intramural migrations as well.

Fetal Brains

Pregnant dams are killed by cervical dislocation (mice) or deep ether anesthesia (rat). The animal is pinned on its back in the laminar flow hood, and the entire ventral surface (head to tail) is saturated with 80% ethanol and allowed to dry. The uterus is rapidly delivered by cesarean section under rigidly sterile conditions, using three sets of sterile instruments: one to reflect the skin, one to open the peritoneum, and one to remove the uterus. The gravid uterus is stored in ice-cold serum and glucose-supplemented, Gey's BSS, after five sequential washes in 100 ml each of the same ice-cold, Gey's BSS. The embryos are removed from each uterine segment, one at a time, and placed in a sterile "dissecting" Maximow depression slide, kept on an ice slab molded in Lucite cylinders (50 × 100 mm). All phases of the dissection procedure are carried out under a stereo microscope in glassware kept on ice slabs, using a fiber-optic light source (Lucida light; Hacker

Instruments, Fairfield, NJ) which is transmitted from below up *through* the ice slab.

The embryo is decapitated with fine scissors, and the skin is removed by peeling it back from the cranium with fine forceps (Dumont, No. 5). The snout is cut off, and with the head on its side, the cranium is cut just above the jaw along its base with very fine scissors (Pascheff-Wolff, Moria). The calvarium is peeled up and separated from its base with fine forceps, allowing the entire brain to be shelled out undamaged. The brain is then transferred with a perforated spatula (Moria) to an embryological watch glass (Thomas) containing ice-cold Gey's BSS, for further subdivision into explants.

Newborn Brains

Craniectomies are performed on newborn mice and rats after hypothermia (cooling in air at 4°C) and cardiac puncture. Each animal is wiped with 80% ethanol and pinned dorsal side up to sterile, gauze-wrapped cardboard (corrugated) with a sterile, 27-gauge needle placed at the rump. The skin is fully saturated with 2% (w/v) tincture of iodine (USP), which is allowed to dry fully before a second, sterile, 27-gauge needle is pinned at the snout. Three sets of sterile instruments are used to remove sequentially: the skin, cranial vault, and brain. The calvarium is removed by cutting with fine scissors (Vannas, Moria) circumferentially through the orbits, along the base of the cranium, and along the sagittal suture. Care must be taken not to damage the underlying brain. The orbital end of each hemicalvarial section is lifted with fine forceps, and a final cut through the sphenoid wing of each temporal bone allows the calvarial segments to be removed *in toto,* exposing the entire intact brain. The brain is cut at the level of the olfactory bulbs and through the myelomedullary junction with a #11 scalpel blade and removed en bloc with curved forceps to a watch glass containing ice-cold Gey's BSS. The veil-like, pia–arachnoid membrane is carefully peeled away completely from the fetal or newborn brain with fine forceps without damaging the underlying tissue.

Subdivision into Explants

Cerebellum

The sausagelike cerebellum is readily separated from the brain stem by two parallel transverse cuts: one just rostral and one caudal to the cerebellum, followed by a cut through the cerebellar peduncles on each side, using an ophthalmic discission knife (Castroviejo-Wheeler, Edward Weck, Long Island City, NY). The cerebellum is transferred with a Pasteur pipette into a well of a 12-well Kline concavity slide (Thomas), which is kept on an ice slab, and then subdivided freehand under microscopic control into eight parasagittal explants. The Kline concavity slide is very practical for preserving the regional origins of all individual explants.

Other Brain Regions

Depending on the other brain regions desired, the rest of the brain is placed either dorsal or ventral side facing upward and cut coronally by freehand section under microscopic control into 300- to 400-μm-thick slices with discission knives. However, for atlas quality, anatomically very precise, coronal sections of the whole brain, we are now preparing explants using the brain-slicing apparatus (at California Institute of Technology, Pasadena, CA) developed by Katz (20), which consists of a spring-driven cutting grid made up of 60 parallel, 6% gold-plated tungsten wires (20 μm thick) (21). Each whole-brain section is transferred to a well of a Kline concavity slide by means of a perforated spatula and further subdivided into the desired brain regions, using a discission knife.

Explants can be maintained as full coronal sections, or further subdivided into hemicoronal or even smaller fragments, and cultured as single explants or cocultures. The thickness of the explants appears to be the limiting factor primarily, since exposure to nutrients and to added test substances, as well as all gaseous exchanges, take place entirely by diffusion through the avascular explant. The optimal thickness appears to be that achieved with the brain slicer, ~360 μm. Explants that are too thick (>400 μm) exhibit a central zone of necrosis in their deepest layers, attributable to both the inadequate inward diffusion of oxygen and glucose and outward diffusion of metabolic waste products. Explants that are too thin (<250 μm), in contrast, tend to spread excessively and lose those three-dimensional cytoarchitectonic relationships which make the Maximow method unique. The overall surface area of the explants, on the other hand, appears to exert little influence on their development.

Hemicoronal explants have proved very useful in the "mirror" paradigm which was developed in our laboratory to compare the responses of organotypic cultures to added substances (22, 23). Mirror explants are right and left homologs (matched pairs) of defined CNS levels that are morphologically and developmentally comparable. One randomly assigned explant of each pair serves as the intrinsic control for such variables as regional differences in development and in neuronal phenotypes, genetic differences between littermates, and the condition of the tissue at explantation.

Maximow Method

Establishing Maximow Double-Coverslip Assemblies

Each collagen-coated coverslip that has been equilibrated in nutrient medium is placed, after draining off the medium, onto a sterile, square coverslip located in a large petri dish (150 × 20 mm; Pyrex) that is lined with black filter paper (Schleicher and Schuell; 15 cm; #551) for enhanced visibility. The round coverslip adheres to the square one by capillarity. (Two 40 × 40 mm square coverslips will fit in these petri dishes.) Depending on their size, explants are then transferred to the collagen-coated coverslips either with curved forceps (Dumont No. 7), a perforated spatula, or with a fire-polished Pasteur pipette that, if necessary, has had its orifice enlarged by breaking the shaft. One Pasteur pipette (bent-tip; Bellco) drop (50 μl) of nutrient medium is added to each round coverslip, and a Maximow depression slide with four *small* daubs of sterile petroleum jelly around the depression is inverted onto the square coverslip. Each Maximow double-coverslip assembly is subsequently exposed in a chamber to sterile 5% CO_2–95% air for 15–30 min, then turned (flipped) so that the culture and drop face downward (hanging drop position), and, using an acrylic paint brush, the edges of the square coverslip are sealed with a paraffin–petroleum jelly mixture (paraffin, mp 54–56°C, 2 lbs; Vaseline, 5.0 g; Tissuemat, mp 56–58°C, 1 square) kept in a water bath at 71°C. The sealed assemblies are flipped back to their original position, placed in racks, and incubated at 34–35°C in the lying drop position (culture faces upward; drop covers the culture as a thin film) (see Fig. 3A–J).

Cultures are viewed in the living state in the hanging drop position, using a standard upright microscope, equipped with long-working-distance (1-mm) lenses. A representative culture is seen in Fig. 4. Great care must be taken (a nonchalant approach is best) in flipping the Maximow assemblies so as to avoid having the drop fly off from the collagen-coated coverslip—a not uncommon hazard unique to this tissue culture method. A drop that is too big will acquire too much momentum and be difficult to control when flipping. Complete loss of the drop, with dryness of the culture, will impair its subsequent development and may lead to cell death. Leaving a dropless culture at room temperature may slow its metabolic rate until the drops can be replenished by refeeding, enabling the culture to survive better.

Refeeding Cultures

Cultures are refed (Fig. 3K–S) two or three times weekly depending on the vigor of their growth, the half-life of any exogenously added substances,

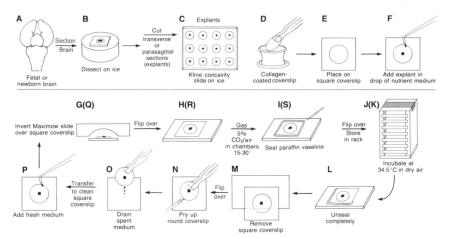

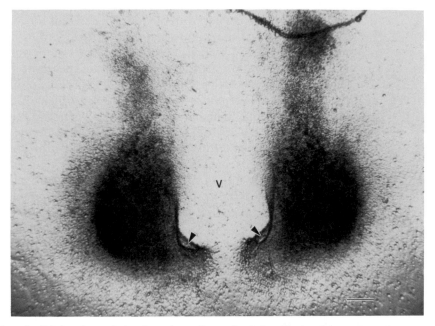

FIG. 3   Preparation of organotypic cultures in Maximow double-coverslip assemblies. For explanations see the text. (A–J) Establishing the cultures; (K–S) refeeding the cultures.

FIG. 4   Living hypothalamic culture from the infundibular (arcuate) region of the newborn mouse, prepared by freehand, coronal section and maintained in Maximow assemblies for 48 days. Note persistence of the anatomy of the two symmetrical, "mirror" explant halves, including preservation of the infundibular recess (arrowheads), and the surrounding zone of outgrowth. V, Ependymal cells of former third ventricle. Bright-field microscopy. Bar, 200 μm.

such as hormones and growth factors, or the nature of the experiment. The procedure for refeeding cultures is basically that described above for their establishment. After the appropriate time interval, the cultures are removed from the incubator, and the paraffin/petroleum jelly seal is scraped completely from all sides of the square coverslip, using a scalpel with a #11 blade. Care must be taken to stabilize the square coverslip to keep it from moving while the seal is being removed, so as to avoid contaminating the underlying culture. The unsealed Maximow assemblies are replaced in their racks in the *hanging drop* position (coverslip facing upward) and transferred to the laminar flow hood. Each Maximow assembly is removed individually from its rack and placed on the working surface of the hood. The square coverslip is then carefully slid forward to a degree just sufficient to allow one corner to be gripped by the thumb and index finger so as to remove the square coverslip from the underlying Maximow slide. The coverslip/culture unit is rapidly inverted (culture facing upward) and placed on an ethanol-wiped, black ceramic tile, placed in a large petri dish. A pair of sterile, flat forceps (Fine Science Tools, Belmont, CA) is used to stabilize the round coverslip, which is then gently pried up with the tip of a #11 scalpel blade, placed on the coverslip's edge at a point exactly opposite to that of the forceps. This positioning is absolutely critical, as the direction of the forces exerted may otherwise lead to breakage of the round coverslip and possible loss of the culture. To prevent breakage, care must be taken not to force the coverslip up. Dull blade tips should be replaced. The loosened, round coverslip is lifted vertically; its spent drop is drained, first onto the center of the used square coverslip and then on the black filter paper in the large petri dish; followed immediately by placement of the round coverslip on a clean square coverslip, as described above. A fresh drop of nutrient medium is added quickly, a clean Maximow slide inverted over the square coverslip, and, after exposure to 5% CO_2, the new Maximow assembly is again sealed with paraffin–petroleum jelly, and the cultures incubated in the lying drop position at 34–35°C. This procedure is repeated as long as one wishes to maintain the cultures—generally for weeks or for months.

Histological Analyses

At appropriate intervals, representative cultures may be fixed and processed as whole mounts or sections for a wide variety of histological, histochemical, or immunocytochemical techniques at both the light and electron microscopic levels. Living cultures may also be prepared for metabolic or electrophysiological studies. For histological procedures requiring sectioning of the explants, we make 22-mm round coverslips from ACLAR (type 33C, 500 mil; Allied Chemical, Morristown, NJ) (10, 24), which can readily be peeled off from the overlying collagen, once the culture has been embedded for frozen, paraffin, or electron microscopic sectioning.

Holmes' Silver Method

Our preferred all-purpose stain for whole mounts is the neuron-specific, Holmes' silver impregnation for neurofibrils, using our modifications of the procedures originally described by Wolf (25) and by Sobkowicz *et al.* (26). A representative explant and a neuron stained by this method are shown in Figs. 5 and 6.

All glassware must be acid-cleaned. Unless otherwise indicated, coverslips and solutions are best handled by placing them in staining jars (Columbia, screw-cap; Thomas).

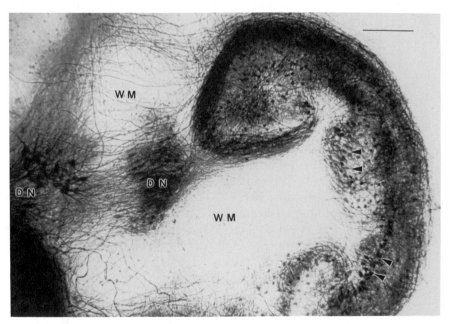

FIG. 5   Holmes' silver-impregnated organotypic explant of the newborn mouse cerebellum, 20 days *in vitro*. Note the organization into cortex with its well-defined Purkinje cell layer (arrowheads) whose axons project to two clusters of deep cerebellar nuclei neurons (DN), and white matter (WM). The axons of both the Purkinje cells and cerebellar nuclei neurons were extensively myelinated in the living state. Bar, 300 μm.

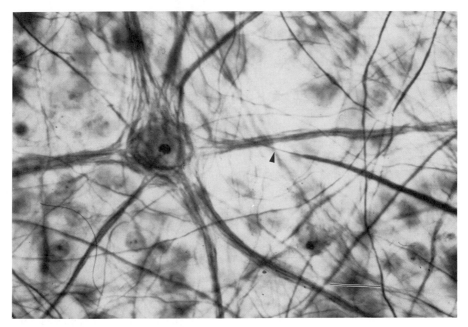

FIG. 6 Holmes' silver-impregnated neuron from a mammillary nucleus of the hypothalamus, 60 days *in vitro*. Note the long, sparsely branching dendrites and the axon
(arrowhead) with its thin initial segment. Bar, 30 μm.

1. Fix cultures without washing or draining off the nutrient medium for 5
   days at 4°C in 10% formalin in boric acid buffer [27.5 ml boric acid (12.4
   g/liter), 22.5 ml sodium borate (19.0 g/liter), 197 ml distilled water].
2. Rinse cultures with distilled water and dehydrate in ascending concentrations of ethanol to 80%. Store in 80% ethanol for 1 month at 4°C.
3. Rehydrate cultures and place in distilled water for 15 min and then transfer, using *plastic* forceps, to 20% (w/v) silver nitrate at room temperature
   for 1.5 hr *in the dark*.
4. Rinse cultures three times for 10 min each in distilled water and then
   transfer with plastic forceps to staining racks (Chen; Thomas) in square
   staining dishes (Thomas) and place in 250 ml *freshly* made impregnating
   solution (4–6 coverslips per 250 ml) on a magnetic stirrer for 3–6 days at
   4°C, *in the dark*.
   The *impregnating solution,* added in the following order, consists of
   110 ml of boric acid (12.4 g/liter), 90 ml of sodium borate (19.0 g/liter), 788
   ml of distilled water. Mix well. Add 2 ml of 1% (w/v) silver nitrate. Mix
   well. Add 10 ml of 10% (v/v) pyridine in water. Mix well.

5. After the appropriate period, and *under dim light,* remove the coverslips from the impregnating solution by draining well but without rinsing, and immediately place for 6 min *in the dark* in freshly made reducing solution warmed to 32°C before use. The *reducing solution* consists of hydroquinone (1 g), sodium sulfite (10 g), distilled water (100 ml).
6. Transfer cultures to running tap water for 10 min, rinse three times with distilled water, and tone in 0.2% (w/v) gold chloride for 4 min *in the dark.* The gold chloride can be saved and reused for many years.
7. Rinse cultures three times in distilled water, transfer to 2% (w/v) oxalic acid for 15 min *in the dark,* rinse three times in distilled water, and place in 5% (w/v) sodium thiosulfate for 5 min *in the dark.*
8. Transfer the cultures to running tap water for 10 min, rinse three times in distilled water, dehydrate in ascending concentrations of ethanol, clear in xylenes, and mount in Permount.

Neurofibrils (the bundles of neuron-specific neurofilaments) in cell bodies and processes are impregnated in shades ranging from jet black to reddish. The intensity of the impregnation appears to be a function of the neurofibrillary content, which is a function of both neuronal phenotype as well as developmental stage. In general, myelinated fibers are more successfully impregnated than unmyelinated ones. Impregnation for long periods of time at 4°C rather than the traditional 40°C, however, enhances dramatically the impregnation of the finest of unmyelinated neurites and neurites with sparse neurofibrils, both of which are notoriously difficult to stain.

The whiteness of the background is significantly enhanced by carrying out steps 3–7 in the dark or dim light. Plastic (*not* metal) forceps must be used for those same steps to prevent the formation of a precipitate that coats the culture and prevents impregnation.

Conclusion

The Maximow method described herein is a particularly useful model system for obtaining long-term cultures of the CNS which exhibit remarkable structural and functional fidelity with the *in vivo* state. Anatomically identifiable regions of the CNS, whose complex organization is enccuraged to develop and be maintained *in vitro,* can be further manipulated in a relatively defined environment. This most complex of all neural culture systems provides a unique approach for supplementing and extending not only *in situ* studies, but may also be useful for comparing the responses obtained from more defined *in vitro* conditions such as those obtained with dissociated cultures.

Despite the limitations imposed by the method, including its labor- and time-intensiveness, the accessibility of CNS regions with intact neural circuits to direct experimental manipulation enables correlative cellular, molecular, and metabolic studies that would not otherwise be currently possible.

Acknowledgments

The work described here has been supported over the years by grants from NIH (HD 08364, NS 18840), NSF (BNS 77-09859; BNS 87-00400), National Multiple Sclerosis Society, March of Dimes Birth Defects Foundation, William T. Grant Foundation, Whitehall Foundation, The Veterans Administration, and by an ADAMHA Research Scientist Development Award (MH-00192).

I am greatly indebted to Dr. Richard P. Bunge and the late Dr. Margaret R. Murray for having introduced me, when they were at the College of Physicians and Surgeons of Columbia University, to long-term organotypic culture of the developing CNS in Maximow assemblies, with its unique and exciting scientific potential and great esthetic satisfaction. I am also grateful to Dr. Robert K. S. Wong for invaluable critical advice regarding the manuscript.

References

1. A. Maximow, *Contrib. Embryol. Carnegie Inst.* **16,** 47 (1925).
2. M. R. Murray, *in* "Cells and Tissues in Culture" (E. N. Willmer, ed.), Vol. 2, p. 373. Academic Press, New York, 1965.
3. S. M. Crain, "Neurophysiologic Studies in Tissue Culture." Raven, New York, 1976.
4. C. D. Toran-Allerand, *Colloq. Int. CNRS* **280,** 759 (1978).
5. B. H. Gähwiler, *Experientia* **40,** 235 (1984).
6. A. Konnerth, T. Takahashi, and B. Sakmann, *Abstr. Eur. Neurosci. Meet., 11th* p. 342 (1988).
7. D. W. Tank, M. Sugimori, J. A. Connor, and R. R. Llinás, *Science* **242,** 773 (1988).
8. R. Traub, R. Miles, and R. K. S. Wong, *Science* **243,** 1319 (1989).
9. C. D. Allerand and M. R. Murray, *Arch. Neurol.* **19,** 292 (1968).
10. C. D. Toran-Allerand, J. L. Gerlach, and B. S. McEwen, *Brain Res.* **184,** 517 (1980).
11. J. Paul, "Cell and Tissue Culture," 3rd ed. Williams & Wilkins, Baltimore, Maryland, 1965.
12. R. L. Ehrmann and G. D. Gey, *JNCI, J. Natl. Cancer Inst.* **16,** 1375 (1956).
13. M. B. Bornstein, *Lab. Invest.* **7,** 134 (1958).
14. D. G. Roufa, M. I. Johnson, and M. B. Bunge, *Dev. Biol.* **99,** 225 (1983).
15. T. Elsdale and J. Bard, *J. Cell Biol.* **54,** 626 (1972).

16. T. Ebendal, *in* "Nerve Growth Factors" (R. A. Rush, ed.), p. 81. Wiley, New York, 1989.
17. E. B. Masurovsky and E. R. Peterson, *Exp. Cell Res.* **76,** 447 (1973).
18. C. D. Toran-Allerand, L. Ellis, and K. H. Pfenninger, *Dev. Brain Res.* **41,** 87 (1988).
19. Y. Bethois, J. Katzenellenbogen, and B. Katzenellenbogen, *Proc. Natl. Acad. Sci. U.S.A.* **93,** 2496 (1986).
20. L. C. Katz, *J. Neurosci.* **7,** 1223 (1987).
21. C. D. Toran-Allerand, *Brain Res. Bull.,* in press (1990).
22. C. D. Toran-Allerand, *Exp. Neurol.* **43,** 216 (1974).
23. C. D. Toran-Allerand, *Brain Res.* **106,** 407 (1976).
24. E. B. Masurovsky, E. R. Peterson, and S. M. Crain, *In Vitro* **6,** 379 (1971).
25. M. K. Wolf, *J. Cell Biol.* **22,** 259 (1964).
26. H. M. Sobkowicz, H. A. Hartmann, R. Monzain, and P. Desnoyers, *J. Comp. Neurol.* **148,** 249 (1973).

Section V

Functional Assessment

[19] Preparation and Use of Morphological Variants to Investigate Neuropeptide Action

John S. Ramsdell

Introduction

The signaling pathways that mediate the prolonged cellular responses of neuropeptides and growth factors are poorly defined. This chapter describes the preparation and use of morphological variants* to investigate several long-term actions of thyrotropin-releasing hormone (TRH) on the GH_4 rat pituitary cell line. GH_4 cells elicit four biological responses to TRH: an acute release of previously synthesized prolactin (PRL) and three prolonged responses (enhanced PRL synthesis via increased gene transcription, enhanced cell–substratum adhesion, and inhibition of cell proliferation).

The approach we use to examine signaling pathways generating prolonged responses in GH_4 cells is based on the isolation and characterization of nonresponsive GH_4 cell variants. The use of somatic cell variants was based on analogous studies in microorganisms and led to new understanding of several signaling mechanisms, including guanine nucleotide-binding proteins, cAMP-dependent protein kinase, and glucocorticoid receptors (1–3). Investigation of cell variants is particularly useful in those systems where the signaling pathways are poorly defined, and because this approach lacks an experimental bias toward known biochemical mechanisms, it may lead to the identification of new signaling mechanisms.

The application of somatic cell variants is limited largely to those systems which permit a selective advantage to the growth or visual identification of nonresponsive cells (4). In mouse S49 lymphoma cells, elevation of the concentration of cAMP or glucocorticoids is cytotoxic to responsive cells (5, 6), and other cell lines have also been found to be growth inhibited by cAMP (reviewed in Ref. 2). Additional methods have been reported for the selective growth of nonresponsive cells, using immunotoxins (7) and complement-mediated lysis (8). Selection based on visual identification of nonresponsive cells, such as replicate plating (9) and adhesion in the presence of a

---

* We use the term "variant" rather than mutant because the latter requires demonstration that the observed phenotype results from altered expression of a specific gene product. The term "variant" does not imply that it is unstable; in fact, the phenotypes of all variants described in this chapter are stable over many passages.

Methods in Neurosciences, Volume 2

mitogenic agent (10), has also been used to isolate nonresponsive variants. The selection we have used is based on a morphological change elicited by TRH, epidermal growth factor (EGF) or 12-O-tetradecanoylphorbol-13-acetate (TPA) and utilizes two steps: one based on increased substratum adhesion and the other on visual identification.

GH$_4$C$_1$ cells have proved useful for the isolation of cell variants because they undergo a reversible morphological change (increased cell–substratum adhesion, also known as stretching) in response to several agents that enhance PRL synthesis. Increased cell–substratum adhesion is not necessary for enhanced PRL synthesis, in part because a selective activator of protein kinase C (bryostatin 1) is an antagonist for GH$_4$ cell–substratum adhesion and an agonist for PRL synthesis (11). However, the fact that many agonists increase each response in these cells suggests that common signaling mechanisms may be involved. With this in mind, we sought to isolate GH$_4$ cell variants that were nonresponsive to TRH-enhanced cell–substratum adhesion, with the objective of investigating signaling mechanisms mediating GH$_4$ cell–substratum adhesion and, possibly, other prolonged cellular responses as well.

Methodology

Donor Cultures

The choice of donor cultures influences the selection of variant phenotypes. Our first selection used GH$_4$C$_1$ cells that had been passaged many (>20) generations. The TRH-nonresponsive variants all had defects in the number of TRH receptor sites. Because TRH receptor number differs between GH clones, altered receptor number may be a common spontaneous defect in these cells. To minimize the selection of preexisting variants with decreased receptor numbers, donor cultures are recently cloned and tested for homogeneity of TRH receptor binding.

Isolation of TRH-Responsive Donor Culture

Because TRH-enhanced cell–substratum adhesion is reversible, it is possible to obtain highly responsive clones in the presence of TRH and then allow them to revert to a nonstimulated phenotype in the absence of TRH. Stock cultures of GH$_4$ cells are maintained in serum-supplemented [15% (v/v) horse and 2.5% (v/v) fetal bovine] Ham's F10 nutrient mixture (F10+) as previously described (12) for a maximum of 10 weekly passages. A single-cell suspension of GH$_4$C$_1$ cells is plated at 5×10^4 cells/100-mm dish and allowed to grow in the presence of 100 nM TRH for 5 days (approximately three cell replications) in F10+. Originally, loosely adherent cells were triturated from the dish each day; however, because of the large population of responsive cells, this enrichment step is not always necessary to isolate donor cultures. Highly flattened colonies are identified visually by phase-contrast microscopy and marked on the underside of the dish with a felt-tip pen. To isolate the selected colonies, the medium is removed, the plates are treated with 5 ml of 0.1% (w/v) Viokase for 1 min, the Viokase is removed, and the dishes incubated for 5 min in a humidified incubator. Five milliliters of F10+ is added very gently to each dish and the marked colony identified using a dissecting or phase-contrast microscope at 50× magnification within a horizontal laminar flow hood. Cell colonies are dislodged with an air bubble behind 5 μl of F10+ from a P-20 Gilson pipetteman and drawn into the pipette tip by suction. The cell suspension is transferred to a 25-mm T-flask containing 4.5 ml of F10+, and the cells are propagated to 10^6 cells in the absence of agonist. Aliquots are frozen [95% fetal bovine serum, 5% (v/v) dimethyl sulfoxide] in nitrogen vapors for 1 hr and stored 5–15 cm above the liquid nitrogen.

Testing for TRH Receptor Homogeneity in Subclones

The second step in obtaining a donor culture is to determine TRH receptor homogeneity. GH_4 cells are cloned by dilution, several clones are propagated to approximately 10^6 cells, and aliquots are stored in liquid nitrogen. Clones are next screened for TRH binding using the high-affinity TRH analog [^{3}H]MeTRH. Cells are plated at 2.5×10^5 cells/35-mm dish and propagated in F10+ for 5 days with two changes of medium. Triplicate dishes are washed once with HBBS (20 mM HEPES, 10 mM glucose, 118 mM NaCl, 4.6 mM KCl, 1.0 mM CaCl$_2$, pH 7.2) and incubated to equilibrium (60 min, 37°C) with one equilibrium dissociation constant (K_d) of [^{3}H]MeTRH (2 nM) in the absence and presence of 100 times K_i of unlabeled TRH (1 μM). Dishes are washed five times with 1 ml of normal saline, and the cells dissolved in 0.5 ml of 1 N NaOH. The extract is collected together with a 0.5-ml wash of H_2O. Radioactivity is quantified by liquid scintillation spectroscopy and receptor number adjusted to cell number. Several clones of the y_{13} donor culture have been examined for [^{3}H]MeTRH binding. Five clones had binding identical to the GH_4C_1 parental cells, whereas one clone (y_{13-5}) had a 67% increase in the number of binding sites/cell without a change in K_d (13).

Pretreatment of Donor Cultures

As a second means to increase the likelihood of variants having a phenotype different from those commonly found in the wild-type population, recently cloned donor cultures are pretreated with a mutagen.

Use of N-Methyl-N'-nitro-N-nitrosoguanidine as Mutagen

The DNA alkylating agent *N*-methyl-*N'*-nitro-*N*-nitrosoguanidine (MNNG) is used to increase the frequency of mutations. MNNG is a commonly used mutagenic agent which methylates predominantly the N-7 of guanine. MNNG is advantageous because it has a half-life of only several hours at physiological pH before it is decomposed to diazomethane, a nontoxic and stable product (14). Contaminated items, such as pipette tips and aliquot tubes, may be immersed in 1 *N* NaOH to inactivate the MNNG rapidly. MNNG should be tested on each cell line prior to the selection because its half-maximal lethal dose (LD_{50}) differs between cell lines and culture conditions. MNNG is prepared in 0.1 *M* acetic acid (pH 5.0) at a concentration of 1 mg/ml, aliquoted, and stored at $-20°C$. Increasing concentrations (1–50 μg/ml) of MNNG are added directly to plated cells grown to near-confluency in F10+. The dishes are washed to remove detached cells at 24 and 48 hr and replenished with fresh medium. Cell number is determined at 48 hr. We find a LD_{50} of 10 μg/ml of GH_4 cells. If a selection is to be performed, the cells are permitted to proceed with one or two replications after treatment with MNNG.

Selection Procedure for Nonresponsive Variants

The selection is based on a morphological change induced by TRH and other agents [including epidermal growth factor (EGF), 12-*O*-tetradecanoyl-phorbol-13-acetate (TPA), sodium butyrate (BUT), and Neplanocin A (NEP)]. The GH_4 cells, which normally grow in a highly rounded and loosely attached configuration, are induced by TRH to become highly flattened and strongly adherent to the tissue culture substratum (Fig. 1). We utilize two different selection steps to isolate nonresponsive variants.

Enrichment of Nonresponsive Variants

The first step in the selection procedure is to enrich the population for nonresponsive cells by collecting poorly adherent, agonist-treated cells. To achieve this, 2.5×10^6 donor cells are plated on 100-mm tissue culture dishes in the presence of 100 n*M* TRH. After 48 hr, poorly adherent cells are removed by gentle trituration of the culture medium with a serological pipette. The cells are transferred to a new dish and incubated for 24 hr; this step is repeated for the next three consecutive days. The repetition of the washes is to ensure that the cells can complete at least one division (because the cells become rounded and loosely attached during the M phase of the cell cycle).

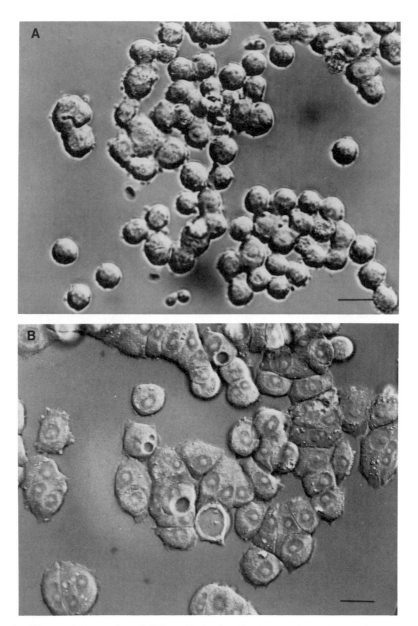

FIG. 1 Photomicrographs of GH$_4$ cells in the absence and presence of TRH. GH$_4$ donor cultures (y$_{13-3}$) were grown on glass coverslips for 5 days in F-10+ and were treated with vehicle (A) or 100 nM TRH (B) for 24 hr. The cells in the absence of TRH are rounded and loosely attached to the substratum, whereas the cells treated with TRH are stretched and firmly attached to the substratum. The photographs were taken using Nomarski optics. Bars, 10 μm.

Visual Identification and Isolation of Nonresponsive Variants

The second step in the selection procedure is visual identification of poorly adherent cells. The enriched population of poorly adherent cells is plated at 5×10^4 cells/100-mm dish and allowed to grow undisturbed in the presence of TRH for 5 days (approximately three cell replications). Highly rounded colonies are identified visually by phase-contrast microscopy and marked on the underside of the dish with a felt-tip pen. Selected colonies are isolated as described above for the donor cultures.

We have isolated several sets of TRH-nonresponsive GH_4 cell variants. Two sets have been isolated as nonresponsive to TRH-enhanced substratum adhesion. The first used a GH_4C_1 donor population that had not been recently cloned nor treated with MNNG. This yielded variants with decreased TRH receptor number. A second set of variants was isolated as nonresponsive to TRH-enhanced substratum adhesion using the recently cloned y_{13-5} donor population treated with MNNG. This set has a normal complement of TRH receptors and probably has a defect in a signaling pathway, although a defect in an end point for adhesion has not yet been entirely discounted.

Preliminary Characterization of Nonresponsive Variants

The preliminary characterization of nonresponsive variants sorts them into one of three general classes of cellular defects (Fig. 2). The first are receptor defects which prevent all responses to TRH but not other agonists. The second class is signaling defects. Signaling defects prevent one or more responses to TRH and may also prevent this action(s) of other agonists that share a common signaling pathway. The third class is end-point defects. These defects represent a final step in agonist-enhanced cell-substratum adhesion (possibly cell adhesion receptors). End-point defects should prevent the action of all agonists to enhance cell–substratum adhesion. Our strategy is to localize the defect within one of the above classes by examining the ability of TRH and other agonists (e.g., TPA, EGF) to elicit several different biological responses (PRL release, PRL synthesis, replication inhibition, and cell–substratum adhesion).

Enhanced Prolactin Release

Cells are plated at 2.5×10^5/35-mm dish and propagated for 5 days with two changes of F10+. Dishes are washed twice with HBBS and incubated in the absence and presence of 100 nM TRH or 100 nM TPA for 30 min on a slide warmer at 37°C. PRL accumulated in the medium is measured by rat PRL radioimmunoassay and the cell number is quantified. Previous studies indi-

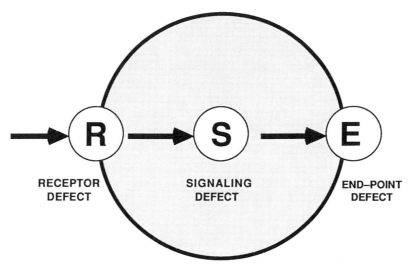

FIG. 2 Diagram illustrating three classes of defects in nonresponsive variants. Non-responsive variants may have (1) receptor defects, (2) signaling defects, or (3) end-point defects.

cate that newly synthesized PRL does not appear in the culture medium until approximately 60 min, indicating that hormone accumulating in medium within 30 min represents the release of previously synthesized hormone (15).

Enhanced Prolactin Production

Cells are plated at 2.5×10^5/35-mm dish and propagated for 5 days with two changes of F10+. Dishes are incubated in the absence or presence of 100 nM TRH, 100 nM TPA, or 10 nM EGF for 72 hr. The medium is collected, centrifuged to remove cells, and PRL measured by radioimmunoassay. Previous studies indicate that PRL accumulation in the medium by GH_4 cells over 72 hr represents >98% newly synthesized PRL, and TRH-enhanced PRL accumulation corresponds closely to enhanced PRL mRNA levels (15, 16).

Inhibition of Cell Proliferation

TRH inhibition of GH_4 cell proliferation has been quantified in several ways (17). The best approach for preliminary characterization of nonresponsive variants is to measure [³H]thymidine incorporation. Cells are plated at 0.5×10^5/16-mm well in 0.3 ml of F10+ containing 2 μCi/ml of [³H]thymidine (specific activity 6.7 Ci/mmol). The cells are treated without and with 100 nM TRH, 100 nM TPA, or 10 nM EGF for 24 hr. Each of these agents inhibit [^{3}H]thymidine incorporation into GH$_4$ cells, and TPA given with TRH or EGF causes an additive effect. The cells are detached from the dish with the addition of 10 μl EDTA (0.1 M) for 10 min at 37°C. The cells are collected, the wells washed with PBS, and the combined suspension centrifuged at 10,000 g for 5 min. The supernatant is removed and the pellet extracted with 10% (w/v) trichloroacetic acid (TCA) for 30 min at 4°C. Acid-insoluble material is separated by filtration (Whatman GFA filters), and trapped radioactivity quantified by liquid scintillation spectroscopy. Cell number is quantified in parallel experiments using a hemocytometer.

Enhanced Cell Substratum Adhesion

Cells are plated at 2.5 $\times$ 10^5/35-mm dish and propagated for 5 days with two changes of F10+. Cultures are treated with 100 nM TRH, 100 nM TPA, or 10 nM EGF, 1 mM BUT, or 2 μg/ml NEP. At 24–72 hr the cells are examined for enhanced substratum adhesion. Cell stretching may be rated from 1 (nonstretched) to 4 (highly stretched) under blind conditions and preferably by several individuals. Cell stretching may also be documented by photomicroscopy. Hoffman interference optics is preferable because it is effective on cells grown on tissue culture plastic. To use Nomarski optics, the cells should be plated on glass coverslips as follows. Cells are seeded on autoclaved 17 $\times$ 35 mm glass coverslips which have been preequilibrated in F10+ for 72 hr. The cells are propagated for 5 days with one change of medium, treated with agonist in fresh F10+, and photographs taken using Nomarski optics.

The first set of variants nonresponsive to TRH showed decreased TRH-enhanced PRL release, PRL production, and inhibition of proliferation (13, 17). Only one variant (GH$_4$S$_1$) has been isolated as entirely nonresponsive to these actions of TRH (and was actually isolated as strongly adhesive in the presence of TRH, yet paradoxically is nonresponsive to TRH actions since it is highly adhesive in the absence of agonist) (13). These cells are nonresponsive to TRH-enhanced PRL release, PRL production (Fig. 3c and d), and inhibition of proliferation (Fig. 4b), but responsive to these actions of TPA and EGF. Because these cells are nonresponsive selectively to TRH actions and have no specific [^{3}H]MeTRH-binding sites, they clearly have a receptor defect. However, additional studies indicate that this variant has other defects involving cell adhesion mechanisms (18). The second set of variants isolated as nonresponsive to TRH-enhanced substratum adhesion (a$_{12}$, a$_{14}$, and others) are responsive to TRH- and TPA-enhanced PRL release and PRL production, yet nonresponsive to TRH and EGF inhibition of cell proliferation (Figs. 3e and f and 4c). Accordingly, they must have functional

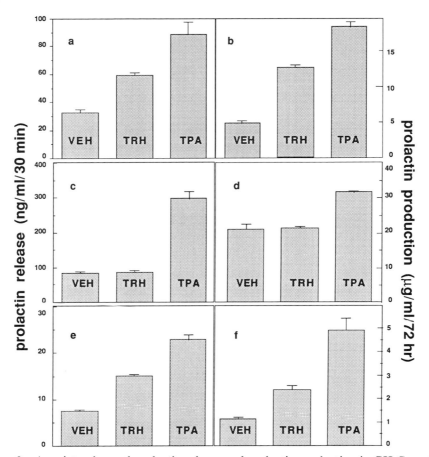

FIG. 3   Agonist-enhanced prolactin release and prolactin production in GH_4C_1 and variant (s_1, a_{12}) cells. GH_4C_1 (a and b) and variant [s_1 (c and d) and a_{12} (e and f) (subclone 5)] cells were plated at 5×10^4 cells/35-mm dish and grown for 5 days in F10+. Dishes were washed, were treated with vehicle, 100 nM TRH or 100 nM TPA, and prolactin release (a, c, and e) and production (b, d, and f) were measured as described in the text. Values given are means $\pm$ SE for triplicate dishes for single experiments repeated at least once.

TRH receptors and for this reason have another type of defect. These variants, in addition to being nonresponsive to TRH-enhanced cell–substratum adhesion, are poorly responsive to this action of EGF (19). However, because they are responsive to TPA-, BUT-, and NEP-enhanced cell–substratum adhesion, they may not necessarily have an end-point lesion. This conclusion depends on whether all agonists act by a common end-point to

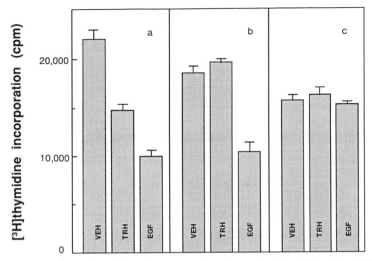

FIG. 4   Agonist inhibition of GH_4C_1 and variant (s_1, a_{12}) cell proliferation. GH_4C_1 (a) and variant [s_1 (b) and a_{12} (c) (subclone 5)] cells were plated at $5 \times 10^4/0.3$ ml of F-10+ containing 2.5 μCi/ml of [^{3}H]thymidine in 16-mm culture wells in the presence of vehicle, 100 nM TRH or 10 nM EGF for 24 hr. The cells were removed and thymidine incorporation was determined as described in the text. Values given are means ± SE for triplicate wells.

enhance GH_4 cell–substratum adhesion. Because the action of each of these agonists to enhance substratum adhesion can be inhibited with the arginine–glycine–aspartate–serine (RGDS) tetrapeptide sequence specific for the fibronectin and vitronectin receptors (19), we believe that a common end-point mediates the action of each agonist to enhance substratum adhesion. If this hypothesis is correct, these variants would have a signaling defect rather than an end-point defect. Additional evidence is necessary to identify conclusively the end-point for agonist-induced cell–substratum adhesion in GH_4 cells, as well as determine whether enhanced cell–substratum adhesion plays a role in the growth inhibitory actions of TRH and EGF.

Characterization of Nonresponsive Variants

Once nonresponsive variants are grouped into one of the three general classes of defects (receptor, signaling, or end-point), the particular defect is examined in greater detail. Below are listed several means we have employed successfully to examine the nonresponsive variants. Other approaches (such as specific protein phosphorylation) may also prove valuable but have not yet been employed.

Receptor Defects

Nonresponsive variants have been found in other systems to have defects that prohibit neurotransmitter–receptor binding or coupling to transducer molecules (i.e., guanine nucleotide-binding proteins) (20).

Thyrotropin-Releasing Hormone Receptor Number

Cells are plated at 2.5×10^5 cells/35-mm dish and propagated in F10+ for 5 days with two changes of medium. Duplicate dishes are washed once with HBBS and incubated to equilibrium (60 min, 37°C) with 0.05, 0.1, 0.2, 0.5, 1.0, 2.0, 5.0, and 10 times K_d of [^{3}H]MeTRH in the absence and presence of 100 times K_d of unlabeled competitor. Dishes are washed five times with 1 ml of normal saline, the cells extracted with 0.5 N NaOH, and radioactivity quantitated by liquid scintillation spectroscopy. The data are transformed by the method of Scatchard, analyzed for B_{max} and apparent K_d by least-squares analysis, and converted to sites/cell. Differences in apparent K_d or B_{max} may yield information of the functional status of the receptor. Such differences might result from altered macromolecular interactions of the TRH receptor with other membrane proteins such as guanine nucleotide-binding proteins.

Thyrotropin-Releasing Hormone Receptor Effector Coupling

Variants having increased apparent K_d or decreased B_{max} are examined for [^{3}H]TRH binding in the presence of nonhydrolyzable guanine nucleotides. Cells are propagated to approximately 5×10^6 cells/100-mm dish, washed twice with normal saline, and treated with TM buffer (20 mM Tris, pH 7.6, 2 mM MgCl$_2$). The hypoisomotic cells are triturated from the dish, collected by centrifugation, and Dounce-homogenized at 4°C. The homogenate is centrifuged at 100 g to remove unbroken cells and nuclei, and the supernatant centrifuged at 5000 g for 10 min and resuspended in TM buffer to approximately 0.5 mg/ml in the absence and presence of 1 μM Gpp(NH)p. [^{3}H]TRH (20 nM in the absence and presence of 1 μM TRH) is added to each group and allowed to incubate for 1 hr at 23°C. Bound ligand is separated from free by filtration through Whatman GFA filters, and the filters counted by liquid scintillation spectroscopy. Nonresponsive variants which show guanine nucleotide-mediated reduction in specific [^{3}H]TRH binding are interpreted as having receptors capable of coupling to guanine nucleotide-transducing proteins.

The variants with receptor defects all have decreased TRH receptor numbers (0 to 265,000 sites/cell) (13, 21). The K_d is similar (1.61 to 1.83 nM) for all variants (13) and specific [^{3}H]TRH binding is reduced by 56 to 71% in the presence of Gpp(NH)p (Fig. 5).

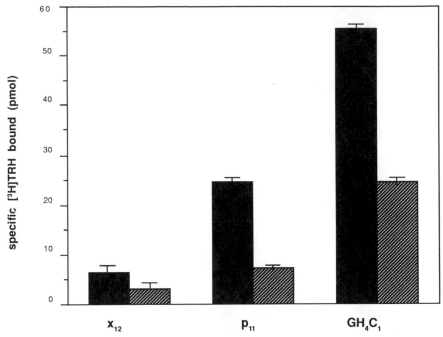

FIG. 5   Guanine nucleotide sensitivity of specific [³H]TRH binding to variants with decreased numbers of TRH-binding sites. GH_4C_1 and variant [x_{12}, p_{11} (subclone 14)] cells were plated at 10^6 cells/100-mm dish and grown for 5 days in F10+. Cells were washed with PBS, were treated with hypotonic buffer, and were Dounce-homogenized. Membranes were prepared as described in the text and were incubated with 20 nM [³H]TRH (±1 μM TRH) in the absence (■) or presence (▨) of 1 μM Gpp(NH)p for 60 min at 23°C. Bound ligand was separated by filtration. Values given are means ± SE for triplicate pairs of samples.

Signaling Defects

TRH-enhanced inositol phosphate accumulation and elevated cytosolic free calcium ($[Ca^{2+}]_i$) have each been used to examine signaling defects in TRH nonresponsive variants. Measurement of $[Ca^{2+}]_i$) is the preferred method because one can assess at least two signaling events (IP_3-mediated release of intracellular calcium stores and the activation of voltage-sensitive calcium conductances) as a continuous function of time. Cells are plated at 10^6 cells in 100-mm dishes and propagated for 5 days in F10+ with two changes of medium. Cells are removed with HBBS–EDTA, washed, and resuspended to 5×10^6 cells/500 μl in HBBS. The suspension is loaded with 0.5 μl of 50 mM quin2/AM for 30 min at 37°C, washed, and resuspended in 2.5 ml of HBBS. Cells are maintained in suspension at 37°C under an excitation wavelength of 340 nm and monitored for 492-nm emission with a spectrofluorometer. TRH (100 nM) is added to the suspension and the fluorescence intensity recorded as a function of time. [Ca^{2+}]$_i$ is calibrated using 25 μM digitonin for F_{max} and 5 mM EGTA in 20 mM Tris (pH 8.3) for F_{min} according to Eq. (1).

$$[Ca^{2+}]_i = 115 \text{ n}M \times (F - F_{min})/(F_{max} - F) \tag{1}$$

The variants with decreased [^{3}H]MeTRH-binding sites have proportional decreases in both TRH-elevated burst and plateau phases of elevated [Ca^{2+}]$_i$ (21). Likewise, TRH-enhanced IP$_3$ accumulation is also decreased in these variants (21). Other variants have not yet been examined.

End-Point Defects

The end point for agonist-enhanced GH$_4$ cell–substratum adhesion is presently unknown. We have attempted to define such an end point to characterize nonresponsive variants better. Substratum adhesion is mediated in large part by a group of cell-surface receptors known as integrins (22). Integrins exist for several different extracellular matrix molecules. Cell attachment to the fibronectin and vitronectin integrins can be blocked by the RGDS tetrapeptide sequence found in fibronectin and vitronectin (both are abundant in the fetal bovine serum component of F10+). RGDS inhibits TRH-enhanced GH$_4$ cell–substratum adhesion with an IC$_{50}$ (concentration to inhibit 50% of binding) similar to its inhibition of GH$_4$ cell attachment to purified fibronectin (Fig. 6). RGDS also inhibits GH$_4$ cell attachment to vitronectin but not collagen IV nor laminin (19). These results suggest that either the fibronectin and/or vitronectin integrin(s) may represent an end point for TRH-enhanced substratum adhesion. To test for this possible end-point defect, the binding of variant cells to several extracellular matrix components is examined. Bacteriological or tissue culture dishes are marked around the periphery with circles (1 cm diameter) on the underside with a felt-tip marker. Within each circle, 10-μl blots (in quadruplicate) of human serum fibronectin, bovine serum vitronectin, and mouse EHS tumor laminin [each prepared at 20 μg/ml in phosphate-buffered saline (PBS)] are incubated for 2 hr at 37°C in a humidified incubator. For coating with mouse EHS tumor collagen IV (20 μg/ml in H$_2$O), 10-μl blots were air-dried overnight. Nonspecific binding sites are blocked with PBS–2% (w/v) bovine albumin followed by two washes with PBS. Cells are removed from stocks flasks with PBS–0.2% (w/v) EDTA, washed twice with Ham's F12–10 mM HEPES, and plated at a concentration of 5 $\times$ 10^5 cells/ml. The cells are incubated at 37°C for 60 min and unattached cells removed by washing four times with F12–HEPES. The attached cells were viewed by phase-contrast microscopy and cells within a 0.5-mm^2 grid counted.

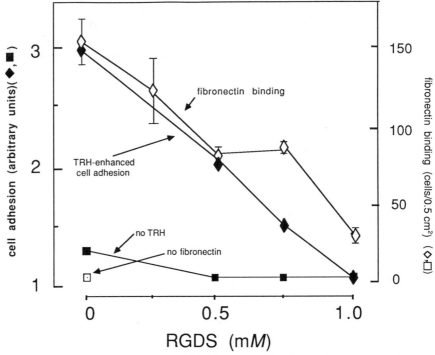

FIG. 6   Dose response for RGDS inhibition of TRH-enhanced GH_4 cell–substratum adhesion and attachment to fibronectin-coated dishes. For the adhesion experiment, cells were plated at $5 \times 10^4/0.25$ ml of F10+ in 16-mm culture wells containing 0, 0.5, 0.75, or 1.0 mM RGDS tetrapeptide. After 30 min preincubation, cells were treated with vehicle or 100 nM TRH. Cell morphology was observed by phase-contrast microscopy and was rated 1 (nonstretched) to 4 (highly stretched) under blind conditions. Values given are the means for triplicate determinations from an experiment repeated four times. For cell attachment to fibronectin, 16-mm wells were coated with 100 μl of fibronectin (20 μg/ml) and nonspecific sites were blocked with 2% bovine albumin in PBS. Cells (5×10^5/ml) were pretreated in the absence or presence of 0, 0.25, 0.5, 0.75, and 1.0 mM RGDS for 10 min and incubated in the fibronectin-coated wells for 60 min at 37°C. The wells were washed to remove unattached cells and the number of attached cells were counted within a 0.5-mm^2 grid at $100\times$ using phase-contrast microscopy. Values given are means $\pm$ SE for six wells.

TRH-nonresponsive variants with receptor defects and those containing TRH receptors attach to fibronectin and vitronectin in a RGDS-displaceable manner that is indistinguishable from that of the donor cultures (19).

Overview of Use of Morphological Variants

Morphological variants with altered responsiveness exist in the wild-type population of GH_4 cells. These variants have decreased numbers of functional TRH receptor-binding sites and their isolation has proved useful to demonstrate that spare receptors do not exist for TRH on GH_4 cells and that the initial actions of TRH occur with a form of the TRH receptor that has rapid dissociation kinetics (13, 21). One variant (GH_4S_1) lacks TRH-binding sites and shows no responses to TRH. Whether this variant expresses altered receptor molecules or fails to express the TRH receptor gene remains to be determined. Two modifications of the original selection procedure have been utilized to obtain a second TRH-nonresponsive variant phenotype. These variants express a wild-type complement of functional TRH receptors and are responsive to certain TRH responses (PRL release, PRL synthesis, but not cell adhesion or inhibition of proliferation). In addition, these variants are poorly responsive to EGF-enhanced cell–substratum adhesion but responsive to this action of TPA, BUT, and NEP. This evidence, together with the finding that these variants possess RGDS-specific binding sites for fibronectin and vitronectin, suggests that the defect is in a signaling mechanism rather than an end point for cell–substratum adhesion. The identification of this signaling mechanism(s) at the molecular level represents a challenging question for the future.

Applications for Neuropeptide Research

Neuronal Cell Lines

Several neuronal cell lines are induced by neuropeptides and neurotransmitters to undergo morphological differentiation. PC12 cells respond to NGF and several mouse neuroblastoma cells respond similarly to acetylcholine, prostaglandin E_2, and several other agents (23, 24) by developing neurite outgrowths. These responses differ from the agonist-enhanced substratum adhesion found in GH_4 cells in that they are irreversible. However, NGF-nonresponsive PC12 cells have still been isolated using both resistance to growth inhibition and the failure to develop neurite outgrowths (25, 26).

Neuropeptides, Growth Factors, and Other Signaling Agents

GH_4 cells contain receptors for a variety of neuropeptides (vasoactive intestinal peptide, somatostatin, and bombesin) and growth factors [EGF, fibroblastic growth factor, platelet-derived growth factor (PDGF), insulin, insulin-like growth factors (IGF-I and IGF-II), transforming growth factors (TGF-α and TGF-β)]. Of these, increased substratum adhesion is observed with EGF, fibroblastic growth factor, PDGF, TGF-α, and TGF-β (27, 28; J. S. Ramsdell, unpublished findings). Morphological variants may also be isolated as nonresponsive to agents known to activate intracellular mechanisms directly, such as phorbol ester, sodium butyrate, or Neplanocin A.

Acknowledgment

I wish to thank Dr. Armen H. Tashjian, Jr. in whose laboratory these studies were initiated and Drs. L. Steven Frawley and G. E. Landreth who provided helpful suggestions in preparing this manuscript. This work was supported by the Medical University of South Carolina Biomedical Support Grant of 1987–1988 and the American Cancer Society Grant #1N-175.

References

1. P. Coffino, H. R. Bourne, U. Friedrich, J. Hochman, P. A. Insel, I. Lemaire, K. L. Melmonn, and G. M. Tomkins, *Recent Prog. Horm. Res.* **32,** 669 (1976).
2. M. M. Gottesman, *in* "Methods in Enzymology (J. D. Corbin and J. G. Hardman, eds.), Vol. 99, p. 197. Academic Press, New York, 1983.
3. K. Yamamoto, U. Gehring, M. R. Stampfer, and C. H. Sibley, *Recent Prog. Horm. Res.* **32,** 3 (1976).
4. L. H. Thompson and R. M. Baker, *Methods Cell Biol.* **6,** 209 (1973).
5. V. Daniel, G. Litwack, and G. M. Tomkins, *Proc. Natl. Acad. Sci. U.S.A.* **70,** 76 (1973).
6. A. W. Harris, *Exp. Cell Res.* **60,** 341 (1970).
7. I. S. Trowbridge and D. O. Domingo, *Nature (London)* **294,** 171 (1981).
8. R. Hymann, *Biochem. J.* **224,** 27 (1985).
9. J. D. Esko and C. R. Raetz, *Proc. Natl. Acad. Sci. U.S.A.* **75,** 1190 (1978).
10. R. M. Pruss and H. R. Herschman, *Proc. Natl. Acad. Sci. U.S.A.* **74,** 3918 (1977).
11. J. S. Ramsdell, G. R. Pettit, and A. H. Tashjian, Jr., *J. Biol. Chem.* **261,** 17073 (1986).
12. A. H. Tashjian, Jr., *in* "Methods in Enzymology" (W. B. Jakoby and I. Pastan, eds.), Vol. 58, p. 527. Academic Press, New York, 1979.
13. J. S. Ramsdell and A. H. Tashjian, Jr., *Mol. Cell. Endocrinol.* **43,** 173 (1985).
14. D. R. McCalla, A. Reuvers, and R. Kitai, *Can. J. Biochem.* **46,** 807 (1968).

15. P. S. Dannies, K. M. Gautvik, and A. H. Tashjian, Jr., *Endocrinology* (*Baltimore*) **98,** 1147 (1976).
16. G. H. Murdoch, M. Waterman, R. M. Evans, and M. G. Rosenfeld, *J. Biol. Chem.* **258,** 15329 (1983).
17. J. S. Ramsdell, *Endocrinology* (*Baltimore*) **126,** 472 (1990).
18. J. S. Ramsdell, *In Vitro Cell Dev. Biol.* **26,** 250 (1990).
19. J. S. Ramsdell and A. H. Tashjian, Jr., *J. Cell. Physiol.* **141,** 565 (1989).
20. G. L. Johnson, H. R. Kaslow, Z. Farfel, and H. R. Bourne, *Adv. Cyclic Nucleotide Res.* **13,** 1 (1980).
21. J. S. Ramsdell and A. H. Tashjian, Jr., *J. Biol. Chem.* **261,** 5301 (1986).
22. R. O. Hynes, *Cell* **48,** 549 (1987).
23. A. S. Tischler and L. A. Greene, *Nature* (*London*) **258,** 341 (1975).
24. J. E. Bottenstein, *in* "Functionally Differentiated Cell Lines" (G. Sato, ed.), p. 155. Liss, New York, 1981.
25. M. Bothwell, A. L. Schecter, and K. M. Vaughn, *Cell* **21,** 857 (1980).
26. S. H. Green, R. E. Ryde, J. L. Connolly, and L. A. Greene, *J. Cell Biol.* **102,** 830 (1986).
27. A. Schonbrunn and A. H. Tashjian, Jr., *J. Cell Biol.* **85,** 786 (1980).
28. N. J. Sullivan and A. H. Tashjian, Jr., *Endocrinology* (*Baltimore*) **113,** 636 (1983).

[20] *In Vivo* Tissue Culture: Use of Ectopic Anterior Pituitary Gland to Study Neuropeptide and Steroid Actions on Adenohypophysis

Frank J. Strobl and Jon E. Levine

Introduction

A variety of cell and tissue culture techniques have been applied to the study of adenohypophyseal hormone secretions, with major advances being gained in understanding the cellular actions of peptide, biogenic amine, and steroid regulators. There are several important neuroendocrine problems, however, which have been difficult to address by conventional *in vitro* approaches. Inhibitory actions of estradiol on luteinizing hormone (LH), for example, have been exceedingly difficult to demonstrate with most superfusion or static culture methods; in most instances, culture conditions would appear to favor the manifestation of stimulatory effects. Moreover, other hormonal effects have been demonstrable in culture, yet their qualitative and quantitative relationships to *in vivo* physiological regulatory mechanisms have been difficult to establish. For these reasons, we developed an *in vivo* isolated pituitary model for the study of adenohypophyseal hormone secretions and their regulation by neurohormonal and endocrine factors. The experimental approach allows for analysis of secretory dynamics in an *in vivo* environment, while offering many of the important advantages of *in vitro* approaches, such as rigorous control of input stimuli, and unambiguous determination of the site of action of various hormone regulators.

Description of Experimental Approach

The *in vivo* isolated pituitary paradigm involves transplantation of adenohypophyseal tissue from donor rats into hypophysectomized host animals, the latter rats then being fitted with a concentric infusion/withdrawal catheter, rodent jacket, tether, swivel, and a system for pulsatile neurohormone delivery. The approach makes use of some established technical procedures [pituitary transplantation (1)], as well as more recently developed experimental

Methods in Neurosciences, Volume 2

methods that we have adapted for use in conscious, free-moving rats (chronic atrial infusion/withdrawal system).

Transplantation Procedures

Hypophysectomized rats are anesthetized with ether or methoxyflurane and receive one or two anterior pituitary transplants under the right kidney capsule. The kidney is exposed through a dorsal incision and held by a pair of hemostats clamped to the surrounding adipose tissue. A fine pair of forceps is used to lift and puncture the capsule at the inferior pole of the kidney. A glass capillary tube previously blunted and fire-polished is then inserted into the opening and used to separate the exposed capsule from the underlying renal tissue to form a pocket into which the anterior pituitary tissue is placed. The anterior pituitaries are obtained from donor rats of the same sex and strain sacrificed by decapitation immediately following exposure of the recipient rat's kidney. Using a scapel, the pituitary is cut in half within the sella turcica and the posterior lobe is removed and discarded. The two anterior pituitary halves are rinsed in sterile saline (Abbott Laboratories, North Chicago, IL) to remove any blood and then placed under the kidney capsule. Using another capillary tube, the transplants are then massaged away from the capsule incision toward the superior pole of the kidney. At this point the hemostat holding the kidney is released and the kidney is assisted back into the abdominal cavity. The abdominal muscles and skin are then sewn closed. During the entire surgical procedure, care must be taken to ensure that both the exposed kidney and pituitary tissue are kept moist with sterile saline.

Infusion/Withdrawal System

On the day following pituitary transplantation, each animal is anesthetized and fitted with an infusion/withdrawal system similar to the one depicted in Fig. 1. The infusion/withdrawal system consists of a concentric atrial catheter and swivel device which allows for both intermittent infusions of luteinizing hormone-releasing hormone (LHRH) and chronic blood sampling. The concentric catheters (PE-10 tubing within PE-90 tubing; Intramedic, Clay Adams, Parsippany, NJ) are introduced into the right atrium through the external jugular vein. The distal ends of the catheters are tunneled subcutaneously to the nape, exteriorized through a small plastic cuff, and guided through a rodent jacket and spring tether to the torque arm of a swivel modified after that described by Brown *et al.* (2). The PE-90 tubing, used for

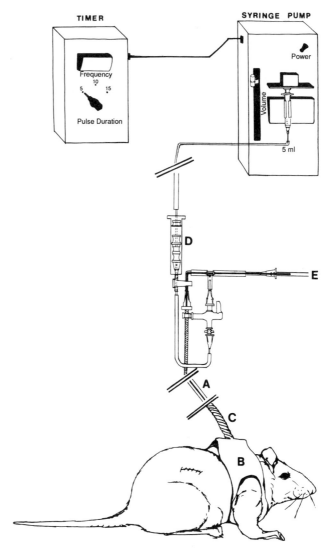

FIG. 1   The *in vivo* isolated pituitary paradigm. A hypophysectomized rat bearing ectopic anterior pituitary tissue under the kidney capsule is fitted with a concentric atrial catheter (A), rodent jacket (B), spring tether (C), and swivel (D), as shown. An electric timer and syringe pump allow automated, pulsatile LHRH infusions to be delivered between the two concentric catheters, and blood samples can be withdrawn upward via the inner catheter (E).

infusion, is connected to the swivel via a t-connector (Endotronics, Coon Rapids, MN), three-way stopcock, and a small length of PE-60 tubing. The smaller PE-10 tubing is extended through the t-connector and glued to a piece of PE-50 tubing within a 20-gauge needle. The swivel is connected by a length of PE-50 tubing to a 5-ml syringe attached to a compact infusion pump (Harvard Apparatus, South Natick, MA). The infusion pump is activated by an electric timer (Dual Trol, Industrial Timer Corp., Waterbury, CT).

Throughout the experiment, the rat remains in its home cage, unrestrained except for the jacket, tether, and swivel. The entire swivel device is held above the cage by a ringstand and clamp. Laboratory rat chow, fresh fruit, and tap water containing 0.9% (w/v) NaCl and 10% (w/v) glucose are available *ad libitum*. Pulsatile infusions of neurohormones are typically initiated immediately following completion of the surgical procedures. In our studies on the regulation of LH secretion by LHRH, frozen aliquots of a LHRH stock solution are thawed and diluted with sodium heparin and sterile saline to a final volume of 5.0 ml. Each aliquot is then drawn into the 5-ml syringe attached to the compact infusion pump. During each pulse infusion, each animal receives a predetermined dose of LHRH and approximately 1 IU heparin/20 g body weight in a 0.1-ml volume of sterile saline. The 250-ng regimen of LHRH infusions used in all of our studies was chosen on the basis of preliminary experiments which showed that this dose was the lowest of those tested (10, 50, 100, 250, and 500 ng) that consistently produced significant LH secretory responses in hypophysectomized, pituitary-grafted (hypox/graft) rats (Fig. 2). The frequency of LHRH stimulation (5-min pulse/hr) was chosen to approximate the frequency of pulsatile LHRH release observed in intact male and female rats.

When required, blood samples can be collected from the atrial catheter by a syringe connected to the free end of the PE-50 tubing extending from the 20-gauge needle. The stopcock, which is closed during blood sampling, prevents withdrawal of the neuropeptide solution from the infusion catheter during blood sampling. If problems with blood collection develop, the position of the withdrawal tubing within the atrium can be adjusted by changing the position of the 20-gauge needle within the t-connector or the entire withdrawal tubing can be removed, flushed, and replaced. When blood is not being collected, the free end of the PE-50 tubing is occluded with a 23-gauge tube. Each sample is dispensed into sample tubes for centrifugation and storage of plasma at −20°C. Following each sampling, an equivalent volume of blood replacement mixture is injected back through the atrial catheter. In our studies, plasma samples are subsequently assayed for immunoreactive LH and follicle-stimulating hormone (FSH). Each blood sampling and replacement procedure takes approximately 5 to 8 min. When needed, the animal can be easily anesthetized by first closing the stopcock, removing the

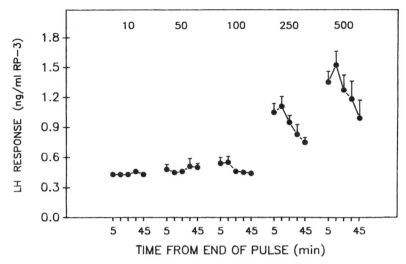

FIG. 2 Mean LH secretory responses to hourly LHRH infusions at each of five doses tested [10 ($n = 5$), 50 ($n = 5$), 100 ($n = 4$), 250 ($n = 5$), and 500 ($n = 6$) ng/5 min/hr] in hypophysectomized, ovariectomized rats bearing two anterior pituitary transplants. Blood samples were obtained on day 4, 5, 6, or 7 at 5, 15, 25, 35, and 45 min following an LHRH infusion.

PE-50 tubing from the swivel, and then placing the animal and the entire swivel device into the anesthesia chamber. Following experiments, vascularization of the pituitary transplant and completeness of hypophysectomy are determined by visual inspection of the kidney bearing the grafted tissue and the sella turcica, respectively, either by dissecting microscope or standard histological techniques.

Precautions and Potential Problems

Potential technical problems that may arise during an *in vivo* isolated pituitary experiment include the following.

1. Pituitary transplant survival. Almost all of our pituitary transplants are revascularized and survive for the duration of experiments. On occasion, however, hormonal and histological evidence may indicate transplant failure. We have found that transplant necrosis is minimized if the following precautions are taken. First, during transplantation procedures, care should be taken to keep the excised tissue moist and free of blood. Second, the

transplants should be positioned away from the capsule incision to prevent the escape of anterior pituitary tissue into the abdominal cavity. Third, position the anterior pituitary halves apart from each other so as to maximize the surface area of pituitary tissue available for penetration and permeation by blood vessels originating from the kidney capsule.

2. Number of anterior pituitaries to be transplanted. The minimum number of pituitaries transplanted into each animal is determined by the amount of adenohypophyseal hormone secreted in response to the administered neurohormone. Ideally, the amount of pituitary tissue transplanted should reinstate physiological levels of the pituitary hormone. For example, we have found that in hypophysectomized male rats bearing a single ectopic pituitary, circulating levels of LH are similar to levels of LH measured in normal pituitary-intact male rats. The maximum number of pituitaries transplanted into each animal should be less than the number which produces supraphysiological concentrations of the adenohypophyseal hormone. Fewer transplants are also preferable to minimize the possible confounding effects of hyperprolactinemia. Since transplantation of a single anterior pituitary in female rats can result in chronic hyperprolactinemia, possible effects of elevated prolactin (PRL) levels on the secretion of the adenohypophyseal hormone of interest should be considered. The problem of elevated PRL levels can be alleviated by daily administration of a dopamine agonist such as CB-154 (2-bromo-α-ergocryptine methane sulfonate). In rats, hyperprolactinemia is associated with reduced gonadotropin levels, particularly those of LH (3). In fact, we have found that hyperprolactinemia likely reduces basal levels of gonadotropin secretion from isolated pituitary tissue; in as much as, treatment of hypox/graft female rats with CB-154 (1 mg/day) results in significantly elevated gonadotropin levels as compared to gonadotropin levels in vehicle-treated hypox/graft rats.

3. Surgical precautions. It is recommended that the size of surgical incisions be minimized, since the hypox/graft animals are maintained on significant levels of sodium heparin, and thus are susceptible to hemorrhage. Particular care should also be exercised to avoid damage to the underlying renal tissue when preparing the kidney capsule for acceptance of the transplant.

4. Maintenance of catheter patency. Our own experience shows that covering the proximal end of the catheter with Silastic tubing and infusion of 1 IU sodium heparin/20 g body weight every hour will normally allow blood samples to be collected for the duration of experiments. Proper positioning of the catheter tip within the right atrium is, however, a critical factor in maintaining catheter patency. The catheter opening should be positioned directly in the center of the right atrium. Significant deviations from this location often result in occlusion of the catheter tip by collapsed venous or atrial tissue and associated thrombi.

5. Verification of hypophysectomy. The validity of results obtained by the *in vivo* isolated pituitary model ultimately rests on the verification that no anterior pituitary tissue remains under endogenous hypothalamic control. Therefore, completeness of hypophysectomy, as determined by visual or histological inspection of the sella turcica subsequent to experiments, is an absolute necessity.

Validation

Several observations from our studies demonstrate that circulating LH and FSH in hypox/graft rats originate solely from the ectopic pituitary tissue; these observations include (1) gonadotropin levels are normally undetectable or present in trace amounts in hypox/graft rats before the initiation of LHRH infusions; (2) plasma LH and FSH remain undetectable in animals without pituitary transplants and in rats in which it was confirmed subsequent to experiments that the transplant had failed to revascularize; (3) in all hypox animals bearing viable pituitary transplants, significant levels of both gonadotropins have been found to be detectable on all days of LHRH infusions (mean levels of LH and FSH in a group of hypox/graft female rats on each of the first 5 days of LHRH infusions are summarized in Table I); and (4) levels of LH typically peak within 15 min following an LHRH infusion and return to prestimulation levels within 45 min. The foregoing results, along with verification of transplant vascularization and completeness of hypophysectomy in our animals, indicate that LH and FSH measured in peripheral plasma in our hypox/graft rats originate from the transplanted pituitaries and are secreted in response to exogenous neurohormone stimulation.

Applications

Examples of our use of the *in vivo* isolated pituitary paradigm to study the direct actions of gonadal steroids on pituitary gonadotropin secretion are given below.

Acute Injections of Steroids

We initially used the *in vivo* isolated pituitary paradigm to investigate the differential feedback actions of estrogen on gonadotropin secretion (4). Hypophysectomized female rats underwent bilateral ovariectomy and pituitary transplantation, and were maintained on a LHRH infusion regimen (250 ng/5

TABLE I   Plasma LH and FSH Levels (ng/ml) in Hypox/Graft Female Rats on
Each of 5 Days of LHRH Infusions[a]

Hormone	Day 1[b]	Day 2	Day 3	Day 4	Day 5
LH	0.25 ± 0.02	1.33 ± 0.35	0.86 ± 0.27	0.56 ± 0.13	0.55 ± 0.18
FSH	6.91 ± 0.37	9.20 ± 0.99	8.30 ± 0.86	9.58 ± 1.14	9.70 ± 0.89

[a] Values are the mean ± SE; $n = 5$ in all groups.

[b] Values on day 1 represent hormone levels in samples obtained prior to the initiation of pulsatile LHRH infusions. The LH levels in 6/10 rats and FSH levels in 3/10 rats were undetectable (<0.21 ng/ml, LH; <5.71 ng/ml, FSH) before the start of LHRH infusions.

min/hr) for 7 days. On the sixth day of LHRH infusions, blood samples were collected 5, 15, 25, 35, and 45 min after each LHRH pulse over a period of 4 hr. At the end of the first hour of sampling, animals were injected subcutaneously with either 2 μg estradiol benzoate (E$_2$B) or oil vehicle. Figure 3 depicts LH secretory responses to hourly LHRH infusions in individual female hypox/graft rats injected with oil or E$_2$B. The FSH secretory responses to hourly LHRH infusions in the same animals are depicted in Fig. 4. During the 4-hr experimental sessions, LH release, but not FSH release, was pulsatile in response to the hourly LHRH infusions. Both LH and FSH secretion in oil-treated animals were undiminished throughout the 4-hr sampling period. In the E$_2$B-treated animals, LH responses to LHRH infusions were blunted by the second hour and reduced to levels near the detectable limits of our radioimmunoassay by the third hour after injection. FSH release was unaffected by E$_2$B. The results demonstrate that a major inhibitory effect of acute estrogen administration on LH secretion is exerted by a direct action on pituitary gonadotropes, and that estrogen can differentially affect the release of LH and FSH by an intrapituitary mechanism.

Steroid Withdrawal

In a second set of experiments (5), we examined the extent to which the negative feedback actions of testicular hormones are exerted directly at the level of the anterior pituitary gland. Hypox/graft male rats were maintained on pulsatile LHRH infusions (250 ng/5 min/hr) for 7 days. On the fifth or sixth day of LHRH infusions, blood samples were collected 2 hr before sham-castration or castration and at 2-hr intervals for 24 hr thereafter. For comparison, blood samples were similarly obtained from a group of normal pituitary-intact male rats. Mean LH levels in male hypox/graft rats following sham-castration or castration are depicted in Fig. 5. Levels of LH in the

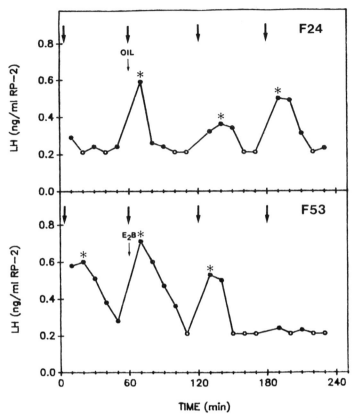

FIG. 3   LH secretory responses to hourly LHRH infusions (250 ng/5 min/hr) before and after the injection of oil vehicle or 2 μg of estradiol benzoate (E₂B) in two individual hypox/graft female rats. The oil or E₂B was administered at the end of the first hour of sampling and is denoted by the smaller arrows. The hourly LHRH infusions are indicated by the larger arrows. ○, Hormone levels that fell below assay sensitivity; *, denotes a pulse.

sham-castrated hypox/graft rats were not significantly changed following surgery. In the castrated hypox/graft animals, LH concentrations increased steadily for 18 hr, reaching a plateau at levels 2- to 3-fold higher than pretreatment levels. Within the first 20 hr following castration, the absolute levels of LH, as well as the trajectory of the LH response in the hypox/graft animals was similar to that observed in pituitary-intact, castrated rats (5). Thereafter, while LH release in the hypox/graft rats remained relatively stable, LH levels in the pituitary-intact rats continued to increase. These

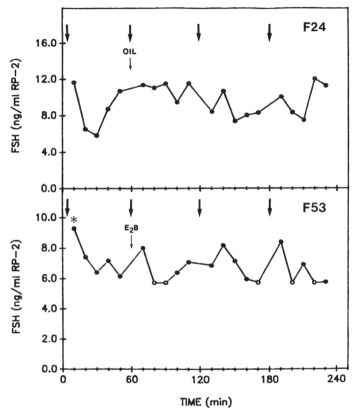

FIG. 4 FSH secretory responses to hourly LHRH infusions (250 ng/5 min/hr) before and after the injection of oil vehicle or 2 μg of estradiol benzoate (E₂B) in two individual hypox/graft female rats. The oil or E₂B was administered at the end of the first hour of sampling and is denoted by the smaller arrows. The hourly LHRH infusions are indicated by the larger arrows. ○, Hormone levels that fell below assay sensitivity; *, denotes a pulse.

studies provide evidence that most of the acute effects of castration on LH secretion are due to pituitary escape from direct testicular negative feedback suppression. The results also suggest that the continued elevation of LH secretion that normally occurs following castration is dependent on some additional stimulatory input. In current experiments, we are attempting to characterize a possible postcastration change in LHRH release, with the aim of accurately reconstructing these patterns to analyze their effects on LH secretion by the isolated pituitary gland.

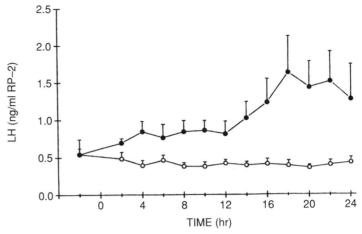

FIG. 5 Plasma LH levels in hypox/graft rats before and after castration ($\bullet$; $n = 5$) or sham-castration ($\bigcirc$; $n = 6$). Each circle represents the mean ± SE LH level for all animals within a group at a particular time point. Statistical analysis of data by ANOVA and *posthoc* comparisons showed that LH levels in the hypox/graft castrates were significantly ($p < 0.01$) elevated by 18 hr following removal of the testes.

Prolonged Steroid Treatment

We recently examined the extent to which the negative and positive feedback actions of estrogen and progesterone are exerted directly at the level of the anterior pituitary (6). Hypophysectomized female rats received two anterior pituitary transplants while also undergoing bilateral ovariectomy. The following day, each hypox/graft rat was fitted with the infusion/withdrawal system and began receiving pulsatile infusions of LHRH (250 ng/5 min/hr). On day 5 of LHRH infusions, blood samples were obtained at 2-hr intervals beginning at 1600 hr and ending at 2400 hr on day 6. Animals received one Silastic capsule containing 17-β-estradiol at 1800 hr on day 5 and two Silastic capsules containing progesterone or oil at 1200 hr on day 6. Control animals received one oil capsule on day 5 and two oil capsules on day 6. Plasma LH levels in three representative experimental animals are depicted in Fig. 6. In the control hypox/graft rats, circulating LH concentrations remained relatively constant throughout the blood sampling period. LH levels in the estrogen-treated hypox/graft rats were inhibited by 54% within the first 4 hr following estrogen administration and then increased steadily to levels 3- to 4-fold higher than suppressed levels by the end of the experiment. Progesterone treatment on day 6 had no additional effect on LH secretion. Possible

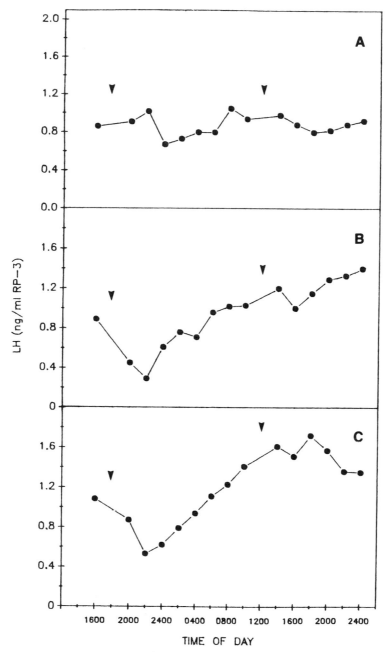

FIG. 6 Plasma LH levels in individual hypox/graft female rats treated with (A) oil, (B) estrogen and oil, and (C) estrogen and progesterone. The time of capsule implantation is indicated by the arrowheads.

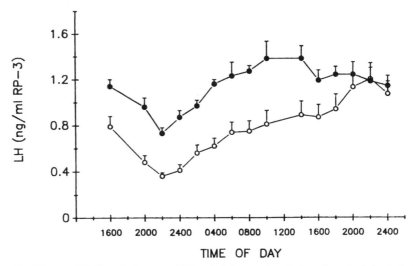

Fig. 7 Plasma LH levels in steroid-treated hypox/graft female rats injected daily with 1 mg of CB-154 (●; $n = 5$) or vehicle (○; $n = 10$). Each symbol represents the mean ± SE LH level for all animals within a group at a particular time point.

effects of hyperprolactinemia on the actions of estrogen and progesterone were assessed by administration of the dopamine agonist CB-154 to a group of identically steroid-treated hypox/graft female rats. A comparison of LH secretion between the CB-154 and vehicle-treated rats (Fig. 7) shows that, although elevated PRL levels had no effect on the course and degree of steroid action, high PRL concentrations did appear to reduce basal LH secretion from the ectopic pituitaries. The data demonstrate that (1) a significant portion of both the negative and positive feedback effects of estrogen on LH secretion occur directly at the level of the anterior pituitary, (2) progesterone's positive actions on LH secretion likely occur at the level of the hypothalamus, and (3) that PRL may act directly at the level of the anterior pituitary to suppress LH secretion. In current experiments, the isolated pituitary paradigm is being used to build on these findings by examining the importance of LHRH pulse parameters and putative priming factors such as neuropeptide Y (7) in generating preovulatory-like LH surges from ectopic pituitaries.

Conclusions

The *in vivo* isolated pituitary paradigm appears to offer a practical alternative approach to the study of neuroendocrine regulatory mechanisms. It has proved particularly useful in the characterization of direct feedback actions of gonadal hormones on adenohypophyseal tissue and holds promise for the analysis of dynamic relationships between hypothalamic peptide release and pituitary hormone secretion. Although we have primarily used this experimental method to study the hypothalamic–pituitary–gonadal axis, it is hoped that the foregoing discussion makes clear its potential usefulness in the integrative analysis of other hormonal systems.

Acknowledgment

This work was supported by NIH grants RO1-HD20677 and PO1-HD21921

References

1. B. K. McLean, N. Chang, and M. B. Nikitovich-Winer, *Endocrinology (Baltimore)* **96,** 196 (1975).
2. Z. W. Brown, Z. Amit, and J. R. Weeks, *Pharmacol. Biochem. Behav.* **5,** 363 (1976).
3. A. Bartke, *Fed. Proc., Fed. Am. Soc. Exp. Biol.* **39,** 2577 (1980).
4. F. J. Strobl and J. E. Levine, *Endocrinology (Baltimore)* **123,** 622 (1988).
5. F. J. Strobl, C. A. Gilmore, and J. E. Levine, *Endocrinology* **124,** 1140 (1989).
6. F. J. Strobl, J. M. Meredith, and J. E. Levine, *Proc. 71st Annu. Meet. Endocr. Soc., 71st* (1989).
7. S. W. Sutton, T. T. Toyama, S. Otto, and P. M. Plotsky, *Endocrinology (Baltimore)* **123,** 1208 (1988).

[21] Evaluation of Catecholaminergic Activity in Hypothalamic Cultures

Barbara A. Bennett, David K. Sundberg, and
Mariana Morris

Introduction

The profound complexity of the mammalian brain is the major deterrent to understanding the intricacies of neuronal systems. One approach in the study of these systems is to use tissue culture methodology, which minimizes the input of other physiological effectors both humoral and neural. In addition, the ability to culture neurons from the mammalian brain has provided a means by which it is possible to examine cellular mechanisms under relatively controlled conditions.

There are two basic types of cell culture: (1) continuous cell lines in which proliferation can be maintained indefinitely and (2) primary culture, where tissue is removed directly from an animal and grown for a limited amount of time (days to months). Two types of primary cultures are used currently: (1) explants of neural tissue and (2) dissociated cell cultures, which also includes reaggregate cultures. Explant cultures offer the advantage of preserving the original cellular interactions, but do not present the optimum conditions for histochemical analyses. Dissociated cultures, on the other hand, permit two-dimensional visualization of individual cells, facilitating both histochemical and electrophysiological studies.

The use of primary dissociated cultures for the study of biochemical and morphological characteristics of both peptide- and amine-containing neurons has increased dramatically in recent years. The presence of a variety of hormones and peptides has been demonstrated in cultures of dissociated hypothalamic cells. Some of these neuromodulators include thyrotropin-releasing hormone (TRH) (1–4), adrenocorticotropic hormone (ACTH) and β-endorphin (5, 6), substance P and neurotensin (7), luteinizing hormone-releasing hormone (LHRH) (8–10), α-melanocyte-stimulating hormone (α-MSH) (10) and neurophysin (10, 11), vasopressin (10, 12), somatostatin (12–14), and corticotropin-releasing hormone (CRF) (12). Dissociated hypothalamic cultures have also been used for characterization by electrophysiological methods (7, 15), including patch–clamp techniques (16, 17). There are also studies which have localized catecholamines using either the gly-

Methods in Neurosciences, Volume 2

oxylic acid technique (8) or immunocytochemistry using the synthetic enzyme, tyrosine hydroxylase (tyrosine monooxygenase) (TH) (18, 19). Other studies have measured TH activity (2, 3). The synthetic enzymes choline acetyltransferase (ChAT) (2, 3, 20) and glutamate decarboxylase (GAD) (2) have been measured in hypothalamic cultures and GABAergic neurons have been visualized both autoradiographically and immunocytochemically (21). Morphological differentiation, including evidence for the occurrence of synaptogenesis (3, 17, 22), has been shown using both light and electron microscopy.

This chapter reviews the methodology for the preparation of dissociated cultures of the medial basal hypothalamus (MBH) and the assessment of catecholaminergic activity by neurochemical and immunochemical means. The MBH consists primarily of the arcuate and periventricular nuclei (dopamine areas A12 and A14) and the median eminence. This area was chosen because of its high concentration of dopamine cell bodies and nerve terminals. We have previously characterized a technique for the study of catecholamine biosynthesis *in vitro* which involves incubation with a labeled precursor followed by separation with high-performance liquid chromatography (HPLC) and quantitation with electrochemical detection (23–29). We have used this technique for the examination of catecholamine biosynthesis in primary cell cultures.

Culture Conditions

Preparation of Dissociated Cultures

Primary cultures are prepared using 3- to 5-day-old Sprague-Dawley rats. Timed-pregnant rats (Zivic-Miller) are received 17 days pregnant and each mother typically delivers 8–10 rat pups. The brains are removed and placed in cold sterile Earle's balanced salt solution (EBSS). The MBH, as defined in these studies, is a piece of tissue bounded by the most anterior and posterior aspects of the median eminence and is a section that is approximately 0.5–1 mm thick consisting primarily of the arcuate/median eminence and the periventricular regions containing both cell bodies and axon terminals. Tissues are washed with calcium- and magnesium-free (CMF) Hanks' balanced salt solution and incubated with neutral dispase (2 U/ml; Boehringer-Mannheim, Indianapolis, IN) in CMF Hanks' for 60 min at 37°C in 95% air–5% CO_2. The dissociation is performed in a CMF solution to promote tissue dissociation and to control enzyme activation by calcium. There is a sufficient amount of calcium in the enzyme preparation and in the tissue to cause activation of the protease. We have tested many different enzyme preparations (i.e., collagenase, protease, DNase, papain, and combinations thereof) and have obtained the best results using dispase alone. We have also found that the age of the animal and the size of the tissue are critical factors in determining the length of incubation time with the enzyme. For this reason, we often perform a test on the desired tissue to determine the optimum incubation time and enzyme concentration. By analyzing the different test conditions for such factors as cell size and shape, presence of clumps, amount of cellular debris and residual processes, we can reasonably establish the appropriate conditions. Using the MBH of 3- to 5-day-old neonatal rats, we found the 60-min time point with 2 U/ml dispase to be optimum. The enzyme solution is removed and the tissues are washed with CMF Hanks' containing 1 mM EDTA in order to chelate calcium and thus inactivate any residual enzyme. Tissues are washed in Dulbecco's modified Eagle's medium (DMEM) and then triturated with fire-polished borosilicate-coated pipettes in DMEM. The initial trituration is made with a large-bore pipette (five passes) and subsequent triturations use increasingly smaller bores until single cells are obtained. The dissociated cells are then centrifuged at 1000 g for 10 min and resuspended in DMEM. This step is repeated once with the final resuspension in DMEM plating media. Cells are counted with a hemocytometer and seeded at either a density of 5 × 10^5 cells (per 16-mm well) or 3 × 10^5 cells (per 10-mm slide well). This procedure yields a cell viability of approximately 95% as estimated by Trypan blue (30). Culture plates (16 mm wells; Falcon Plastics, Oxnard, CA) are used for the biochemical evaluation, and slide dishes (10 mm wells; Miles Scientific, Naperville, IL) are used for the immunochemical analyses.

Culture Substratum

Cells are normally in contact with an extracellular matrix (ECM) which consists of proteins and polysaccharides and comprises the space between cells. It is thought that ECMs play an important role in the regulation of proliferation, migration, cytodifferentiation, morphogenesis, as well as in cellular adhesion (31). Since enzymatic treatment removes the ECM, the dispersed cells require an artificial matrix for optimal adherance. Commonly used attachment factors are collagen, gelatin, fibronectin, laminin, and polylysine. Eventually, cells under *in vitro* conditions will synthesize ECM molecules, but this appears to be influenced by the type (32) and the pH (33) of the media used. In addition, the type of substratum influences the responses of various cultured cells to hormones and growth factors (34, 35).

We have tested various attachment factors and obtained the best results using poly(L-lysine). A stock solution of polylysine (1 mg/ml in distilled water; Sigma, St. Louis, MO; MW 70,000–150,000) is stored at 4°C until use.

It is diluted to a final concentration of 100 μg/ml, filter sterilized (0.22-μm pore size), and both glass and plastic surfaces are precoated overnight. The wells are rinsed with sterile distilled water and air dried in a laminar flow hood. These dishes can be stored (4°C) or used immediately after rinsing with culture media.

Media and Supplements

The medium used is serum-supplemented (SSM) as opposed to serum-free (SFM) or chemically defined media. The main advantage in using SFM is that undefined biological fluids in serum are replaced with known amounts of growth factors, hormones, trace elements, etc. (36). In addition, there appears to be less glial proliferation in cultures grown in SFM (2). On the other hand, cultures in SSM tend to survive longer than cultures maintained in SFM. Glial proliferation can be arrested by the use of antimitotics (i.e., cytosine arabinoside or fluorodeoxyuracil). Glial overgrowth can affect the survival of the neuronal cell population and thus must be controlled. Specific antisera against a component of the glial cells (glial fibrillary acidic protein, GFAP) are available for use as a glial-specific marker. The basal medium used is Dulbecco's modified Eagle's medium (DMEM, 4.5 g glucose/liter) which is supplemented with 10% (v/v) fetal calf serum, 2 mM glutamine, 100 μg/ml streptomycin, 100 U/ml penicillin (all GIBCO, Grand Island, NY), and 10^{-5} M ascorbate. Stock solutions of the additives are aliquoted and stored at -20°C. Ascorbate is added to the medium for three reasons. First, ascorbate is a cofactor in the enzymatic conversion of dopamine to norepinephrine by dopamine β-monooxygenase (37). Second, ascorbate prevents the oxidation of the amines that occurs when amines are incubated in the presence of intact cells or cell membrane preparations (38, 39). Third, ascorbate is one of several soluble factors that influence the synthesis of the ECM (40). The culture medium is filter-sterilized on Millipore filter (0.22 μm) and can be stored for 7 days at 4°C. The medium is adjusted to the proper temperature and pH before addition to the cultures. Antimitotics are added to the medium (10 μM cytosine arabinoside) on days 3–5 to inhibit nonneuronal cell growth.

Incubation

Although a systematic study of the effects of various gases on different cell populations has not been undertaken, there are indications that dissociated cells show a greater sensitivity to high oxygen levels than do explant cultures (41). The hypothalamic cells are maintained in a 5% carbon dioxide–95% air mixture, the air providing approximately 18% oxygen. Carbon dioxide/bicarbonate is the natural buffering system in blood and is the combination most commonly used in cell culture.

Catecholamine Biosynthesis Methodology

The MBH contains both noradrenergic and dopaminergic nerve terminals, but only dopaminergic cell bodies. Therefore, levels of norepinephrine (NE) decline to nondetectable levels over several days, as seen in hypothalamic explants of the paraventricular and supraoptic nucleus (25). We chose to examine dopaminergic activity by measuring the appearance of newly synthesized dopamine (DA) after administration of the labeled precursor, [³H]tyrosine. High-performance liquid chromatography (HPLC) coupled with electrochemical detection is ideally suited for this purpose since it allows for separation as well as quantitation of newly synthesized amines.

The biosynthesis experiments are performed after the dissociated cells have been in culture for 6 days. This amount of time *in vitro* was found to be sufficient for recovery from the initial trauma of dissociation and for growth and differentiation. The culture medium is removed and cells are washed with EBSS, pH 7.4, and incubated in 200 μl of EBSS containing 10 μCi of [³H]tyrosine per well (38 Ci mmol; Amersham, Arlington Heights, IL). The radioactive medium is removed from the wells, acidified to 0.1 N with HCl, and frozen until extraction. Catecholamines are analyzed by electrochemical (EC) methods which have been previously described (23, 24, 27). Briefly, catecholamines are adsorbed with alumina and quantitated by EC detection after separation by reversed-phase HPLC. The eluant fractions are then collected and monitored for radioactivity.

One precaution in using this technique is the necessity to analyze the eluant fractions carefully. When ascorbate is present in the medium, a large peak of radioactivity is found which migrates very close to NE. This peak does not represent any of the major metabolites of either DA or NE. Since ascorbate is known to be a very reactive substance and a strong reducing agent, we believe this peak is due to the action of ascorbate on [³H]tyrosine. This emphasizes that it is incorrect to assume that all radioactivity adsorbed by the alumina represents ³H-labeled amine. There are alternatives to using ascorbate in tissue culture (such as superoxide dismutase and catalase) which others have found to be effective in preventing the oxidation of amines (42).

A time course was performed to determine the appropriate time of incuba-

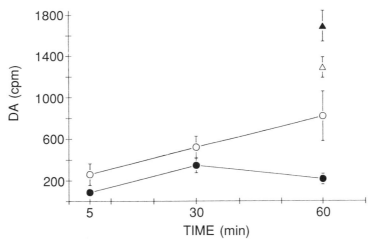

FIG. 1 Time course for dopamine biosynthesis in 6-day MBH-dissociated cultures
(● and ○) and fresh tissue (▲ and △). (△ and ○) Medium levels. (▲ and ●) Tissue
levels. $n = 6$–10. [From Bennett and Morris (29), reprinted with permission.]

tion. As shown in Fig. 1, DA biosynthesis was measured after 5, 30, and 60
min of incubation with the tritiated precursor. At every time point there is a
greater amount of labeled DA in the medium than in the tissue, indicating a
preferential release of newly synthesized DA. Dopamine biosynthesis was
also examined in fresh, undissociated (0 day) tissue and this is compared to
DA biosynthesis in the cultured cells. There is less newly synthesized DA in
the medium of the 0 day MBH, suggesting that the cultured cells may have
an altered ability to either take up or store the newly synthesized amine. This
is in agreement with studies by other investigators who found an increased
amount of amine present in the medium (from brain stem explants) (43). This
suggests that cultured neurons maintain considerable synthetic activity, but
appear to have an altered uptake capacity.

To verify the biosynthesis experiments, the rate-limiting enzyme, TH, was
inhibited using α-methyl-p-tyrosine (α-MT) and the effects on biosynthesis
determined. This is a necessary control experiment that shows the radioactive product which is measured in medium and tissue is indeed [^{3}H]DA and
not a product derived from the nonenzymatic conversion of tyrosine to other
metabolites. As shown in Fig. 2, α-MT significantly inhibited the amount of
newly synthesized DA present in the medium and tissue. These results
provide further evidence that hypothalamic cultures contain viable catecholaminergic cells, as determined by their ability to synthesize dopamine.

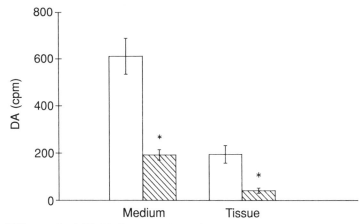

FIG. 2   Effects of α-MT (10^{-5} M) on dopamine (DA) biosynthesis in 6-day cultures of dissociated MBH. ($\square$) Control. ($\boxtimes$) α-MT treated. $n = 6$–8; *, $p < 0.05$. [From Bennett and Morris (29), reprinted with permission.]

Immunocytochemical Methods

Immunocytochemical studies provide information on the types of cells present in culture. The precise method of fixation and staining will vary depending on the specific antiserum to be used. The fixatives most commonly used in immunocytochemical studies are chosen for their ability to retain the antigenicity of peptides and proteins. The fixative we typically use is acrolein, which is an unsaturated monoaldehyde capable of preserving fine structural detail. Acrolein is very reactive and rapidly stabilizes proteins and even very small peptides *in situ* (44).

For the immunocytochemical studies, we use Lab-Tek slide chambers (1 cm²; Miles) with each well seeded with approximately 3 × 10⁵ cells. The cultures are fixed with a 5% (v/v) solution of acrolein in 0.1 M phosphate-buffered saline (PBS, pH 7.4, room temperature) for 5 min. The cultures are rinsed with PBS, incubated for 15 min with 0.005 M sodium periodate, rinsed, and then incubated with 0.03 M sodium borohydrate. These last two incubations are included to remove residual aldehydes (45). Nonspecific staining is reduced by incubating the tissue with a 1% (w/v) solution of normal goat serum (NGS) in PBS for 20 min. Primary antisera diluted in PBS containing 0.1% (v/v) Triton X-100 (Sigma) and 1% NGS are incubated with the cultures for 24–48 hr at 4°C. Antisera can be reused for several months if stored at 4°C. After removal of the antisera, tissues are rinsed with PBS several times and then processed using the Vectastain protocol (Vector

Labs, Burlingame, CA) with diaminobenzidine tetrahyrochloride (Polysciences, Warrington, PA) as the chromogen. The antisera include those against tyrosine monooxygenase (TH, 0.1 U/ml; Eugene Tech., Allendale, NJ), dopamine β-monooxygenase (DBH, 1 : 1000; generously supplied by R. Grzanna, Baltimore, MD), and neuron-specific enolase (NSE, 1 : 5000; Polysciences). Immunoreacted slides are dehydrated in a graded ethanol series, cleared in xylene, and coverslipped with permount.

Figure 3 shows dissociated cultures (7 days) from the MBH which have been stained immunochemically for NSE and TH. NSE is an isoenzyme of the glycolytic enzyme enolase which is different from all other known enolases. NSE is specifically localized to neurons and neuroendocrine cells and labels the cell soma and fibers (46, 47). Labeling with NSE gives an indication of the total neuronal population present in the cultures. The TH-positive cells, on the other hand, yield an index of the number of catecholminergic neurons in the cultures or, more specifically, the dopaminergic neuronal populations, since this region is composed primarily of dopamine cell bodies. This is further supported by the fact that there is no evidence of staining for DBH. As seen in Fig. 3, the density of dopaminergic cells is much less than the general neuronal population. The dopaminergic cells are typically bipolar with a fusiform shape and average size of 10–15 μm. Approximately 10% of the TH-positive cells were multipolar.

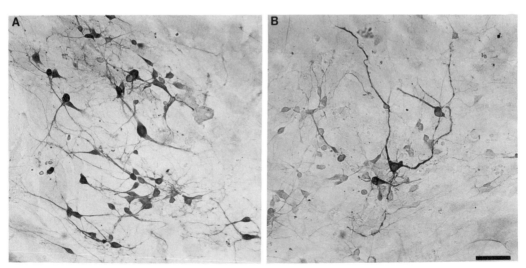

FIG. 3   Photomicrographs of dissociated MBH in culture for 7 days. Cultures were stained immunocytochemically for (A) NSE and (B) TH. The NSE-positive cells are more dense whereas the length of processes is much greater for the TH-positive neurons. Bar, 50 μm.

Morphometric Analysis

It is advantageous to have a morphometrics system for the evaluation of the immunocytochemical results due to the volume of measurements that are necessary. There are many software packages available with various degrees of sophistication. We use a planar morphometry package from Southern Micro Instruments (Atlanta, GA) that allows the analysis of cell size; the number, frequency, and density of cell type; as well as the number and length of processes. In addition, the program contains a statistical package that can perform basic statistical analysis and Student's *t*-test on acquired data. The data files can also be transferred to Lotus 1-2-3. In each experiment, we compare the number of neurons (positive for NSE) to the number of cells which are immunoreactive for specific neuroproteins (i.e., TH). This is an important analysis since it provides an indication of the viability of different types of neuronal populations and their distribution under different conditions.

The morphometric analysis (shown in Table I) of 3-, 6-, and 9-day cultures determined cell size, density of distribution, and length of processes. The cell size had the least variation, with the cell soma of TH neurons averaging 138 μm^2 [in agreement with studies by Puymirat *et al.* (19)] which is slightly smaller (85%) than that of the total neuronal population. This is probably due to the fact that the neuronal population comprises many different cell types. The TH-positive neurons averaged 7.7, 7.1, and 5.5% of all neurons present at 3, 6, and 9 days, respectively. There is a slight reduction in NSE-positive staining at 9 days, although this is not statistically significant. TH neuronal processes are significantly longer than NSE processes on days 6 and 9, and there is an increase in process length over time (3 to 6 day) for dopaminergic neurons. These results indicate that TH-positive neurons undergo maturation and elongation during the period in which they are maintained in culture.

TABLE I Morphometric Analysis of Cultured Hypothalamic Cells[a,b]

Culture (days)	Cell size (μm)		Density (cells/mm^2)		Length of processes (μm)	
	TH	NSE	TH	NSE	TH	NSE
3	136 ± 10	154 ± 12	11 ± 3	143 ± 4	78 ± 7	77 ± 7
6	142 ± 9	180 ± 15	11 ± 2	154 ± 7	117 ± 11[c]	82 ± 7
9	136 ± 4	153 ± 5	8 ± 1	146 ± 4	115 ± 10[c]	72 ± 6

[a] From B. A. Bennett and M. Morris (29), reprinted with permission.
[b] Tissues were fixed on days 3, 6, and 9 of culture and stained with either TH or NSE.
[c] $p < 0.05$ different from NSE-positive cells; $n = 20$ observations per data point.

Summary

These studies demonstrate the utility of cultured neonatal nerve cells dissociated from a specific brain region, the medial basal hypothalamus. The cultured catecholamine neurons continue to synthesize dopamine, as evidenced by the incorporation of [³H]tyrosine. This is also supported by the immunocytochemical studies which show a significant percentage of TH cells. Morphometric analysis shows that 7% of these neurons are TH-positive (putative DA) and may have significantly longer processes, but similar cell body size compared to the mean neuronal (NSE) population. Although primary cell culture of specific brain areas is still in its infancy, there are ever increasing numbers of laboratories that are undertaking this endeavor. Using established tissue culture methodology, we have developed a suitable preparation for the *in vitro* examination of catecholamine-mediated events. This chapter describes a tissue culture model that may have applications to other neuronal systems in which this methodology may prove useful.

Acknowledgments

We would like to thank Ms. Jill Clodfelter for her technical expertise in the maintenance of the tissue cultures. This work was supported in part by NIH Grants NS-22492, NS-24723 and AHA-NC Affiliate Grant #1988-89-A-15.

References

1. A. Faivre-Bauman, A. Nemeskeri, C. Tougard, and A. Tixier-Vidal, *Brain Res.* **185,** 289 (1980).
2. A. Faivre-Bauman, E. Rosenbaum, J. Puymirat, D. Grouselle, and A. Tixier-Vidal, *Dev. Neurosci.* **4,** 118 (1981).
3. J. Puymirat, C. Loudes, A. Faivre-Bauman, A. Tixier-Vidal, and J. M. Boure, *Cold Spring Harbor Cell Proliferation* **9,** 1033 (1982).
4. C. Loudes, A. Faivre-Bauman, A. Barrett, J. Puymirat, and A. Tixier-Vidal, *Dev. Brain Res.* **9,** 231 (1983).
5. A. S. Liotta, C. Loudes, J. F. McKelvy, and D. T. Krieger, *Proc. Natl. Acad. Sci. U.S.A.* **77,** 1880 (1980).
6. S. J. Lolait, A. T. Lim, D. Dahl, B. A. K. Khalid, B. H. Toh, and J. W. Funder, *Neuroendocrinology* **37,** 111 (1983).
7. D. E. Vaccaro, S. E. Leeman, and A. Messer, *J. Neurobiol.* **11,** 417 (1980).
8. K. M. Knigge, G. Hoffman, D. E. Scott, and J. R. Sladek, Jr., *Brain Res.* **120,** 393 (1977).

9. S. Daikoku, H. Kawano, H. Matsumura, and S. Saito, *Cell Tissue Res.* **194,** 433 (1978).
10. G. Jirikowski, I. Reisert, and C. Pilgrim, *Neuroscience (Oxford)* **6,** 1953 (1981).
11. K. L. Schilling and C. Pilgrim, *J. Neurosci. Res.* **19,** 27 (1988).
12. M. J. O. Clarke, P. Lowry, and G. Gillies, *Neuroendocrinology* **46,** 147 (1987).
13. R. Gamse, D. E. Vaccaro, G. Gamse, M. Dipace, T. O. Fox, and S. E. Leeman, *Proc. Natl. Acad. Sci. U.S.A.* **77,** 5552 (1980).
14. H. H. Zingg and Y. C. Patel, *J. Clin. Invest.* **70,** 1107 (1982).
15. Z. Ahmed, J. A. Connor, D. W. Tank, and R. E. Fellows, *Dev. Brain Res.* **28,** 221 (1986).
16. E. Marani, M. Corino, R. J. van den Berg, W. J. Rietveld, M. Deenen, and W. Windhorst, *Neuroendocrinology* **48,** 455 (1988).
17. P. Legendre, A. Tixier-Vidal, J. L. Brigant, and J. D. Vincent, *Dev. Brain Res.* **43,** 273 (1988).
18. J. Puymirat, A. Barrett, A. Vigny, C. Loudes, A. Faivre-Bauman, and A. Tixier-Vidal, *Neuroscience (Oxford)* **10,** 801 (1983).
19. J. Puymirat, A. Barrett, A. Faivre-Baiman, C. Loudes, and A. Tixier-Vidal, *in* "Fetal Neuroendocrinology" (F. Ellendorf, P. D. Gluckman, and N. Parvizi, eds.), p. 121. Perinatology Press, Ithaca, New York, 1984.
20. P. Honneger and D. Lenoir, *Brain Res.* **199,** 425 (1980).
21. I. Reisert, G. Jirikowski, C. Pilgrim, and M. L. Tappaz, *Cell Tissue Res.* **229,** 685 (1983).
22. P. Benda, F. De Vitry, R. Picart, and A. Tixier-Vidal, *Exp. Brain Res.* **23,** 29 (1975).
23. B. A. Bennett and D. K. Sundberg, *Life Sci.* **28,** 2811 (1981).
24. B. A. Bennett and D. K. Sundberg, *Mol. Cell. Endocrinol.* **30,** 149 (1982).
25. M. Morris, B. A. Bennett, N. Alexander, and D. K. Sundberg, *in* "Brain and Blood Pressure Control" (K. Nakamura, ed.), p. 377. Elsevier, Amsterdam, 1986.
26. D. K. Sundberg, B. A. Bennett, O. T. Wendel, and M. Morris, *Res. Commun. Chem. Pathol. Pharmacol.* **3,** 599 (1980).
27. D. K. Sundberg, B. A. Bennett, and M. Morris, *in* "Methods in Enzymology" (P. M. Conn, ed.), Vol. 103, p. 493. Academic Press, Orlando, Florida, 1983.
28. B. A. Bennett and C. R. Freed, *J. Neurochem.* **47,** 472 (1986).
29. B. A. Bennett and M. Morris, *Dev. Brain Res.* **491,** 109 (1989).
30. K. Manford and J. R. Patterson, *in* "Methods in Enzymology" (W. B. Jakoby and I. Pastan, eds.), Vol. 58, p. 141. Academic Press, New York, 1979.
31. J. Sanes, *Annu. Rev. Physiol.* **45,** 581 (1983).
32. M. Nathanson, *Dev. Biol.* **96,** 46 (1983).
33. S. Lie, V. McKusick, and E. Neufeld, *Proc. Natl. Acad. Sci. U.S.A.* **69,** 2361 (1972).
34. J. Bottenstein and G. Sato, *Exp. Cell Res.* **129,** 361 (1980).
35. D. Salomon, L. Liotta, and W. Kidwell, *Proc. Natl. Acad. Sci. U.S.A.* **78,** 382 (1981).
36. J. Bottenstein and G. Sato, *Proc. Natl. Acad. Sci. U.S.A.* **76,** 514 (1979).
37. E. Y. Levin, B. Levenberg, and S. Kaufman, *J. Biol. Chem.* **235,** 2080 (1960).

38. P. Cuatrecasas, G. P. E. Tell, V. Sica, I. Parikh, and K. Chang, *Nature* (*London*) **247,** 92 (1974).
39. B. B. Wolfe, J. A. Jirrolli, and P. B. Molinoff, *Mol. Pharmacol.* **10,** 582 (1974).
40. S. Murad, D. Grove, K. Lindberg, G. Reynolds, A. Sivarajh, and A. Pinnell, *Proc. Natl. Acad. Sci. U.S.A.* **78,** 2879 (1981).
41. C. Nissen, J. Ciesielski-Treska, and L. Hertz, *J. Neurochem.* **20,** 1029 (1973).
42. L. C. Mahan and P. A. Insel, *Anal. Biochem.* **136,** 208 (1984).
43. M. Schlumpf, W. J. Shoemaker, and F. E. Bloom, *Proc. Natl. Acad. Sci. U.S.A.* **74,** 4471 (1977).
44. J. C. King, R. M. Lechan, G. Kugel, and E. D. L. P. Anthony, *J. Histochem. Cytochem.* **31,** 62 (1983).
45. M. Schachner, E. T. Hedley-Whyte, D. W. Hsu, G. Shoonmaker, and A. Bignami, *J. Cell Biol.* **75,** 67 (1977).
46. V. Pickel, D. J. Reis, P. J. Marangos, and C. Zonzely-Neurath, *Brain Res.* **105,** 184 (1975).
47. D. E. Schmechel, P. J. Marangos, and M. W. Brightman, *Nature* (*London*) **276,** 834 (1978).

[22] Receptors for Bombesin/Gastrin-Releasing Peptide and Epidermal Growth Factor on Central Nervous System Cells

Terry W. Moody, Julie Staley, Mei Lee, and Richard M. Kris

Introduction

The development, differentiation, and maintenance of central nervous system (CNS) cells may be regulated by growth factors. The most well studied of these is nerve growth factor (NGF), a 118-amino acid polypeptide which facilitates differentiation of sympathetic neurons (1). Also NGF matures and maintains cholinergic neurons which are deficient in Alzheimer's disease (2).

Methods in Neurosciences, Volume 2

Immunoreactive NGF has been detected in the cortex, where it may bind to receptors and undergo retrograde transport to cell bodies in the septohippocampal area and nucleus basalis of Meynert (3). NGF enhances choline acetyltransferase activity, resulting in increased levels of the neurotransmitter acetylcholine (4). Because NGF partially restores learning ability in rats with a cholinergic deficit caused by lesioning the septal area (5), there is great interest in the use of NGF to restore memory deficits in Alzheimer's patients.

Other growth factors, including epidermal growth factor (EGF) and bombesin/gastrin-releasing peptide (BN/GRP), may play a role in brain plasticity. EGF is a 53-amino acid polypeptide which stimulates the growth of neuronal and nonneuronal cells (6). These actions may be mediated by the endogenous EGF which has been detected in the neonatal and adult rat brain (7). EGF receptors have been detected in the neonatal rat cortex (8) and EGF induces enzymatic activity of glial cells (9). Also, EGF enhances tyrosine monooxygenase activity in rat sympathetic superior cervical ganglia (10). It has been demonstrated that neuropeptides such as BN/GRP stimulate the growth of the neuroendocrine tumor small cell lung cancer (SCLC) (11). BN is a 14-amino acid peptide initially isolated from frog skin; its mammalian equivalent is the 27-amino acid peptide GRP (12). The peptide is made in and secreted from SCLC cells, where it binds to cell-surface receptors and stimulates tumor growth (13). Because both peptides (14) and receptors (15) for BN/GRP are present in discrete regions of the rat brain, this neuropeptide may be biologically active in brain cells. In this regard, BN or GRP stimulates phosphatidylinositol turnover in rat cortical slices (16) and causes depolarization of rat hippocampal neurons (17). Also, BN causes increased grooming (18), decreased food intake (19), and altered hormone secretion (20) after injection into the rat CNS. The structures of EGF, BN, and GRP are shown in Table I.

EGF, a polypeptide of 53 amino acids, is derived from a 1217 amino acid precursor (21). It is posttranslationally processed by enzymes to form an

TABLE I   Structure of Growth Factors[a]

	1	10	20	30	40	50
hEGF	NSDSEC PLSHDGY C LHDGV CMY I EALDKYACNCVVGYIGERCQYRDLKWWELR					
hGRP	VPLPAGGGTV LDKMY PRGNHWAVGHLM *					
BN	p QQRLGNQWAVGHLM *					

[a] The amino acid sequences of human (h) EGF and GRP and BN are shown using standard abbreviations. For BN, the amino terminal is a pyroglutamate, pQ; the carboxy terminal of GRP and BN is amidated, *. hEGF, hGRP, and BN are composed of 53, 27, and 14 amino acids, respectively, and 9 of the 10 carboxyl-terminal amino acids of BN and GRP are identical.

acidic polypeptide containing three disulfide bridges. EGF has sequence homology with transforming growth factor α (TGFα), and both EGF and TGFα bind with high affinity to the EGF receptor (22). The EGF receptor has been cloned and is composed of 1186 amino acids (23). This includes a 621-amino acid extracellular domain, which binds EGF, a 23-amino acid transmembrane domain, and a 542-amino acid cytoplasmic domain that has tyrosine kinase activity. Within seconds after binding EGF, intracellular Ca^{2+} levels increase (24) and there is elevated transport of amino acids and glucose (25). Because the EGF receptor has tyrosine kinase activity, it stimulates the phosphorylation of tyrosine amino acid residues in numerous proteins, including the EGF receptor itself (26). A functional tyrosine kinase is essential for EGF to stimulate proliferation as determined by [^{3}H]thymidine uptake in mouse fibroblast cell lines (27). The EGF receptor gene is overexpressed and amplified in human epidermoid carcinoma cell line A431, which has approximately 2,000,000 EGF receptors per cell (28). The EGF receptor gene is also amplified in some glioblastoma cells (29), which have 100,000 EGF receptors per cell. In addition, EGF receptors have been detected in normal brain cells, such as rodent astrocytes and oligodendrocytes (6, 30).

BN/GRP is synthesized as a 148-amino acid precursor protein and is posttranslationally processed by trypsinlike enzymes to a 30-amino acid form (31). The dibasic amino acid sequence at the carboxy terminal is removed by carboxypeptidase B-like enzymes to yield GRP–glycine, which is biologically inactive. An amidating enzyme then metabolizes the substrate GRP–glycine to yield the biologically active product GRP, which has an amidated carboxy terminal. Nine of the 10 carboxy-terminal amino acid residues of GRP and BN are identical, and they both bind with high affinity to BN/GRP receptors. Using Swiss 3T3 cells, which have 100,000 receptors/ cell, ^{125}I-labeled GRP can be cross-linked to a 75,000-Da glycoprotein (32). Because treatment with N-glycanase reduces the molecular weight of the ^{125}I-labeled GRP–receptor complex to 45,000, the BN/GRP receptor has carbohydrates linked to asparagine amino acid residues (33). After binding to receptors in Swiss 3T3 cells, BN or GRP stimulates phosphatidylinositol turnover (34). The resulting inositol 1,4,5-trisphosphate released causes release of Ca^{2+} from intracellular pools (35), elevating the intracellular Ca^{2+} from 150 to 400 nM in Swiss 3T3 cells. The released diacylglycerol activates protein kinase C, which phosphorylates the EGF receptor, resulting in inhibition of EGF receptor binding (36). BN or GRP stimulates the growth of Swiss 3T3 cells, resulting in increased [^{3}H]thymidine uptake (37). In SCLC cells, BN also stimulates phosphatidylinositol turnover, resulting in increased cytosolic Ca^{2+} (38, 39). (Psi^{13,14}, Leu^{14})BN functions as a BN receptor antagonist in that it inhibits the increase in cytosolic Ca^{2+} and clonal growth of SCLC cells caused by BN (40). Recently, high-affinity BN receptors were detected in human glioblastoma cell lines (33). In this review, BN and EGF receptors in normal and malignant CNS cells are discussed.

In Vitro Autoradiography

BN/GRP and EGF receptors have been localized to discrete regions in the rat brain using ^{125}I-labeled ligands and *in vitro* autoradiographic techniques. (Tyr⁴)BN was iodinated using the chloramine-T procedure and used as a BN receptor probe. (Tyr⁴)BN (1.8 μg in 10 μl of 0.5 M NaHPO₄, pH 7.4) was incubated with ^{125}I (2 mCi, Amersham Corp., Arlington Heights, CA) and 9 μg of chloramine-T (in 30 μl of H₂O) was added. After 60 sec the reaction was quenched with 21 μg of sodium metabisulfite (30 μl in H₂O). The radiolabeled peptide was separated from the free ^{125}I by chromatography on a 0.7 × 15 cm Sephadex LH-20 column using methanol/acetic acid/H₂O [10/2/1 (v/v/v)] as an eluant. The first peak of radioactivity was the radiolabeled peptide, whereas the second peak of radioactivity was ^{125}I. Routinely, the specific activity of the monoiodinated (Tyr⁴)BN was 1100 Ci/mmol. ([^{125}I]Tyr⁴)BN which had been oxidized to the sulfoxide during the iodination was then reduced using 1 M dithiothreitol at 80°C for 2 hr. Routinely, the frozen tracer was stable for 3 weeks in receptor binding assays, then it promptly lost biological activity and the receptor binding activity was negligible. Also, ^{125}I-labeled GRP (2200 Ci/mmol) was purchased from Amersham Corp. and ^{125}I-labeled EGF (1000 Ci/mmol) was purchased from ICN Biomedicals (Cleveland, OH) for use as BN/GRP and EGF receptor probes, respectively. In general, the radiolabeled EGF was less susceptible to radiolysis than was radiolabeled (Tyr⁴)BN.

BN/GRP and EGF receptors were localized to rat brain regions using *in vitro* autoradiographic techniques. For the BN/GRP receptors, 12-μm-thick sections of rat brain were sliced on a cryostat and placed onto glass slides or coverslips. Sections were air dried and incubated with assay buffer composed of 130 mM NaCl, 5 mM MgCl₂, 5 mM KCl, 1 mM EGTA, 100 μg/ml of bacitracin, and 0.1% (w/v) bovine serum albumin (BSA) in 10 mM HEPES–NaOH plus radiolabeled peptide at 22°C in the presence or absence of competitor. After incubation, free radiolabeled peptide was removed by two consecutive washes in buffer at 4°C, followed by a brief rinse in H₂O. The sections on coverslips, which contained bound peptide, were crushed and assayed for radioactivity, or apposed to LKB Ultrofilm. After 2 weeks the film was developed and the grain density analyzed using a RAS 1000 densitometer (Amersham Corp.). EGF receptors have been localized previously (8). In general, BN/GRP receptors were very labile and only fresh frozen brains could be used, whereas EGF receptors were very stable and, consequently, the tissue could be stored frozen at $-80°C$ with minimal loss of ^{125}I-labeled EGF binding.

([^{125}I]Tyr^4)BN bound with high affinity (K_d = 4 nM) to a single class of sites (B_{max} = 130 fmol/mg protein) in coronal adult rat brain slices containing the caudate putamen. Similarly, using homogenate derived from the whole rat brain, ([^{125}I]Tyr^4)BN bound with high affinity (K_d = 4 nM) to a single class of sites (80 fmol/mg protein) (41). In both assays, the carboxy terminal of BN or GRP, but not the amino terminal was essential for high-affinity binding activity. Figure 1 shows that high densities of BN/GRP receptors were present in the nucleus accumbens. Moderate grain densities were present in the ventral caudate putamen, olfactory tubercle, septohippocampal nucleus, and layers V and VI of the neocortex. Low grain densities were found in the dorsal caudate putamen, lateral septal nucleus, and layers I–IV of the parietal cortex. Grains were absent in the corpus callosum. Other areas having a high density of BN/GRP receptors include the olfactory bulb,

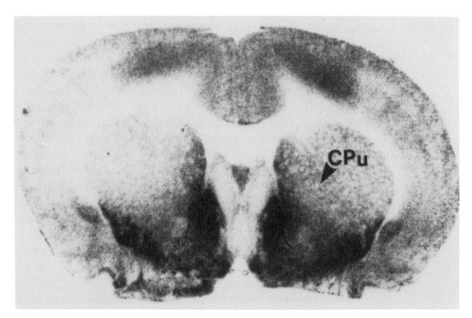

FIG. 1 Distribution of rat brain BN/GRP receptors. The density of ([^{125}I]Tyr^4)BN-binding sites was determined using *in vitro* autoradiographic techniques in a coronal section of rat brain derived from Paxinos and Watson coordinates 10.2 mm [G. Paxinos and C. Watson (eds.), "The Rat Brain in Stereotaxic Coordinates." Academic Press, New York, 1982]. The dark areas indicate high densities of BN/GRP receptors. CPu, Caudate putamen.

suprachiasmatic and periventricular nuclei of the hypothalamus, central medial thalamic nucleus, medial amygdaloid nucleus, hippocampus, dentate gyrus, subiculum, nucleus of the solitary tract, and substantia gelatinosa. Recently, we found that high densities of BN receptors develop in fetal cortex transplants 3 weeks after transplantation into the adult rat brain (42). Therefore, BN receptors may play a role in the differentiation of fetal brain tissue. Previously, Quirion *et al.* (8) detected EGF receptors in the fetal but not adult rat brain. In particular, high grain densities were present during the first postnatal week in the cortex, nucleus accumbens, and caudate putamen. Moderate grain densities were detected in the lateral septum and olfactory bulb as well as tubercle, and low grain densities in the corpus callosum. Because ^{125}I-labeled EGF binding sites are present in high densities in the neonatal but not adult rat brain, EGF receptors also may play a role in brain development.

Binding to Cell Lines

Because BN/GRP and EGF receptors are found in the mammalian brain, it was of interest to determine if they are found in cell lines derived from neurons or glia. Human glioblastoma cell lines were cultured as continuous clonal adherent cell lines. The cells were cultured in Dulbecco's modified Eagle's medium (DMEM) with 10% (w/v) fetal bovine serum in a humidified incubator at 37°C. For receptor binding studies, U-118 cells were cultured in 24-well plates treated with human fibronectin (20 μg/well). When a monolayer of cells formed (3 days), receptor binding studies were performed using 0.8 nM ([^{125}I]Tyr^4)BN or ^{125}I-labeled EGF. The cells were rinsed four times with DMEM/20 mM HEPES–NaOH (pH 7.4). Routinely, radiolabeled peptide (100,000 cpm/250 μl) was added in DMEM/HEPES containing 0.1% BSA and 100 μg/ml bacitracin in the presence or absence of competitor. After 30 min at 37°C, free peptide was removed and the cells rinsed with 250 μl of cold PBS/0.1% BSA. The cells, which contained bound peptide, were solubilized with 0.2 N NaOH and counted in a gamma counter.

Table II shows that total ([^{125}I]Tyr^4)BN binding to U-118 was 3713 cpm, whereas nonspecific binding in the presence of 1 μM unlabeled BN was 605 cpm. The difference between the two represents specific binding, and the ratio of specific/nonspecific binding was approximately 5/1. The concentration of unlabeled BN required to inhibit 50% of the specific ([^{125}I]Tyr^4)BN bound (IC$_{50}$) as 3 nM. Because the IC$_{50}$ values for GRP, GRP$^{14-27}$, and GRP$^{1-16}$ were 1, 10, and >10,000 nM, respectively, the carboxy-terminal of GRP is essential for high-affinity binding activity. EGF or insulin (1 μg/ml) had no effect on ([^{125}I]Tyr^4)BN binding. Total binding of ^{125}I-labeled EGF

TABLE II   Binding of ([^{125}I]Tyr^4)BN and ^{125}I-Labeled
EGF to U-118 Cells^a

Addition	([^{125}I]Tyr^4)BN bound	^{125}I-Labeled EGF bound
None	3713 ± 422	1860 ± 250
BN (10 nM)	1071 ± 105	1355 ± 55
BN (1 μM)	605 ± 71	ND
EGF (1 μg/ml)	4053 ± 474	320 ± 30
Insulin (1 μg/ml)	3793 ± 290	ND

^{a} ([^{125}I]Tyr^4)BN and ^{125}I-labeled EGF (0.8 nM) were incubated with U-118
cells (5 × 10^5) for 30 min at 37°C. The mean cpm bound ± SD of four
determinations is indicated. ND, Not determined.

was 1860 cpm and nonspecific binding was 320 cpm. The ratio of specific to
nonspecific ^{125}I-labeled EGF binding was approximately 5/1. The IC$_{50}$ for
EGF was approximately 10 ng/ml. Surprisingly, 10 nM BN inhibited significantly about 35% of the specific ^{125}I-labeled EGF binding at 37°C, whereas it
had no effect on EGF binding at 4°C. These data suggest that BN may
indirectly affect the EGF receptor at 37°C but not at 4°C. Subsequently, in
Swiss 3T3 cells, it was demonstrated that BN stimulates protein kinase C
activity, resulting in phosphorylation of the EGF receptor and decreased
ability of the receptor to bind ^{125}I-labeled EGF (36). Thus there is cross-talk
between BN/GRP and EGF receptors.

The internalization of the bound growth factors was investigated.
([^{125}I]Tyr^4)BN was incubated with U-118 cells for 2 hr at 4°C in the presence
or absence of competitor. Free ([^{125}I]Tyr^4)BN was removed by washing with
buffer. The cells were then divided into two groups: one group was incubated for an additional 10 min at 4°C and a second group was incubated at
37°C for 10 min. Internalized versus cell-surface ^{125}I-labeled GRP was assessed by dissociation of the peptide with acid. The cells containing bound
([^{125}I]Tyr^4)BN were treated with 0.5 ml of 0.5 M acetic acid, 0.15 M NaCl
(pH 2.5) at 4°C. After 5 min, the supernatant was removed and counted in a
gamma counter. This fraction represented acid-dissociable ([^{125}I]Tyr^4)BN,
which was presumably bound to the cell surface. The pellet was dissolved in
NaOH and was also counted in a gamma counter. This fraction represented
acid-resistant ([^{125}I]Tyr^4)BN, which was internalized. Figure 2 shows that, at
4°C, approximately 90% of the specifically bound ([^{125}I]Tyr^4)BN was acid
dissociable and hence may represent binding to cell-surface receptors. In
contrast, after incubation at 37°C for 10 min, approximately 70% of the
specifically bound ([^{125}I]Tyr^4)BN was acid resistant because it had been internalized. Similar experiments with rat pituitary GH$_4$C$_1$ cells showed ap-

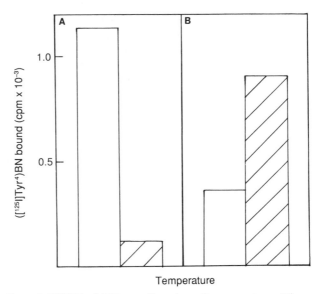

FIG. 2   Binding of ([^{125}I]Tyr^4)BN as a function of temperature. The amount of specific ([^{125}I]Tyr^4)BN binding that was acid dissociable (□) and acid resistant (▨) was determined after (A) a 130-min incubation at 4°C and (B) a 2-hr incubation at 4°C followed by a 10-min incubation at 37°C. The mean value of four determinations is indicated.

proximately 90% of the specifically bound ([^{125}I]Tyr^4)BN was on the cell surface at 4°C, whereas approximately 55% was internalized at 37°C (43). Internalized ([^{125}I]Tyr^4)BN was hydrolyzed to yield free ^{125}I-labeled tyrosine at 37°C but not at 4°C. Because this degradation of ligand was inhibited by chloroquine, it was postulated that ([^{125}I]Tyr^4)BN was internalized in lysozomes (43). Similarly, at 37°C, bound ^{125}I-labeled EGF is rapidly internalized. These data suggest that the glioblastoma (Tyr^4)BN–receptor complex, as well as the EGF–receptor complex, is internalized at 37°C. It remains to be determined if BN/GRP and/or EGF receptors are present on neuroblastoma cell lines.

Cross-Linking

Cross-linking studies were performed to identify the cellular binding component for BN/GRP. Because (Tyr^4)BN has no functional groups available for cross-linking, ^{125}I-labeled GRP, with a free amino group at Lys^{13}, was used as a ligand. The cross-linking studies were performed as follows. Swiss 3T3 cells, NIH-3T3 cells or human glioblastoma cells were seeded (10^5 cells/well) in 6-well tissue culture dishes and grown to confluence. The cells were washed three times with DMEM medium containing 20 mM HEPES–NaOH (pH 7.4). Then ^{125}I-labeled GRP (0.5 nM) was added in 1 ml of DMEM/ HEPES. After 2 hr at 4°C, the cells were washed three times with cold DMEM/HEPES to remove unbound radiolabeled GRP, and rinsed once with cold PBS. The bound ^{125}I-labeled GRP was cross-linked with the homobifunctional reagents (1 mM) disuccinimidyl suberate (DSS) or disuccinimidyl tartarate (DST). After 30 min at 4°C, the cross-linking reaction was stopped by the addition of 10 μl of 2 M Tris-HCl (pH 8.0) and the cells rinsed once with cold PBS. Eighty microliters of Laemmli sample buffer (44) preheated to 95°C was added to the cells and the cells scraped into an Eppendorf tube (1.5 ml). Samples were sonicated briefly, heated to boiling, and subjected to electrophoresis on an 8% (w/v) sodium dodecyl sulfate (SDS) gel using the previously described buffer system (44). Gels were dried and exposed on Kodak XAR-5 film for 3–4 days at −80°C using image-intensifying screens.

Figure 3 shows that ^{125}I-labeled GRP was cross-linked to a radioactive band of molecular weight 65,000, 75,000, and 75,000 using cell lines NIH-3T3-1, Swiss-3T3, and glioblastoma line G-340 (lanes a, c, and e), respec-

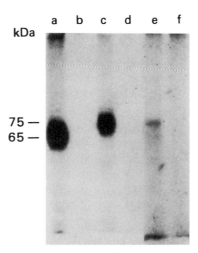

FIG. 3   Cross-linking of ^{125}I-labeled GRP. ^{125}I-Labeled GRP (0.5 nM) was incubated with NIH-3T3-1 (a and b), Swiss 3T3 (c and d), and human glioblastoma GM-340 cells (e and f) in the absence (a, c, and e) and presence (b, d, and f) of 1 μM GRP. The bound peptide was cross-linked to BN/GRP receptors using 1 mM DSS and analyzed after SDS gel electrophoresis and autoradiography. [Reproduced from Kris *et al.* (33) with permission.]

tively; the NIH-3T3-1, Swiss-3T3, and glioblastoma cell lines have 80,000, 100,000, and 30,000 BN/GRP receptors, respectively. No labeling was detected when 1 μM GRP was present during the incubation (Fig. 3, lanes b, d, and f). Similarly, cross-linking of ^{125}I-labeled GRP to Swiss 3T3 cells with 6 mM ethylene glycol bis(succinimidyl succinate) yielded a radiolabeled protein with a molecular weight of 75,000–85,000 and an isoelectric point of 6.0–6.5 (32). The binding subunit for GRP is a glycoprotein monomer (33). Additional studies indicated that the glioblastoma EGF receptor is a 170,000 protein monomer (29).

Phosphatidylinositol Turnover

After binding to central receptors, BN or EGF may stimulate signal transduction through second messenger systems. Peptide binding to BN/GRP receptors stimulates phosphatidylinositol turnover in Swiss 3T3 cells (34). The assay for BN/GRP-stimulated phosphatidylinositol turnover in rat brain slices is described below. Male Sprague-Dawley rats (200–300 g) were decapitated and the brains removed. The rat frontal cortex was dissected and slices (250 μm) prepared using a McIlvain tissue chopper. The slices were agitated in Kreb's buffer containing 10 mM glucose at 37°C for 30 min with two changes of buffer. [^{3}H]Inositol (14 Ci/mmol, New England Nuclear, Boston, MA) was purified on a 0.75-ml Dowex-1 formate column and eluted with 1 ml of water to remove impurities. Three microcuries of purified [^{3}H]inositol was added to 215 μl of Kreb's buffer which contained 7.5 mM LiCl followed by the addition of 75 μl of brain slices (1 mg of protein). The solutions were gassed with 95% O_2/5%CO_2 and shaken at 37°C for 30 min. Then the peptides were added and after 120 min the reaction was terminated by the addition of 940 μl of chloroform/methanol [1/2 (v/v)]. After 16 hr, 310 μl each of chloroform and water were added, the sample vortexed, and centrifuged at 1000 g for 15 min. The water-soluble inositol phosphates in the upper layer (700 μl) were applied to a Dowex-1 formate column (0.5 ml) and the unreacted [^{3}H]inositol removed by five consecutive washes (3 ml) with 5 mM unlabeled myoinositol. [^{3}H]Glycerol, [^{3}H]inositol 1-phosphate ([^{3}H]IP$_1$), [^{3}H]inositol 4,5-bisphosphate ([^{3}H]IP$_2$), and [^{3}H]inositol 1,4,5-trisphosphate ([^{3}H]IP$_3$) were eluted with 1 ml each of 5 mM sodium tetraborate/60 mM sodium formate, 0.2 M ammonium formate/0.1 M formic acid, 0.4 M ammonium formate/0.1 M formic acid, and 1 M ammonium formate/0.1 M formic acid, respectively. The protein content of each assay tube was determined using the Lowry method (45).

The basal cpm/mg protein was approximately 20, 135, 128, and 46 for [^{3}H]glycerol, [^{3}H]IP$_1$, [^{3}H]IP$_2$, and [^{3}H]IP$_3$, respectively. BN or GRP

TABLE III   Ability of BN and GRP to Stimulate
Phosphatidylinositol Turnover in
Rat Brain Slices[a]

Addition	IP_1 response (%)
None	100 ± 4
GRP (1 μM)	112 ± 2*
BN (1 μM)	123 ± 4*
GRP (1 μM) + insulin (2 μg/ml)	131 ± 4*
BN (1 μM) + insulin (2 μg/ml)	179 ± 6**

[a] The mean value $\pm$ SD for four determinations is indicated.
* $p < 0.05$; ** $p < 0.01$.

(1 μM) significantly increased the [³H]IP$_1$ but not [³H]IP$_2$, [³H]IP$_3$, or [³H]glycerol relative to controls. Table III shows that BN and GRP (1 μM) significantly increased the [³H]IP$_1$ levels by 12 and 23%, respectively. When insulin (2 μg/ml) was added in the presence of BN or GRP (1 μM), the IP$_1$ levels significantly increased by 31 and 79%, respectively; insulin alone had no effect on the basal IP$_1$ levels. These data indicate that BN or GRP and insulin are synergistic at stimulation of phosphatidylinositol turnover. Similarly, BN and insulin are synergistic at stimulating phosphatidylinositol turnover (34) and [³H]thymidine uptake (37) in Swiss 3T3 cells. Table II shows, however, that insulin has no effect on binding of ([¹²⁵I]Tyr⁴)BN to cell line U-118.

Cytosolic Ca^{2+}

After stimulation of phosphatidylinositol turnover, the resulting diacylglycerol released stimulates protein kinase C, resulting in phosphorylation of cellular proteins (36). Also, the IP$_3$ released causes release of cytsolic Ca^{2+} from intracellular pools (35). For the cytosolic Ca^{2+} determination, the glioblastoma cells were cultured on fibronectin-treated coverslips in DMEM with 10% fetal bovine serum. When a monolayer of cells had formed (3–5 days), the serum-supplemented medium was removed and the cells fed DMEM and cultured for an additional 16 hr. The cells were rinsed with incubation buffer [150 mM NaCl, 1 mM $CaCl_2$, 1 mM $MgCl_2$, 10 mM glucose, 5 mM KCl, and 20 mM HEPES–NaOH (pH 7.4)] which contained 1 % BSA and 0.04% (w/v) pluronic acid and then incubated in 1.5 ml of this buffer with 1.3 μM fura-2 for 20 min at 25°C. After fura-2 loading, the cells were washed in incubation buffer which containing 1 mM EGTA and no Ca^{2+}. Fluorescence excitation was at 340, 355, and 370 nm, and emission at 510 nm was monitored at 20-sec interval in a SPEX fluorolog at 37°C in 2 ml of Ca^{2+}-free incubation buffer. The free Ca^{2+} concentration was determined by a computer algorithm which compared the relative fluorescence intensities at these three wavelengths to that determined using Ca^{2+} standards.

The basal Ca^{2+} concentration in cell line U-118 was 150 nM. Figure 4 shows that, when 10 nM BN was added, there was a transient increase in the cytosolic Ca^{2+} concentration to 300 nM within 15 sec. After a brief steady state, the cytosolic Ca^{2+} concentration declined to basal levels, possibly due to receptor desensitization. The decline was not due to depletion of intracellular Ca^{2+}, because addition of another stimulus, EGF (100 ng/ml), increased the cytosolic Ca^{2+} from 150 to 200 nM. These data indicate the BN and EGF elevate cytosolic Ca^{2+} through distinct receptors.

The structure–activity relationship for BN-like peptides was investigated. BN increased cytosolic Ca^{2+} in a dose-dependent manner and the ED_{50} was approximately 5 nM. Similarly, 10 nM GRP or GRP^{14-27} strongly increased cytosolic Ca^{2+}, whereas 1 μM GRP^{1-16} was inactive. The BN receptor antagonist (Psi^{13,14},Leu^{14})BN (1 μM) had no effect on the cytosolic Ca^{2+}, but it inhibited the increase in cytosolic Ca^{2+} caused by BN (10 nM). The role of

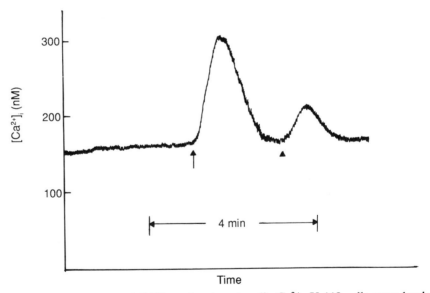

FIG. 4   Ability of BN and EGF to elevate cytosolic Ca^{2+}. U-118 cells were loaded with the fluorescent Ca^{2+} indicator fura-2/AM. The ability of 10 nM BN (arrow) followed by 100 ng/ml EGF (arrowhead) to elevate cytosolic Ca^{2+} levels was determined.

BN/GRP or EGF in stimulating the growth of glioblastoma cell lines remains to be determined.

Acknowledgments

The authors thank Drs. J. Schlessinger and C. Linden for helpful discussions and R. Getz and H. Prasad for technical assistance. Supported in part by NSF grant 88-15133 and NCI grant CA-48071.

References

1. R. Levi-Montalcini and P. Calissano, *Trends NeuroSci. (Pers. Ed.)* **9**, 473 (1986).
2. F. Hefti and W. J. Weiner, *Ann. Neurol.* **20**, 275 (1986).
3. M. Seiler and M. E. Schwab, *Brain Res.* **300**, 33 (1984).
4. B. H. Gahwiler, A. Enz, and F. Hefti, *Neurosci. Lett.* **75**, 6 (1987).
5. B. Will and F. Hefti, *Behav. Brain Res.* **17**, 17 (1985).
6. D. L. Simpson, R. Morrison, J. de Villis, and H. R. Herschman, *J. Neurosci.* **8**, 153 (1982).
7. J. H. Fallon, K. B. Seroogy, S. E. Loughlin, S. D. Morrison, R. A. Bradshaw, D. J. Knauer, and D. D. Cunningham, *Science* **224**, 1107 (1984).
8. R. Quirion, D. Araujo, N. P. V. Nair, and J. G. Chabot, *Synapse* **2**, 212 (1988).
9. P. Honneger and B. Guentert-Lauber, *Dev. Brain Res.* **11**, 245 (1983).
10. H. R. Herschman, R. Goodman, C. Chandler, D. Simpson, D. Cawley, R. Cole, and J. de Villis, "Nervous System Regeneration," p. 79. Liss, New York, 1983.
11. F. Cuttitta, D. N. Carney, J. Mulshine, T. W. Moody, J. Fedorko, A. Fischler, and J. D. Minna, *Nature (London)* **316**, 823 (1985).
12. T. J. McDonald, J. Jornvall, G. Nilsson, M. Vagne, M. Ghatei, S. R. Bloom, and V. Mutt, *Biochem. Biophys. Res. Commun.* **90**, 227 (1979).
13. D. N. Carney, F. Cuttitta, T. W. Moody, and J. D. Minna, *Cancer Res.* **47**, 821 (1987).
14. P. Panula, *Med. Biol.* **64**, 177 (1986).
15. M. Zarbin, M. J. Kuhar, T. L. O'Donohue, S. S. Wolf, and T. W. Moody, *J. Neurosci.* **5**, 429 (1985).
16. V. N. H. Prasad and T. W. Moody, *Peptides* **9**, 1345 (1988).
17. J. Dodd and J. S. Kelly, *Brain Res.* **205**, 337 (1981).
18. D. Gmerek and A. Cowan, *Life Sci.* **31**, 2229 (1982).
19. J. A. Stuckey, J. Gibbs, and G. P. Smith, *Brain Res. Bull.* **8**, 617 (1982).
20. Y. Tache and M. Gunion, *Life Sci.* **37**, 115 (1985).
21. A. Gray, T. J. Dull, and A. Ullrich, *Nature (London)* **303**, 722 (1983).
22. H. Marquardt, M. W. Hankapiller, L. E. Hood, and G. J. Todaro, *Science* **223**, 1079 (1984).
23. T. Hunter, *Nature (London)* **311**, 414 (1984).

24. W. H. Moolenaar, L. C. Tertoolen, and S. W. de Laat, *J. Biol. Chem.* **258,** 2041 (1983).
25. G. Carpenter and S. Cohen, *Annu. Rev. Biochem.* **48,** 193 (1979).
26. H. Ushiro and S. Cohen, *J. Biol. Chem.* **255,** 8363 (1980).
27. A. M. Honnegar, D. Szapary, A. Schmidt, R. Lyall, and E. VanObberghen, *Mol. Cell. Biol.* **7,** 4568 (1987).
28. R. N. Fabricant, J. E. Delarco, and G. L. Tadaro, *Proc. Natl. Acad. Sci. U.S.A.* **74,** 565 (1977).
29. T. A. Libermann, H. R. Nusbaum, N. Razon, R. Kris, I. Lax, H. Soreq, N. Whittle, M. D. Waterfield, A. Ullrich, and J. Schlessinger, *Nature (London)* **313,** 144 (1985).
30. A. Leutz and M. Schachner, *Neurosci. Lett.* **30,** 179 (1982).
31. E. R. Spindel, W. W. Chin, J. Price, L. H. Rees, G. M. Besser, and J. F. Habener, *Proc. Natl. Acad. Sci. U.S.A.* **81,** 5699 (1984).
32. I. Zachary and E. Rozengurt, *J. Biol. Chem.* **262,** 3947 (1987).
33. R. M. Kris, R. Hazan, J. Villines, T. W. Moody, and J. Schlessinger, *J. Biol. Chem.* **262,** 3947 (1987).
34. J. P. Heslop, D. M. Blakeley, K. D. Brown, R. F. Irvine, and M. J. Berridge, *Cell* **47,** 703 (1986).
35. S. A. Mendoza, J. A. Schneider, A. Lopez-Rivas, J. W. Sinnett-Smith, and E. Rozengurt, *J. Cell Biol.* **102,** 2223 (1986).
36. I. Zachary, J. W. Sinnett-Smith, and E. Rozengurt, *J. Cell Biol.* **102,** 2211 (1986).
37. E. Rozengurt and J. Sinnett-Smith, *Proc. Natl. Acad. Sci. U.S.A.* **80,** 2936 (1983).
38. R. Heikkila, J. B. Trepel, F. Cuttitta, L. M. Neckers, and E. A. Sausville, *J. Biol. Chem.* **262,** 16456 (1987).
39. T. W. Moody, A. Murphy, S. Mahmoud, and G. Fiskum, *Biochem. Biophys. Res. Commun.* **147,** 189 (1987).
40. S. Mahmoud, E. Palaszynski, G. Fiskum, D. H. Coy, and T. W. Moody, *Life Sci.* **44,** 367 (1989).
41. T. W. Moody, C. B. Pert, J. Rivier, and M. R. Brown, *Proc. Natl. Acad. Sci. U.S.A.* **75,** 5372 (1978).
42. R. Getz, T. W. Moody, and J. M. Rosenstein, *Neurosci. Lett.* **79,** 97 (1987).
43. J. Westendorf and A. Schonbrunn, *J. Biol. Chem.* **258,** 7527 (1983).
44. U. K. Laemmli, *Nature (London)* **277,** 680 (1970).
45. O. H. Lowry, N. J. Rosenbrough, A. L. Farr, and R. J. Randall, *J. Biol. Chem.* **193,** 265 (1951).

[23] Use of Hypothalamic Cell Cultures to Study Role of Diffusible Factors in Phenotypic Expression of Central Nervous System Neurons

Andrée Tixier-Vidal and Annie Faivre-Bauman

Introduction

During their development *in vivo,* central nervous system (CNS) neurons are exposed to a combination of extracellular signals of various origin: components of the extracellular fluid medium, membrane glycoproteins mediating cell-to-cell interaction, and macromolecules of the extracellular matrix. By definition, diffusible factors are soluble components of the extracellular fluid medium. During fetal life the composition of the brain extracellular fluid certainly differs from that of the adult. The fetal cerebrospinal fluid (CSF) contains high concentrations of high-molecular-weight plasma proteins which originate from a combination of uptake from plasma and *in situ* synthesis, such as fetuin, α-fetoprotein, albumin, and transferrin (1, 2). Moreover, the brain extracellular fluid also contains small molecules which can diffuse short distances in such hydrated tissues. This may be the case for neurotransmitters and neuropeptides which are synthesized in the brain at early fetal stages as well as for fetal peripheral hormones carried by the fetal circulation. The concentrations of these components can be assumed to be very low and to vary along with the perinatal life.

In this chapter, we first briefly review the classes of diffusible factors which are known to play a role in neuron development. Then, we discuss the most appropriate strategies to study their effects on the expression of neuronal phenotype in culture. In the last sections, we present findings mostly obtained in our laboratory with hypothalamic cell cultures that use these strategies and show that the successive steps of the expression of neuronal phenotype can be independently regulated by diffusible factors and that the

Methods in Neurosciences, Volume 2

responses to a given factor can vary depending on the brain area as well as the neuronal specialization.

Classes of Diffusible Factors Acting on Neuron Development

Our definition of diffusible factors is based on the *in vivo* situation. In consequence, we do not include any soluble substance which can be added to the culture medium and promotes neuron development yet is not necessarily important *in vivo*. Moreover, we decided to exclude growth factors such as nerve growth factor (NGF), which is secreted by neuron target cells and transported retrogradely in afferent neurons, and other types of neurotrophic factors whose physiological roles during brain development *in vivo* are not always clear (see Ref. 3).

Two main classes can be distinguished among diffusible factors which are potential regulators of neuron development: those of endogenous origin, such as hormones and neurotransmitters, and those provided by the diet, i.e., nutrients. The role of hormones in neuron development *in vivo* is largely documented for sexual steroids (see Ref. 4) and for thyroid hormones (see Ref. 5). They are necessary at transient, critical periods of the development, for example, sexual steroids before puberty in mammals, thyroid hormones at perinatal periods. They act at the genomic level and their receptors in the brain have been purified and, for most of them, localized by immunocytochemistry or by *in situ* hybridization. Evidence for a role of polypeptide hormones and neurotransmitters *in vivo* or *in vitro* in neuron development has appeared more recently. In contrast to steroids and thyroid hormones, polypeptide hormones and neurotransmitters have their effects initiated at the membrane level and mediated by second messengers which can mimic their effects. Of particular importance for *in vitro* studies are the very low concentration of all of these components in plasma and CSF (below the nanomolar range).

As concerns factors provided by the diet, the most important for neuron development are vitamins and essential fatty acids. Among vitamins (see Ref. 6), vitamin C is known to be highly concentrated in the brain, although there is apparently no explanation for that observation. Vitamin E, which has strong antioxidizing properties, prevents the peroxidation of polyunsaturated fatty acids, which are particularly concentrated in synaptosomal and synaptic vesicle membranes. The latter components can be synthesized only from their precursors, linoleic acid and linolenic acid, which are essential fatty acids provided by the food. The lack of these components in the food at early steps of brain development is known to have dramatic consequences (see Ref. 7).

Strategies

The selection of strategies to study the effects of diffusible factors on the expression of neuronal phenotype in culture depends on two parameters: (1) the medium composition and (2) the neuronal phenotype.

Culture Medium

Obviously, the best strategy consists of the use of a chemically defined, serum-free medium. This is the only way to control the concentration of a given component, a parameter of particular importance for biologically active substances which act in a very precise and often narrow dose range. Indeed, sera should be avoided because of their ill-defined composition and their variations from batch to batch. Other alternatives can be utilized in the case of hormones, such as serum extraction (Sephadex LH-20, charcoal, dextran), or use of castrated or thyroidectomized animals as donors. However, this often alters the concentration of other components of the serum. In the case of components which are not present in serum, commercially available "serum substitutes" which contain ill-defined macromolecules and serum-supplemented medium may remain a valid tool.

The literature on the advantages and development of serum-free medium is rather large. It is now clear that each cell type has its specific requirements for growth, and many optimized chemically defined media specific for the growth of differentiated cells lines have been established (see Refs. 8–10).

With regard to primary cultures of CNS neurons, several successful attempts were made separately to obtain their survival and differentiation in serum-free chemically defined medium (11–15). Our studies on hypothalamic cells were based on the pioneering work of Bottenstein and Sato (16), who developed a simple medium (N2) which supports the growth of a rat neuroblastoma cell line. We first determined the minimum conditions to obtain cell survival and expression of several neuron-specific functions. Deletion of transferrin or of selenium resulted in rapid cell death, whereas deletion of insulin or putrescine greatly limited duration of cell survival (13). Then, we progressively improved the composition of the culture medium and the nature of the culture substratum (see Ref. 17). The conditions which we now use in routine are described in Table I. They permit the survival and complete differentiation of hypothalamic neurons for up to 50 days in culture. The proportion of astrocytes is low for the first week in culture (1 out of 5–6 neurons); however, they then slowly proliferate. Thus for long-term cultures, cytosine arabinoside is added after 5 days. These conditions (Table I) are also suitable for culturing fetal brain hemisphere cells.

TABLE I   Methods to Culture Mouse Fetal Hypothalamic
Neurons in Chemically Defined Medium[a]

I. Preparation of plastic tissue culture dishes or glass coverslips
   1. Incubation with gelatin (250 μg/ml distilled water), 30 min, room temperature
   2. Incubation with poly(L-lysine) MW 90,000–120,000 (10 μg/ml in 0.15 M sodium borate buffer, pH 8.4), 1.5 hr, two rinsings in phosphate-buffered saline (PBS), one rinsing in distilled water
   3. Ultraviolet irradiation for 3 hr. The dishes can be then stored at 37°C in an incubator
   4. Before cell seeding, incubation for 30 min at room temperature in 10% (v/v) fetal calf serum in PBS, then withdrawn
II. Cell dissociation and seeding
   1. Hypothalami from mouse fetuses taken on day 14–16 of gestation are dissected out and minced with scissors in Ca^{2+},Mg^+-free PBS supplemented with D-glucose (6 mg/ml)
   2. Mechanical dissociation through a Pasteur pipette in 10% fetal calf serum in Ham's F12/Dulbecco's modified Eagle's medium (DMEM) [1/1 (v/v)]
   3. Centrifugation for 10 min (450 g) followed by suspension of the cell pellet in serum-free medium (SFM). Yields a single-cell suspension
   4. Seeding the cells in SFM; 6–7 × 10⁵ cells/ml (one hypothalamus yields 1400 cells/mm²)
III. Culture medium

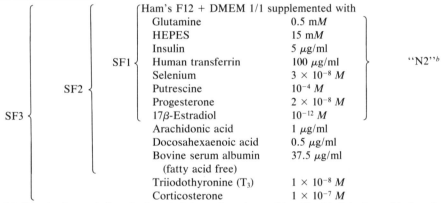

Medium is changed after the first 4–5 days. Cytosine arabinoside (10⁻⁶) is then added to the medium, which is renewed every 2–3 days
IV. Special notations
   Water quality is critical. Use thrice-distilled or pyrolyzed (Pyrodistillator, Institut Pasteur, Paris, France)
   Origin of chemicals: gelatin, polylysine, HEPES, human transferrin, putrescine, hormones, and fatty acid-free serum albumin are purchased from Sigma (St. Louis, MO); ethanol from Merck (Rahway, NJ); and sodium selenite from Johnston Matthey (Roissy, France)
   Ham's F12 and DMEM are purchased as powders (GIBCO, Grand Island, NY) for 1 liter, supplemented with NaHCO₃ and with HEPES (N-2-hydroxyethylpiperazine-N'-2-ethanesulfonic acid), pH 6.9–7.0. The solutions are sterilized on Millipore filters (0.22 μm), aliquoted, and stored at 4°C for up to 1 month. Antibiotics are generally avoided
   Stock solutions of supplements are aliquoted and stored at −20°C (avoid freezings and thawing) except when indicated. Glutamine (400×) is dissolved in water. Putrescine (100×) and human transferrin (100×) are made in PBS. Bovine insulin (200×) is dissolved in 0.1 N HCl and after dissolution brought to 0.01 N HCl with water (stored at 4°C)

(continued)

TABLE I (*continued*)

Sodium selenite (100×) is dissolved in water adjusted to pH 7.4 and kept at room temperature. Steroid hormones are dissolved and serially diluted in 80% (v/v) ethanol to 1000×

Triiodothyronine is dissolved (10^{-3} M) in siliconized glassware in 80% ethanol and subsequent dilutions are made in 0.1 N NaOH (stored at 4°C)

Polyunsaturated fatty acids (PUFAs) are bound to free fatty acid bovine serum albumin (25 μg/1 μg PUFAs) diluted in F12–DMEM mixture as 100× solution, and aliquoted in siliconized glassware

Solutions made in water or PBS are sterilized on Millipore filters before aliquoting

Culture medium: F12 and DMEM solutions are mixed in equal volume, glutamine is added, and then hormones and other supplements. The mixture is then aliquoted (100 ml) and kept for a week at 4°C

[a] From A. Faivre-Bauman, J. Puymirat, C. Loudes, and A. Tixier-Vidal, *in* "Methods for Serum-Free Culture of Neuronal and Lymphoid Cells" (D. W. Barnes, D. A. Sirbasku, and G. H. Sato, eds.), p. 37. Liss, New York, 1984.

[b] From J. E. Bottenstein and G. H. Sato, *Proc. Natl. Acad. Sci. U.S.A.* **76,** 514 (1979).

Neuronal Phenotype

It is now clear that the acquisition of the neuronal phenotype involves a sequence of developmental steps from neuroblast mitosis, neurite initiation, neurite elongation and branching, to synapse formation. These morphological events are accompanied by a sequence of biochemical events, in particular the capacity to synthesize, store, and release neurotransmitters and neuropeptides. The time course *in vivo* of this differentiation program varies depending on the neuronal specificity and on the brain region. In the case of the mouse hypothalamus, the last mitosis of neuron precursors occurs between 11 and 14 days of gestation. Neurite initiation and elongation rapidly follow the last neuroblast mitosis, as well as the expression of neurotransmitter-synthesizing enzymes and neuropeptides. In contrast, synaptogenesis begins at birth and develops postnatally (see Ref. 17). This sequential feature of the neuronal differentiation program should be taken into consideration for selection of components. This is illustrated in the following sections by reviewing the effects of diffusible factors at progressive steps of the differentiation of hypothalamic neurons in culture.

Fate of Neuron Precursor Cells

Because of their early appearance in the developing hypothalamus, the role for neurotransmitters or neuropeptides on the fate of precursor cells has been investigated. A few examples of such effects have been reported.

Choice of Precursor Cell Fate

The demonstration *in vitro* of an effect of a neurotransmitter on the commitment of hypothalamic precursor cells to a precise biochemical phenotype would require initiation of the cultures during or before the mitotic phase, i.e., 10–12 days of fetal life. This would be hard to realize, since the anatomical delineation of the hypothalamus coincides with the positioning of dividing precursors. An alternative approach to this problem has been the use of the multipotent hypothalamic cell line F7, initially obtained by SV40 transformation of 14-day mouse fetal cells (18). The phenotype of these primitive nerve cells was found to be modified by the environment. Appropriate culture conditions induced in these cells the expression of a serotoninergic phenotype characteristic of hypothalamic neurons, i.e., the capacity to synthesize serotonin (5-HT) from 5-hydroxytrytophan but not from tryptophan (18). This was obtained in the following conditions. The cells seeded in serum-supplemented medium were transferred after 24 hr in a serum-free medium (Table II) for 2 days. The capacity to synthesize [^{3}H]5-HT was

TABLE II   Composition of Serum-Free Medium Devised for
Expression of Serotoninergic Properties by
F7 Hypothalamic Cell Line[a]

Component	Composition
Ham's F12 : DME. C6 L15-conditioned medium	1 : 2 : 1, by volume
Insulin	10 μg/ml
Transferrin	25 μg/ml
L-Glutamine	2.4 mM
Parathyroid hormone	4 ng/ml
Ethanolamine	0.1 mM
D(+)-Galactose	10 mM
L-Tyrosine	10 nM
L-Tryptophan	10 nM
5-HTP	0.1 μM
Progesterone	1 nM
Corticosterone	10 pM
Triiodothyronine	10 pM
Retinol	1 nM
Lys-vasopressin	2.5 IU/ml
Dibutyryl-cAMP	100 μM
EDGF	7.5 SU/ml
8- to 10-day-old mice brain extract	50 μl/ml
LSD	10 μM

[a] From F. de Vitry, J. Catelon, M. Dubois, J. Thibault, D. Barritault, J. Courty, S. Bourgoin, and M. Hamon, *Neurochem. Int.* **9**, 43 (1986).

reduced by 30% when eye derived growth factor (EDGF) and the serotonin agonist LSD were simultaneously deleted from the medium. This was the first indication of a possible role of serotonin in the induction of its own synthesis.

Fate of Postmitotic Cells Already Committed to Neuronal Phenotype

Three examples of an effect of a single added component on the expression of neuronal phenotypes have been reported. In the two first cases, the number of neurons has been augmented, whereas in the third case the intracellular content was enhanced.

Initiation and Autoamplification by Serotonin of the Serotoninergic Phenotype (19)

Hypothalamic cultures initiated at early stages of fetal development (12–15 days) and grown in routine conditions (Ham's F10, 15% heat-inactivated horse serum, 2.5% fetal calf serum) contain a small proportion of 5-HT neurons which have the capacity to decarboxylate 5-HTP neurons into 5-HT as revealed immunocytochemically. The number of 5-HT cells slightly increases with age in culture and with the stage of culture initiation (from 12 to 15 fetal days), but their proportion remains low: 1.5 to 2.5% of the total number of neurons in culture after 10 days. The repetitive addition to the medium of a stable serotoninergic agonist, 8-hydroxy-2-[di(n-propyl)amino]-tetralin (8-OH-DPAT) (10 nM), increased the proportion of 5-HT positive cells to 5–6% of total neuron number, whereas the total number of neurons was not affected. This response to the serotonin agonist was observed at a transient period of development: only with cells taken at embryonic days 12 to 14. Appropriate controls indicated that this effect was mediated by 5-HT receptors. The fact that the total number of neurons was not affected and that numerous ovoid neuroblasts were present among the newly formed positive cells suggests the recruitment of cells already committed to the serotoninergic phenotype. Such an autoregulatory mechanism as found here for serotonin may play an important role at early stages of development of neurotransmitter-synthesizing neurons.

Promotion by Angiotensin II of Development of Neurophysin Neurons (20)

In these experiments, also performed in a serum-supplemented medium (Ham's F10, 15% fetal calf serum), rat hypothalamic cells were taken at 18 days of gestation, that is, a relatively late fetal stage. Continuous treatment with angiotensin II (2×10^{-9} M) induced after 16 days *in vitro* a drastic augmentation (10–13 fold) of the number of neurophysin-immunoreactive neurons without affecting the total number of neurons in culture. Interestingly, it increased the number of a subpopulation of small ovoid cells, most probably immature neurons. This suggests that angiotensin II treatment recruited precursor cells already commited to the neurophysin phenotype. The fact that angiotensin II did not induce the appearance of neurophysin neurons in other brain areas where the neurophysin phenotype is not expressed *in vivo* suggests that angiotensin II did not influence the transmitter choice of neuropeptide neuron precursors. In this study, the mechanism of this effect of angiotensin II was not investigated. In any case, this provides one of the very few examples of an heteroregulation of a neuropeptide neuronal phenotype.

Supplementation with Ascorbate to Increase Thyroliberin Cell Content (21)

Ascorbic acid is known to be a cofactor of the peptidyl glycyl α-amidating monooxygenase (EC 1.14.17.3), the amidation enzyme of many neuropeptides, including thyroliberin (TRH). It is absent in many basal nutrient media. When added (50 nM) at initiation of cultures to SF3 medium (see Table I), it greatly enhanced TRH cell content at all stages in culture ($4\times$ after 9 days), for up to 16 days at least (21). In that case, the number of TRH neurons was not apparently affected. Moreover, the somatostatin cell content was not changed, consistent with the fact that this peptide is not amidated (unpublished).

Neurite Elongation and Branching by Specified Neurons

Because of the central role of the hypothalamus in the neuroendocrine control of reproduction, studies on hormonal control of neuron morphogenesis in this brain area started with sexual steroids. In a series of studies, Toran-Allerand demonstrated the role of sex steroids on neurite outgrowth from explants of newborn mouse hypothalamus/preoptic area and dendrite induction from soma (22, 23). These experiments were performed on medium supplemented with high concentrations of steroid-deficient (gelded horse) serum and high concentration of 17β-estradiol (up to 3×10^{-6} M). Moreover, these effects were not ascribed to a precise neuronal phenotype.

In the case of dopaminergic (DA) hypothalamic neurons both a regional and hormone specificity of the responses were observed.

Enhancement by Triiodothyronine of Morphogenesis of Dopaminergic Hypothalamic Neurons but not of Dopaminergic Mesencephalic Neurons

In this study (24), cultures were initiated with 16-day-old mouse fetal cells as described on Table I. The culture medium was the N2 mixture of Bottenstein and Sato (16) supplemented with 10^{-12} M 17β-estradiol only (SF1). Triiodothyronine (T$_3$) was added at initiation of culture from 10^{-13} to 10^{-9} M, the dose which gave the optimum morphogenetic response. DA neurons were identified either by immunocytochemistry or by autoradiography after specific uptake of [^{3}H]dopamine. The latter identification served for the morphometric analysis, which was performed after 8 days in culture. DA neurons in hypothalamic cultures are relatively few (0.1% of total number of neurons). Addition of T$_3$ at initiation of cultures did not increase their number, but significantly enhanced perikarya size, neurite length, and neurite branching as appreciated by an index of neurite density (see Table III). In contrast, the number of neurites per soma did not seem to be modified. These morphogenetic effects were associated with an increase of [^{3}H]DA uptake. The demonstration of the presence of T$_3$ nuclear binding sites in neuron-enriched hypothalamic cultures grown in similar conditions, but in absence of T$_3$, argues in favor of a direct receptor-mediated action at the

TABLE III Comparison of Effects of Triiodothyronine (10^{-9} M) on Morphogenesis in Culture of DA Hypothalamic versus Mesencephalic Neurons[a,b]

Origin of neurons	Number of DA neurons		DA cell surface (μm^2)		Index of neurite density	
	Control	T$_3$	Control	T$_3$	Control	T$_3$
Hypothalamic	185 ± 34	189 ± 29 NS	87.5 ± 5	126 ± 9**	1387 ± 100	1821 ± 80**
Mesencephalic	214 ± 2	245 ± 90 NS	111 ± 3	143 ± 3*	2167 ± 171	2345 ± 167 NS

[a] The total number of DA neurons visualized by autoradiography was counted at 100× magnification in 15-mm culture dishes. Each value represents the mean of three different experiments. The surface of DA neuron perikarya was measured with a planimeter on microphotographs (650×) of DA neurons visualized by autoradiography. The index of neurite density was determined by counting the number of intersections of any labeled neurite with a square grid superimposed on the same microphotographs. A total of 80–100 neurons was scored from three different experiments. NS, Not significant. Significantly different from control: *, $P \leq 0.01$; **, $P \leq 0.001$.

[b] J. Puymirat, A. Barret, R. Picart, A. Vigny, C. Loudes, A. Faivre-Bauman, and A. Tixier-Vidal, *Neuroscience (Oxford)* **10**, 801 (1983); J. Puymirat, A. Faivre-Bauman, A. Barret, C. Loudes, and A. Tixier-Vidal, *Dev. Brain Res.* **23**, 315 (1985).

neuronal level (25). Moreover, nuclear thyroid hormone receptors were immunocytochemically demonstrated in DA neurons of fetal rat hypothalamus in culture, indicating that these neurons are direct targets for thyroid hormone (26). However, the fact that pure hypothalamic astrocytic cell cultures also possess T_3 nuclear binding sites of the same affinity, albeit three times less in number than in neurons, raises the question of a role of astrocytes in neuron responses. Although the proportion of glial cells is low in cell cultures in hypothalamic serum-free medium, this possibility cannot be excluded.

A similar study performed with mouse mesencephalic cells taken from 14- and 16-day-old mouse fetuses and grown in the same conditions as described above gave different results (27). T_3 had no effect on the index of neurite density and [^{3}H]Da uptake, although it significantly enhanced perikarya size (Table III). These discrepancies between the effects of T_3 on hypothalamic and mesencephalic neurons *in vitro*, which agree with biochemical data obtained *in vivo*, may have several explanations (see Ref. 28).

Enhancement by 17β-Estradiol of Morphogenesis of Dopaminergic Mesencephalic Neurons but not of Dopaminergic Hypothalamic Neurons

Another example of a regional specificity of the hormonal control of DA neurons morphogenesis has been reported by Reisert *et al.* (29), concerning the effects of sex steroids. In these experiments, the cells were taken from 14-day-old rat fetuses and grown for 6 days in Eagle's basal medium supplemented with 10% castrated horse serum. The situation is reverse to that observed with T_3. Sex steroids (17β-estradiol and testosterone) (10^{-8}–10^{-10} M) enhanced neurite length of DA mesencephalic neurons, but not of DA diencephalic neurons.

These studies emphasize the importance of studying the effect of a given diffusible factor on neurite morphogenesis of a specified neuronal phenotype and in a precise brain area.

Synapse Differentiation

Synapse differentiation will be considered here from two points of view: morphological and functional, i.e., ability to release neurotransmitters or neuropeptides.

Morphological Differentiation

The ability of dissociated fetal rodent brain cells to form synapses *de novo in vitro* has been reported for cells grown in serum-supplemented media and taken from various brain regions, including the hypothalamus (for review, see Ref. 30). Using mouse hypothalamic cells taken on day 16 of gestation, we previously observed fully differentiated synapses at 10–12 days *in vitro*. Thus, we have looked for the time of appearance and the morphological quality of synapses in serum-free medium as a function of medium composition. The presence of synapses was shown by electron microscopy (30) and by immunofluorescence localization of synaptophysin, an integral membrane protein characteristic of synaptic vesicles (31, 32). We compared three medium compositions: SF1, SF2, and SF3 (see Table I).

The onset of synapse formation was not affected by the medium composition, suggesting that the time required for synapse formation corresponds to the execution of an intrinsic, genetically determined, program. Similarly, synaptophysin immunofluorescent signal in perikarya was detected at a very early stage, 24 hr in culture, whatever the medium composition (unpublished).

In contrast, the morphological features of synapses were found to be under the major control of polyunsaturated fatty acids (PUFAs) (SF2). The main differences concerned synaptic vesicles. In SF1, the synapses displayed a few synaptic vesicles, which were irregular in shape and diameter and were apparently rare. Addition of hormones to SF1 [T_3 or T_3 + corticosterone (Cs)] did not affect these features. In contrast, addition of polyunsaturated fatty acids alone (SF3) was sufficient to improve the density and quality of synaptic vesicles, which displayed a regular diameter (40–50 nm) and a rounded shape. At the same time, synapses became more frequent and acquired complex configuration with time in culture. These features were undistinguishable from those observed in SF3 or in serum-supplemented medium. This effect is consistent with the exceptional richness in PUFAs of synaptosomes and synaptic vesicles. It is correlated with a previous biochemical study which showed that brain hemisphere and hypothalamic cultures grown in SF1 for 8 days had a dramatic deficiency of PUFAs in cell membranes and that this was overcome by adding arachidonic acid and docosahexaenoic acid in a ratio of 2 : 1 (17, 33).

The addition to SF2 of T_3 and Cs could not improve the quality of the synapses, which was already excellent in their absence. However, in complete medium (SF3) we could keep the cells, with many mature synapses, for up to 50 days, as revealed by synaptophysin immunofluorescence (Fig. 1) and electron microscopy.

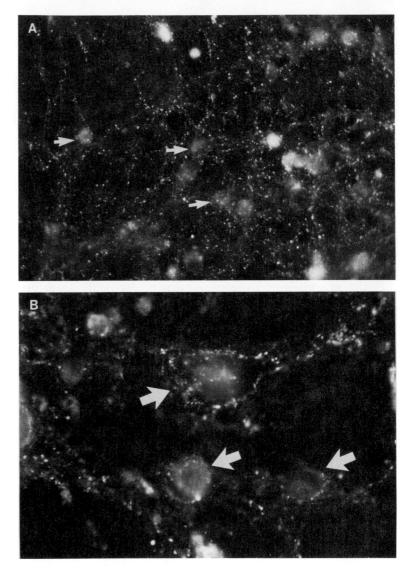

FIG. 1 Immunofluorescence localization of synaptophysin in a primary culture of 16-day-old mouse fetal hypothalamic cells grown for 48 days in SF3 Medium. The immunostaining was performed as previously described [A. Tixier-Vidal, A. Faivre-Bauman, R. Picart, and B. Wiedenmann, *Neuroscience (Oxford)* **26,** 847 (1988)] using a monoclonal antibody SY38 directed against synaptophysin, a transmembrane protein characteristic of synaptic vesicles. (A) At low magnification, numerous labeled particles representing varicosities and synaptic boutons can be seen. Perikarya (arrows) are not in focus. ×325. (b) At high magnification, note the cage of synaptic boutons around several perikarya (arrows). ×650.

Functional Differentiation

The functional differentiation of synapses was appreciated by their ability to release DA, a classical neurotransmitter, and TRH, a neuropeptide, in response to potassium depolarization.

Dopamine Release (34)

In hypothalamic cultures initiated with cells taken on day 16 of gestation and grown in SF2 medium, DA neurons progressively acquire the functional properties of adult DA neurons as concerns DA synthesis, [³H]DA uptake, and DA release (34). Exposure for 3 min to a high potassium concentration (60 mM) stimulated the release of exogenous [³H]DA as well as of endogenous DA, in a strict Ca^{2+}-dependent manner. After 15 days in culture, the percentage of the tissue [³H]DA store released increased 2–2.5 times in response to 60 mM K^+.

The effects of medium components on the response to K^+ depolarization are summarized in Table IV. Deletion of PUFAs, supplementation with T_3 ($10^{-9} M$) or corticosterone ($10^{-7} M$), or both, did not affect the percentage of [³H]DA store released, neither basal nor stimulated. In the case of T_3, although the absolute amount of stored [³H]DA was increased, this did not modify the percentage of content released. Thus, the medium requirements for DA neurons to acquire in culture the functional properties of adult DA neurons appear relatively simple.

TABLE IV Effects of Medium Components on Release of Newly Taken up [³H]DA by Mouse Fetal Hypothalamic Cells Taken from 16-Day-Old Fetuses and Grown for 15 Days[a]

Culture medium	Tissue [³H]DA store released/3 min (%)	
	3 mM K^+	60 mM K^+
SF1	8 ± 0.8	18.4 ± 2.1 (14)
SF2	9.3 ± 0.8 NS	14.8 ± 2.1 NS (7)
SF1 + Cs	8.6 ± 0.5 NS	20.9 ± 1.3 NS (2)
SF1 + T_3	7.3 ± 1 NS	14.7 ± 2.1 NS (2)
SF1 + Cs + T_3	6.9 ± 0.8 NS	19.8 ± 2.1 NS (6)
SF3	5.2 ± 0.5**	19.6 ± 1.7 NS (13)

[a] Symbols for culture medium refer to Table I. Number of experiments given in parentheses. NS, Not significant as compared to SF1 in the same column. **, Different from SF1, $p \leq 0.05$ (Student's t test). [From J. Puymirat, A. Barret, A. Faivre-Bauman, and A. Tixier-Vidal, *Dev. Biol.* **119**, 75 (1987).]

TRH Release (35, 36)

In hypothalamic cultures initiated with 16-day-old fetal cells and grown in SF1, the TRH cell content increases with time in culture and TRH neurons identified by immunostaining differentiate up to synapse formation (10–12 days in culture). However, the capacity of mature TRH neurons to release TRH within 3 min in basal conditions of K^+ concentration (3 mM) was very low (0.5% of intracellular TRH content) and reached 4% only after exposure to 60 mM K^+. Supplementation of SF1 with PUFAs or T_3 or Cs did not change these features. In contrast, simultaneous addition of these three components (SF3 medium, see Table I) increased up to a total of 5% the percentage of TRH cell content released in basal conditions of K^+ and up to a total of 15% the percentage released in presence of 60 mM K^+. These differences are not the consequence of an increase of TRH content which was unchanged whatever the medium composition (35). They most probably reflect the maturation of morphological and biochemical mechanisms necessary for the release of TRH, such as membrane structure, transduction mechanisms, and second messengers. Indeed, this medium condition has permitted the determination of the ionic dependency of TRH release and the involvement in TRH release of different types of calcium channels and activation of protein kinase C (36).

These differences in medium requirements for basal or K^+-stimulated release between DA neurons and TRH neurons reveal that the effects of diffusible factors vary depending on the neuronal specificity. Reciprocally, they disclose new aspects of the respective properties of a catecholamine-synthesizing neuron and a neuropeptide-synthesizing neuron.

Another example of hormonal control of the secretion of a neuropeptide was reported for somatostatin secretion by cultured neocortical cells (37). In that case, the cells were cultured for 7 days in serum-supplemented medium which was then replaced by a serum-free nutrient medium supplemented or not with thyroid hormones (T_3, 0.1–1, nM; T_4, 1–10 nM). Chronic treatment with these hormones for up to 50 hr suppressed release of somatostatin (basal or potassium-induced depolarization) and decreased cell content. Other authors observed a dose-dependent biphasic effect: stimulation or inhibition of thyroid hormones on somatostatin secretion and biosynthesis by rat hypothalamic cells and rat cortical cells (38). In the latter case, larger dose ranges of hormones were used, making comparisons with previous work difficult.

Conclusion

This brief review shows that it is possible to study the effects of diffusible factors in culture on a precise step of the program of differentiation of specified neurons in a precise brain area. It also shows the advantages of using a serum-free medium with a rather limited number of supplements; this greatly helps to define the role of a single factor. The more numerous the components, the more complex are the interactions between them.

The analysis of the mechanism of action of epigenetic diffusible factors remains to be elucidated. There are several possibilities. They may act on neuron gene expression either directly or indirectly through paracrine or autocrine relays. They may also act primarily on glia gene expression. Finally, they may regulate the production and/or action of local growth factors which are produced either by neurons or by glia or both.

Acknowledgments

Work from our laboratory presented in this chapter was supported by grants from Centre National de la Recherche Scientifique (UA 1115), Institut National de la Santé et de la Recherche Médicale (83-4018, 856022, 856025), and Direction Générale de la Recherche Scientifique et Technique (78-7-2761, 81E-0540). Parts of these studies were presented at the ETP Autumn School: "Genetic and Epigenetic Control of Phenotypic Expression in Nerve Cells." We acknowledge the skillful technical assistance of A. Barret and J. Catelon (CNRS) in preparation of cell cultures.

References

1. N. R. Saunders and K. Mollgard, *Trends NeuroSci. (Pers. Ed.)* **4**, 56 (1981).
2. K. Mollgard, K. M. Dziegielewska, N. R. Saunders, H. Zakut, and H. Soreq, *Dev. Biol.* **128**, 207 (1988).
3. Y. A. Barde, *Trends NeuroSci. (Pers. Ed.)* **11**, 343 (1988).
4. B. S. McEwen, *Science* **211**, 1303 (1981).
5. J. Legrand, *J. Physiol. (Paris)* **78**, 603 (1983).
6. H. J. Romijn, F. Van Huizen, and P. S. Wolters, *Neurosci. Biobehav. Rev.* **8**, 301 (1984).
7. J. M. Bourre, M. François, A. You-You, O. Dumont, M. Piciotti, G. Pascal, and G. Durand, *J. Nutr.* **119** (1990).
8. J. Bottenstein, I. Hayashi, S. Hutchings, H. Matsui, J. Mather, D. B. McClure, S. Ohasa, A. Rizzino, G. Sato, G. Serrero, R. Wolfe, and R. Wu, *in* "Methods in Enzymology" (W. B. Jacoby and I. Pastan, eds.), Vol. 58, p. 94. Academic Press, New York, 1979.
9. R. G. Ham and W. L. McKeehan, *in* "Methods in Enzymology" (W. B. Jakoby and I. Pastan, eds.), Vol. 58, p. 44. Academic Press, New York, 1979.

10. R. G. Ham, *in* "Methods for Preparation of Media, Supplements, and Substrata for Serum-Free Animal Cell Culture" (D. W. Barnes, D. A. Sirbasku, and G. H. Sato, eds.), p. 3. Liss, New York, 1984.

11. P. Honegger, D. Lenoir, and P. Favrod, *Nature (London)* **282**, 305 (1979).

12. U. Di Porzio, M. C. Daguet, J. Glowinski, and A. Prochiantz, *Nature (London)* **288**, 370 (1980).

13. A. Faivre-Bauman, E. Rosenbaum, J. Puymirat, D. Grouselle, and A. Tixier-Vidal, *Dev. Neurosci.* **4**, 118 (1981).

14. J. Puymirat, C. Loudes, A. Faivre-Bauman, A. Tixier-Vidal, and J. M. Bourre, *Cold Spring Harbor Conf. Cell Proliferation* **9**, 1033 (1982).

15. H. J. Romijn, A. M. M. C. Habets, M. T. Mud, and P. S. Wolters, *Dev. Brain Res.* **2**, 583 (1982).

16. J. E. Bottenstein and G. H. Sato, *Proc. Natl. Acad. Sci. U.S.A.* **76**, 514 (1979).

17. A. Faivre-Bauman, J. Puymirat, C. Loudes, and A. Tixier-Vidal, *in* "Methods for Serum-Free Culture of Neuronal and Lymphoid Cells" (D. W. Barnes, D. A. Sirbasku, and G. H. Sato, eds.), p. 37. Liss, New York, 1984.

18. F. de Vitry, J. Catelon, M. Dubois, J. Thibault, D. Barritault, J. Courty, S. Bourgoin, and M. Hamon, *Neurochem. Int.* **9**, 43 (1986).

19. F. de Vitry, M. Hamon, J. Catelon, M. Dubois, and J. Thibault, *Proc. Natl. Acad. Sci. U.S.A.* **83**, 8629 (1986).

20. G. Jirikowski, I. Reisert, and C. Pilgrim, *Dev. Brain Res.* **14**, 179 (1984).

21. A. Faivre-Bauman, C. Loudes, A. Barret, C. Patte, and A. Tixier-Vidal, *Dev. Brain Res.* **40**, 261 (1988).

22. C. D. Toran-Allerand, *Brain Res.* **189**, 413 (1980).

23. C. D. Toran-Allerand, K. Hashimoto, W. T. Greenough, and M. Saltarelli, *Dev. Brain Res.* **7**, 97 (1983).

24. J. Puymirat, A. Barret, R. Picart, A. Vigny, C. Loudes, A. Faivre-Bauman, and A. Tixier-Vidal, *Neuroscience (Oxford)* **10**, 801 (1983).

25. J. Puymirat and A. Faivre-Bauman, *Neurosci. Lett.* **68**, 299 (1986).

26. J. Puymirat, M. Luo, and J. H. Dussault, *Neuroscience* **30**, 443 (1989).

27. J. Puymirat, A. Faivre-Bauman, A. Barret, C. Loudes, and A. Tixier-Vidal, *Dev. Brain Res.* **23**, 315 (1985).

28. J. Puymirat, *Neurochem. Int.* **7**, 969 (1985).

29. I. Reisert, V. Han, E. Lieth, D. Toran-Allerand, C. Pilgrim, and J. Lauder, *Int. J. Dev. Neurosci.* **5**, 91 (1987).

30. A. Tixier-Vidal, R. Picart, C. Loudes, and A. Faivre-Bauman, *Neuroscience (Oxford)* **17**, 115 (1986).

31. B. Wiedenmann and W. W. Franke, *Cell* **41**, 1017 (1985).

32. A. Tixier-Vidal, A. Faivre-Bauman, R. Picart, and B. Wiedenmann, *Neuroscience (Oxford)* **26**, 847 (1988).

33. J. M. Bourre, A. Faivre, O. Dumont, A. Nouvelot, C. Loudes, J. Puymirat, and A. Tixier-Vidal, *J. Neurochem.* **41**, 1234 (1983).

34. J. Puymirat, A. Barret, A. Faivre-Bauman, and A. Tixier-Vidal, *Dev. Biol.* **119**, 75 (1987).

35. C. Loudes, A. Faivre-Bauman, A. Barret, D. Grouselle, J. Puymirat, and A. Tixier-Vidal, *Dev. Brain Res.* **9,** 231 (1983).
36. C. Loudes, A. Faivre-Bauman, C. Patte, and A. Tixier-Vidal, *Brain Res.* **456,** 324 (1988).
37. R. A. Peterfreund, P. E. Sawchenko, and W. Vale, *Brain Res.* **328,** 259 (1985).
38. M. T. de los Frailes, L. Cacicedo, M. J. Lorenzo, G. Fernandez, and F. Sanchez-Franco, *Endocrinology* **123,** 898 (1988).

Section VI

Cell Lineage

[24] Microinjectable Probes for Tracing Cell Lineage in Development

Duncan K. Stuart, Steven A. Torrence, and
Gunther S. Stent

Origins of Cell Lineage Studies

Studies of developmental cell lineage, i.e., of the mitotic pedigrees of individual cells in an embryo, were begun in the 1870s, in the context of the controversy then raging about Ernst Haeckel's "biogenetic law." That law seemed to imply that in animal development the cells of early embryos recapitulate the nondifferentiated tissues of a remote, spongelike evolutionary ancestor. Only after gastrulation would the germ layers—ectoderm, mesoderm, endoderm—be destined to take on the tissue differentiation characteristic of more recent metazoan ancestors. To test this implication, Charles O. Whitman (1) observed the cleavage pattern of early leech embryos and followed the fate of individual cells from the egg to the germ-layer stage. He concluded that, contrary to the implication of the biogenetic law, a definite developmental fate can be assigned to each identified embryonic cell and to the clone of its descendants. These findings suggested that the differentiated properties which characterize a given cell of the mature animal are causally linked with the cell's developmental line of descent.

Despite these highly promising beginnings, the study of cell lineage went into decline after the turn of this century. It remained a biological backwater for the next 50 years, while the attention of embryologists focused on cell interactions rather than on cell lineage as causal factors in cell differentiation. About 20 years ago, interest revived in the developmental role of cell lineage. Novel techniques, capable of revealing the line of descent of single, identified cells came into use, such as direct observation of embryogenesis by differential interference contrast microscopy (2), photoablation of specified precursor cells by laser microbeams (3), generation of embryos whose tissues are mosaics of genetically different cells (4), and cell labeling with intracellular lineage tracers (5–8). The last of these techniques is the subject of this chapter. This technique consists of microinjecting into an embryonic cell a tracer molecule that is passed on to all of the lineal descendants of the injected cell, but to no other cells. To this end, the tracer molecule must be large enough not to pass through the intercellular gap junctions that link many embryonic cells. The descendant cells can be identified at a later developmental stage by observing the distribution of the tracer within the embryonic or postembryonic tissues (Fig. 1). Initially developed for cell lineage analysis in leeches (6), microinjectable lineage tracers have been subsequently used in diverse animals, including the frog (e.g., Ref. 9), mouse (e.g., Ref. 10), fish (e.g., Ref. 11), ascidians (e.g., Ref. 12), echinoderms (e.g., Ref. 13), and chick (e.g., Ref. 14).

A very powerful extension of the cell lineage tracer method has recently been introduced, based on the use of a genetically engineered retrovirus with

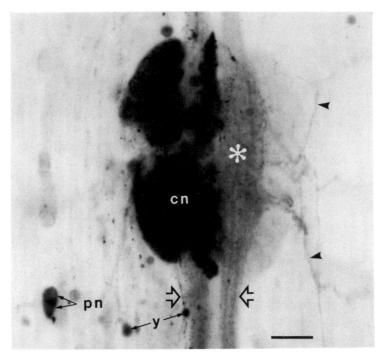

FIG. 1   Lineage tracer in embryonic leech neurons and their axons. An early precursor blastomere of the nervous system was injected with the lineage tracer tetramethylrhodamine–dextran–amine (RDA), and the embryo was fixed and dissected later in development, after formation of the ventral nerve cord. In this negative photomicrograph of a segmental ganglion and the surrounding periphery, the red fluorescence of the RDA appears dark against a lighter autofluorescent background. Clusters of central neurons (cn) in the left half of the ganglion and a few peripheral neurons (pn) contain the tracer. The labeled axons of these neurons and their homologs in adjacent segments are also visible in the interganglionic connective nerves (open arrows), contralateral neuropil (asterisk), and periphery (arrowheads). y, Yolk granules. Bar, 20 μm.

a genome encoding a tracer enzyme whose reaction product can be visualized by histochemistry. An embryo, or part of an embryo, is injected extracellularly with a sufficiently low concentration of the tracer virus so that only one cell or a few widely separated cells become infected. Although the tracer virus replicates in the infected cells, it is engineered so that its progeny cannot infect neighboring cells. Instead, the viral genome, and hence the capability of producing the tracer enzyme, is passed on only to the lineal descendants of the infected cell (15). Because the tracer in this technique is a self-replicating entity, it is not diluted in the course of the cell growth attending each cell division, as occurs in the development of mammalian embryos. This technique permits lineage tracing over many cell generations not only in embryos where microinjected, nonreplicating lineage tracers are diluted excessively, but also where individual embryonic cells are too difficult to impale. However, the retroviral tracers available thus far cannot be targeted precisely to a particular cell.

Comparison of Intracellularly Injectable Tracers

Enzyme Tracers

The first (6) and still most widely used enzymatic lineage tracer is horseradish peroxidase (HRP), which is detected by means of a standard histochemical reaction. The permanent reaction product is visible in a conventional light microscope, exhibits excellent contrast when observed with differential interference contrast or phase-contrast optics, and, because it is osmiophilic, is also well-suited for electron microscopy. HRP histochemical methods have been reviewed by M.-M. Mesulam (16).

A major limitation of HRP as a lineage tracer is that it cannot be visualized in a living embryo, since the embryo must be fixed for the histochemical reaction. Hence, HRP cannot be used for observations of an individual embryo over a series of developmental stages. Another drawback to the use of HRP is the toxicity of the histochemical reagents for the experimenter.

The enzyme β-galactosidase has also been used as a microinjectable lineage tracer (17).

Biotinylated Tracers

A tracer composed of biotin coupled to a dextran carrier to prevent its passage through gap junctions has recently been devised (18). Biotinylated dextran is visualized by staining with an avidin-linked probe. As is the case for enzyme tracers, the embryo must first be fixed. Because a wide variety of avidin-linked probes are available, a biotinylated tracer has the advantage of being visualizable in many different ways, such as by enzyme histochemistry (e.g., HRP, β-galactosidase, alkaline phosphatase) or by a variety of fluorescent labels. As noted below, the lack of light absorbance of the biotin tracer in living embryos can be used to advantage in some experiments.

Fluorescent Tracers

Fluorescent lineage tracers consist of fluorophores coupled to large carrier molecules. They offer the advantage of being detectable in the living embryo, provided that the embryo is sufficiently transparent. This allows the distribution of lineage tracer to be surveyed repeatedly in a single embryo at progressive developmental stages and permits labeled cells to be examined by methods requiring living specimens such as intracellular electrophysiological recording (19).

Currently available fluorescent lineage tracers provide three distinguishable colors: the yellow-green of fluorescein, the reds of rhodamine and its derivatives (including Texas Red), and the blue of coumarin derivatives and the recently developed, proprietary fluorophore *Cascade Blue* (Molecular Probes, Eugene, OR). Restrictions on experimental design imposed by the limited number of distinguishable fluorophores can sometimes be overcome by use of both nonfixable and fixable forms of the tracers. For instance, a nonfixable tracer with a given fluorophore can be used to study cell lineage relations in the living embryo and then be rinsed away when the embryo is fixed. The same fluorophore may then be employed to stain the fixed embryo by indirect immunofluorescence.

The first fluorescent cell lineage tracers to be developed consisted of rhodamine or fluorescein coupled to a dodecapeptide that was synthesized from D-amino acids to provide resistance to digestion by intracellular proteases (7). These tracers have now been supplanted by conjugates of fluorophores to dextrans of low molecular weight. Available dextran-based tracers include the fixable fluorescein–dextran–amine (FDA), tetramethylrhodamine–dextran–amine (RDA), and Texas Red–dextran–amine (TxRDA), in which lysine residues are coupled to the dextran molecule in addition to the fluorophore (8), and the nonfixable (nonlysinated) fluorescein–dextran (FDX) and tetramethylrhodamine–dextran (RDX). [Texas Red (20) is a derivative of rhodamine, which absorbs and emits light at longer wavelengths than tetramethylrhodamine and thus provides superior spectral separation from fluorescein.] The fixable dextran tracer based on Cascade Blue is the best of the blue-fluorescing tracers that we have tested so far. These tracers, as well as other dyes coupled to dextrans of molecular weight 10,000 or larger, are available from Molecular Probes, Inc. (Eugene, OR).

Certain fluorophores have the very useful property of also serving as specific photosensitizers. That is, cells containing tracers based on such fluorophores can be photoablated by intense irradiation with light of the wavelength that excites the fluorophore while adjacent, unlabeled cells are not harmed by the same irradiation (21–23). Thus, cells belonging to a specific, labeled cell lineage that are either too numerous or too small to be killed by direct microinjection, can be ablated specifically, with the embryo being raised to a later stage to examine the developmental effects of the ablation. Photoablation is attributed to the generation of oxygen free radicals, which cause the cell in which they are generated to disintegrate, but which do not diffuse far enough to damage adjacent cells.

Of the dextran tracers we have tested thus far, only those containing fluorescein or eosin (24) fluorophores serve as effective lineage-specific sensitizers for photoablation in leech embryos. The eosin–dextran tracer is a more effective photosensitizer than fluorescein–dextran, but it may not be completely nontoxic to unirradiated cells (25). Lucifer yellow, which has been used as a photosensitizer in adult neurons (26), should also be effective when coupled to dextran. These fluorophores photobleach rapidly when intensely excited. Because rhodamine- and Texas Red-based tracers (RDX, RDA, TxRDA) photobleach more slowly and are less effective photosensitizers, they are the tracers of choice for *in vivo* observations in which photoablation is undesirable or in which repeated observations must be made.

A source of concern about the interpretation of results obtained by sensitized photoablation is that irradiated, labeled cells may remain viable despite their lineage tracer having been bleached to invisibility, thus giving the false appearance of a successful ablation. This possibility is difficult to disprove rigorously, and the interpretation of the results must depend on the experimental context. A convincing demonstration of successful photoablation consists of demonstrating by morphological or immunochemical methods that structures usually derived from the putatively ablated cells are, in fact, absent from the embryo; or, if such structures are present, demonstrating by lineage tracing methods that the structures have been regenerated from some other source. Another demonstration of successful photoablation consists of coinjecting with the photosensitizing tracer a second tracer, such as the biotin tracer, which does not absorb light of the wavelength employed for ablation. If this second tracer is also absent from the area of irradiated cells, it can be inferred that photoablation has indeed taken place. Our experience suggests that, in leech embryos, irradiated but viable photosensitized cells remain at least faintly visible.

A general problem presented by the visualization of fluorescent labels in thick specimens such as whole-mounted embryos is that fluorescent emission from planes above and below the plane of focus can seriously degrade the microscopic image. Scanning confocal microscopy (27) solves this problem by collecting information only from the plane of focus. This method also allows a series of closely spaced optical sections to be recombined by computer into a high-resolution, thicker section or a three-dimensional projection.

The major disadvantage of fluorescent lineage tracers is that they photobleach while they are being examined under the microscope and that they fade with time, even in the dark. Photobleaching during observation can be substantially reduced in fixed tissue by using free radical scavengers, such as *n*-propyl gallate (28) or *p*-phenylenediamine (29) in the mounting medium. Fixable fluorescent lineage tracers generally require formaldehyde fixation, because fixation with gluteraldehyde generates substantial autofluorescence. Antibleaching reagents cannot be used *in vivo,* so fluorophore bleaching often limits the number of live observations that are possible.

Another disadvantage of fluorescent lineage tracers is that they cannot be detected directly under the electron microscope. However, the fluorophore can be converted into an electron-opaque enzymatic reaction product by treatment with HRP-conjugated antibodies directed against the fluorophore (30).

Considerations in Experimental Design

Dilution and Degradation of Tracers

There are several factors that limit the usefulness of microinjected substances for lineage tracing. One of these is dilution of the tracer attending the growth in total cell volume with each division of the injected cell and its descendants. Such tracer dilution may limit the number of cell generations that an experiment can span. Dilution does not occur, however, if the cells divide without growth, as is the case during early embryonic cleavage divisions.

Another limitation is the progressive sequestration of lineage tracers into cytoplasmic vesicles and their eventual degradation. Even before the tracer is degraded, its sequestration into vesicles may prevent interpretation of cell shape, or, in irregularly shaped cells, may even prevent discrimination of which cells are labeled. The rate at which such sequestration occurs varies, with dodecapeptide tracers becoming vesicularized more quickly than dextran tracers. Dextrans of lower molecular weight (about 5,000) appear to vesicularize less rapidly than those of higher molecular weight (about 10,000). The fluorescent dextran tracers can remain visualizable in leech embryos maintained at 20°C for at least 2 months.

Intracellular Distribution of Tracers

Lineage tracers differ in their intracellular distribution, which appears to depend on several variables, including the net charge carried by the tracer molecule, the type of cell containing the tracer, and the length of time the tracer has been present in the embryo. In leech embryos, tracers carrying a net positive charge tend to be concentrated in cell nuclei, whereas neutral or negatively charged tracers are sometimes preferentially excluded from nuclei. Preferential labeling of cell nuclei can be useful for identifying and counting the exact number of cells containing the tracer.

Amount of Tracer Injected

It is critical for the interpretation of lineage tracing experiments that the tracer does not itself affect the course of development. Useful tracers have the property that the cellular distributions they reveal are independent of the amount of tracer injected over a wide range, from barely detectable to quite intense labeling. In conjunction with the absence of developmental abnormalities observable by other methods, this dose-independence provides evidence for the developmental neutrality of the tracers.

Even the most innocuous substance will damage a cell if enough of it is injected, and there is a maximum useful dose of any tracer in a given cell. Exceeding this maximum by a modest amount causes development of abnormal patterns of labeled descendant cells; substantial excess will kill the injected cell outright. Thus, for any new combination of tracer and cell, the largest amount of tracer that can be injected without producing abnormalities must be ascertained by injecting a wide range of amounts. Especially when lineage tracing is to be employed to interpret the effects of experimental perturbations of development, less than the maximum neutral amount of tracer should be used.

Limitations on Visibility

In some favorable cases, it is possible to observe the distribution of lineage tracer-labeled cells in whole mounts or deep within living embryos (31). In less favorable cases, a labeled cell of interest may be obscured by another cell lying above it. Information may also be lost through optical dispersion as the light passes through thick tissues. In such cases it may be necessary to cut histological sections. Alternatively, confocal microscopy of fluorescent tracers can solve some superposition problems.

Combining Labels

It has been our experience that combining HRP with fluorescent tracers in the same specimen is rarely satisfactory. The gluteraldehyde fixation and histochemical reaction for the HRP generally add to the background fluorescence and may also reduce the intensity of the fluorescent tracer, while the opaque reaction product of the enzyme can obscure tracer fluorescence deeper in the tissue.

In contrast, multiple-label experiments in which two or three differently labeled fluorescent lineage tracers are injected into a single embryo and then visualized individually under the epifluorescence microscope by means of appropriate filters are quite feasible. Fixed embryos containing a fluorescent lineage tracer can also be stained by indirect immunofluorescence using a second antibody with a complementary fluorescent label. Green- (fluorescein), red- (rhodamine derivatives), and blue- [aminomethylcoumarin acetate (AMCA) (32) or Cascade Blue; Molecular Probes] fluorescing second antibodies, among others, are commercially available. The distribution of cells containing lineage tracer can then be directly compared to the distribution of antibody label in intact or partially dissected embryos, or in histological sections (14, 33–37). Counterstains for fluorescent labels are generally limited to other fluorescent stains, such as the nuclear stains Hoechst 33258 (blue) and propidium iodide (red).

Methods for Employing Tracers

Injection Solutions

Stock solutions of fluorescent dextrans (100 mg/ml) or HRP (Sigma type IX, 40 mg/ml) in 200 mM KCl (for pressure injection) or distilled water (for iontophoresis) are adjusted to a pH of about 7 and passed through filters of 0.2-μm pore size (Millipore, Bedford, MA, Ultrafree-MC filter unit, 0.22-μm Durapore), divided into 3- or 5-μl portions, and stored at $-70°C$ in small plastic vials. For pressure injection, 1–2 μl of a solution of 40 mg/ml Fast

Green FCF (Sigma) in 200 mM KCl, also filtered at 0.2 μm, is added to a freshly thawed vial of tracer.

Pressure Injection

Pressure injection allows rapid delivery of large volumes of tracer into large blastomeres and may be used with all available tracers. In small cells, however, the volume of tracer delivered may be too difficult to regulate.

Micropipettes

We find that short (approximately 1 cm), abruptly tapering micropipettes clog least, and the stiffness of such pipettes aids in penetrating tough embryonic envelopes. Thin-walled borosilicate glass micropipettes (Sutter Instruments, Novato, CA, #BF 100-78-10; 1.0 mm outside diameter, 0.78 mm inside diameter, with capillary filament) are pulled (Sutter Instruments Model P-80/PC) to give a tip resistance of 25–50 MΩ when filled with the injection solution. They are filled by dipping the blunt end in a drop of injection solution. After filling, micropipettes are beveled to 2–5 MΩ either by holding them briefly in a stream of 120-grit silicon carbide particles suspended in distilled water and expelled from a wash bottle, or by touching them briefly to a rotating glass disk coated with 0.05-μm alumina silicate particles in polyurethane varnish.

Apparatus

The specimen chamber consists of a 60-mm-diameter plastic petri dish half filled with polymerized Epon, which is either transparent or made opaque by inclusion of powdered charcoal. The embryo is held in a funnel-shaped depression in the surface of the Epon. This depression connects to polyethylene tubing embedded in the Epon, which connects in turn to a 1-ml syringe with a screw-driven plunger used to regulate holding suction. The leech embryos we use in our experiments range in diameter from 0.4 to 2 mm. For smaller embryos, a fire-polished glass holding pipette mounted on a micromanipulator may be a more appropriate holding device.

The embryo in the specimen chamber is illuminated from the side by a fiber-optic illuminator (Dolan-Jenner, Woburn, MA, model 180) and viewed through a dissecting microscope. Side illumination is useful for opaque embryos; transparent embryos are better visualized by transillumination with a dark-field condenser (Leitz model 513-356). The holder (E. W. Wright, Guilford, CT) for the injection micropipette is mounted on a micromanipulator and is connected to a device (Picospritzer II, General Valve, Fairfield, NJ) that delivers brief, controlled pressure pulses from a tank of compressed nitrogen. A microelectrode amplifier and oscilloscope for measuring the electrical potential across an impaled cell's membrane are optional. The specimen chamber, micromanipulator, and dissecting microscope are mounted on a vibration-resistant table.

Procedure

The specimen chamber and half of the polyethylene tubing of the holding device are filled with embryo medium made up without divalent cations. An embryo to be injected is maneuvered into a favorable orientation in the holding depression, and gentle suction is applied with the syringe. The target cell is impaled with the micropipette and a series of pressure pulses (typically 3–10 pulses of 10–50 msec each at 50 psig) is applied to fill it with tracer.

The rate of tracer ejection from a pipette may vary over a series of injections if the tip becomes partially clogged with tracer aggregates, cytoplasm, yolk, or bits of embryonic envelope. The volume of tracer injected is therefore judged visually by how deeply colored by Fast Green the cell becomes. The amount of tracer that may be injected without causing abnormal development varies from cell to cell, and must be determined empirically.

Iontophoretic Injection Method

Iontophoresis is well suited for injection into small cells, but is usable only with electrically charged tracers, such as the fixable dextrans.

Micropipettes

Thick-walled borosilicate glass micropipettes (Sutter Instruments #BF 100-50-10; 1.0 mm outside diameter, 0.50 mm inside diameter, with capillary filament) are pulled to give a resistance of 80–120 MΩ and beveled to 60–80 MΩ after filling with the injection solution. Alternatively, thin-walled micropipettes (as above) are pulled to give a tip resistance of 50–60 MΩ, and are used without beveling. In either case, the tips are backfilled with tracer solution and the rest of the electrode is backfilled with water.

Apparatus

An anodized aluminum plate, somewhat larger than the stage of the microscope, is affixed to the mechanical stage of a compound microscope so that it may be moved with the slide-positioning controls. A specimen chamber of the type described above and the manipulator head of a remote-control micromanipulator (Narishige model MO-102) are mounted on this plate. Side-illumination of embryos in the specimen chamber is provided by a fiber-optic illuminator. The micropipette holder is mounted on the manipulator head and is connected via a microelectrode amplifier (Getting Instruments, Iowa City, IA, model 5A) to an oscilloscope. A chlorided silver wire immersed in the specimen chamber provides a ground electrode. The microscope is mounted on a vibration-resistant table and equipped with long-working-distance objectives (Zeiss Neofluar 6.3× NA 0.2; UD40/0.57 with adapter 462990-9901, effectively 25× NA 0.41; achromat 40× water immersion NA 0.75) and epifluorescence illumination.

Procedure

An embryo is held in a favorable orientation as for pressure injection. The target cell is impaled and depolarizing DC current (typically 3–10 nA for 2–10 sec), supplied by the microelectrode amplifier, is passed through the micropipette to eject one of the positively charged, fixable dextran tracers. The amount of tracer injected is judged visually by how brightly fluorescent the cell becomes.

Care of Injected Embryos

After pressure or iontophoretic injection, embryos are returned to standard culture medium, which may be supplemented with 50 μg/ml tetracycline hydrochloride, 100 U/ml potassium penicillin G, and 100 μg/ml streptomycin sulfate. Embryos injected with HRP require no other special care. Embryos injected with fluorescent dextran tracers are cultured in the dark to minimize the chance of photodamage to tracer-labeled cells. Such embryos may, however, be examined briefly under an epifluorescence microscope if the exciting illumination is attenuated by neutral density filters.

Photoablation of Fluorescein-Labeled Blastomeres

Apparatus

A low-power argon ion laser (Lexel model 65, Palo Alto, CA) equipped with a tunable rear prism for single-line emission and a compound microscope equipped with epifluorescence illumination are mounted together on a vibration-resistant table. Zeiss epifluorescence filter set 487717 is used for fluorescein-sensitized photoablation. The laser beam passes through a shutter and a focusable beam expander (Newport, Fountain Valley, CA) and is directed into the microscope by first-surface mirrors. The port through which the laser beam enters the optical path of the microscope is mounted between the mercury arc lamp and the horizontal arm of the epifluorescence illumination system, and consists of a black-anodized aluminum housing holding a beam splitter (Melles Griot model 03 BSC 011 or 03 BTF 023) which joins the illumination from the two sources. The housing is designed to permit placement of neutral density filters in the beam from the mercury arc lamp without affecting the laser beam. The beam splitter simplifies targeting by allowing simultaneous illumination of an embryo with the mercury arc lamp and the laser; the attendant 50% reduction in beam intensity is of little practical significance. Alternatively, a housing holding a rotatable first-surface mirror (Zeiss model 467049-9901) may be used, but does not permit simultaneous use of both sources. In either case, a lens (spherical achromat, $f = 100$ mm; Melles Griot model 01 LAU 033), mounted where the laser beam enters the housing, brings the beam to focus in the conjugate plane of the specimen.

Procedure

The laser is tuned to 488 nm (near the fluorescein absorption peak) and adjusted to yield a beam power of 5–20 mW before the entry of the beam into the optical path of the microscope. By focusing the beam expander, the beam diameter at the specimen plane of the microscope is adjusted to be slightly smaller than the target cells. The beam is aligned to coincide with centered targeting cross hairs in the microscope eyepiece. A 1- to 2-μm-thick slice of polymerized Epon, which is brightly autofluorescent, makes a convenient alignment target.

Oxygen is bubbled through embryo medium containing 0.5% (w/v) methyl cellulose (A4M Premium, Dow Chemical, Midland, MI). An embryo containing fluorescein-labeled blastomeres is immersed in this oxygenated medium and sucked up into a capillary tube (diameter 0.5 or 0.7 mm, wall thickness 0.01 mm; Uni-Mex Co., Valparaiso, IN) of approximately its own diameter. The ends of the tube are sealed with molten paraffin, and the tube is placed in a groove in the upper surface of a Lucite block (50 × 75 × 5 mm) mounted on the microscope stage. The embryos are viewed through water-immersion objectives (Zeiss Plan Neofluar 16× NA 0.5 or 40× NA 0.9) using illumination from the mercury arc lamp attenuated with neutral density filters. The tube is rotated until the target cells are uppermost. Alternatively, a specimen chamber such as is used for injections is mounted on the microscope stage and filled with oxygenated embryo medium (without methyl cellulose). An embryo is manipulated into position so that the target cells are uppermost and is held by gentle suction.

The shutter is then opened and the target cells are bleached by irradiation with the laser beam. If several adjacent cells are to be ablated, the mechanical stage controls are used to move the embryo so that each cell is irradiated in turn. Although the tracer is almost never bleached to complete invisibility, exposure times of 10–15 sec per cell are usually sufficient to bleach it to a small fraction of its initial brightness. Successful ablation is associated with rapid bleaching; if substantial bleaching requires several minutes, the ablation is usually unsuccessful.

Irradiated embryos are returned to antibiotic-supplemented embryo medium for culture to later stages.

Observation Methods

HRP

Embryos of the leech *Theromyzon rude* are fixed for 2–6 hr, on ice, in half-strength Karnovsky's fixative (38) (final concentrations: 2% (w/v) paraformaldehyde, 2.5% (v/v) glutaraldehyde, 1 mM CaCl$_2$, 50 mM sodium cacodylate buffer, pH 7.4), rinsed first in the cacodylate buffer, then in 50 mM sodium HEPES buffer, pH 7.6, and soaked for 15 min in a solution of 1 mg/ml diaminobenzidine tetrahydrochloride (DAB; Polysciences, Warrington, PA) in the HEPES buffer. The HRP histochemical reaction is initiated by adding 10 μl of 0.5% (v/v) H$_2$O$_2$. When the reaction product is sufficiently dark, the reaction is halted by rinsing the embryos in the HEPES buffer without DAB. Tissue preservation is improved and the reaction product intensified by an optional postfixation in 1% (w/v) OsO$_4$ in 50 mM s-collidine buffer, pH 7.4. The embryos are dehydrated in ethanol and embedded in Epon for histological sectioning. If a soft Epon mixture is used (omit stock solution B from the mixture), thick (50–100 μm), freehand sections, suitable for differential interference contrast microscopy, may be cut with a razor blade (39).

Embryos of the leech *Helobdella triserialis* are apparently impermeable to DAB. These are fixed for 4 hr in 2.5% glutaraldehyde in 100 mM sodium cacodylate buffer, pH 7.4, rinsed first in this cacodylate buffer and then in 8% (w/v) sucrose in water, soaked for 10 min in a saturated solution of benzidine dihydrochloride in distilled water, and reacted as above (6). The reaction is halted by rinsing the embryos in embryo medium, and the embryos are dehydrated and embedded in Epon. Because the benzidine reaction product is soluble in ethanol, dehydration must be carried out as rapidly as possible.

Fluorescent Dextrans

Embryos are fixed in buffered paraformaldehyde. [Leech embryos are fixed for 18–24 hr at 4°C in 20 mg/ml paraformaldehyde in 50 mM sodium HEPES buffer, pH 7.4. Embryos old enough to have begun muscular contractions are relaxed in ice-cold embryo medium containing 80 mM chlorobutanol

(Sigma, St. Louis, MO) and pinned on Sylgard before fixation.] If no other blue-fluorescing label is to be used, 5 μg/ml of the DNA-specific, fluorescent dye Hoechst 33258 (Aldrich, Milwaukee, WI) is added to the fixative. After fixation, the embryos are rinsed several times in a buffered saline (HBS) containing 50 mM sodium HEPES, pH 7.4, 145 mM NaCl, and 15 mM sodium azide, and stored at 4°C for up to several weeks.

Embryos to be whole-mounted are cleared and mounted under coverslips in a solution containing, by volume, 80% glycerol, 20% 100 mM Tris-HCl buffer, pH 9, and 40 mg/ml n-propyl gallate. (To make this solution, dissolve the n-propyl gallate in the glycerol before adding the buffer.) Leech yolk reacts with n-propyl gallate; either the yolk must be dissected out before clearing or the n-propyl gallate must be omitted. The edges of the coverslips are sealed with Fluoromount (Gurr, via Bio/medical Specialties, Santa Monica, CA) or nail polish. The slides are stored at −20°C.

Embryos to be embedded for histological sectioning are dehydrated in a graded concentration series of glycol methacrylate monomer (charcoal-filtered to reduce background fluorescence) in HBS and embedded in glycol methacrylate resin (Sorvall JB4). Ethanol dehydration is avoided as it quenches some fluorophores. Sections are cut on glass knives by conventional techniques and mounted in buffered 80% glycerol with n-propyl gallate as above. Sections are examined by differential interference contrast or phase-contrast microscopy in addition to epifluorescence.

Fluorophores are distinguished under the epifluorescence microscope by appropriate filters. Suitable Zeiss filter sets include 487717 for fluorescein, 487715 for tetramethylrhodamine, 487700 for Texas Red, and 487701 or 487702 for Cascade Blue, AMCA, and Hoechst 33258. To maximize image brightness as well as resolution, objectives of the highest available numerical aperture are desirable for epifluorescence observations. However, apochromatic objectives may be unsuitable for observation of blue fluorophores, because they may attenuate the exciting illumination.

Embryos are photographed on Kodak T-Max 100, T-Max 400, Ektachrome 160 Professional, or Ektachrome 400 film. Micrographs showing two different labels in the same specimen are taken as double exposures, using first the filter set appropriate for one of the labels, then the filter set appropriate for the other label. When fluorescence photomicrographs are printed in black and white, we find that negative images, in which fluorescence is rendered dark against a light background (Fig. 1), allow more delicate reproduction of fine detail than do conventional positive images. To make negative prints, micrographs on Ektachrome films are printed directly from the transparencies onto Kodak Panalure or Panalure II Repro panchromatic enlarging papers. Micrographs on black and white negative films are converted to interpositives by projecting the original negatives onto Polaroid Type 55 film, and prints are made from the interpositives.

Synthesis of Fluorescein–Dextran and Rhodamine–Dextran Tracers

Dextran Carriers

Three different dextran carriers are used: *amino-dextran* for the fixable tracers FDA, RDA, and TxRDA; *carboxy-dextran* for the nonfixable rhodamine–dextran tracer RDX; and pure, unsubstituted dextran for the nonfixable fluorescein–dextran tracer FDX.

Preparation of Amino-Dextran (40)

Dextran (500 mg; Research Plus, Bayonne, NJ, MW 4000–6000 or Sigma, MW 9000) is dissolved in 50 ml of distilled water and the pH is adjusted to 10.8 ± 0.1 with 1 *N* NaOH. Cyanogen bromide (200 mg; Sigma) is added with continuous stirring. The pH is monitored continuously and kept between 10.7 and 10.9 by repeated addition of small drops of 1 *N* NaOH. When the pH has stabilized (15–20 min), 1.72 g of lysine monohydrochloride (Sigma) is added and the pH is adjusted to 8.35 with 6 *N* NaOH. The solution is stirred overnight at 4°C, dialyzed for 2 days in Spectraphor 3 membrane tubing (MW cutoff 3500) against at least three 1-liter changes of distilled water, and lyophilized. The amino-dextran product is stored at −20 or −70°C.

These conditions are designed to bind 2–3 lysine residues to each dextran molecule. This ratio may be estimated by the following trinitrobenzene sulfonate assay for free amino groups (41). A 0.4 m*M* solution of the dextran-amine to be assayed, standard solutions of 0.2, 0.5, 1.0, 2.0, and 4.0 m*M* ethylamine hydrochloride (Aldrich), and spectrophotometric blanks of distilled water and 0.4 m*M* dextran are prepared. To 2-ml samples of each is added 2 ml of 4% sodium bicarbonate, pH 8.5, followed by 2 ml of 1 mg/ml 2,4,6-trinitrobenzenesulfonic acid (picrylsulfonic acid; Sigma). The reaction is allowed to proceed for 2 hr at 40°C, and then is terminated by the addition of 2 ml of 1.0 *M* HCl. A 0.5-ml sample of each solution is diluted with 9.5 ml of 0.01–0.05 *M* HCl. The absorbance of each sample at 335 nm is measured, the water solution serving as a blank for the ethylamine hydrochloride standards and the dextran solution as a blank for the dextran–amine solution. A standard curve is constructed and the concentration of amino groups (bound lysine residues) in the amino-dextran sample is read from the curve.

Preparation of Carboxy-Dextran (8)

Dextran (500 mg, as above) is dissolved in 100 ml of distilled water at room temperature and the pH is adjusted to 10.8 ± 0.1 with 0.1 *N* NaOH. Cyanogen bromide (250 mg) is added with continuous stirring, and the pH is kept steady between 10.7 and 10.9 by repeated addition of small drops of 1 *N* NaOH. When the pH has stabilized, 1 g of glycine (Sigma) is added to the activated dextran and the pH is brought to 8.35 with 6 N NaOH. The solution is stirred overnight at 4°C, dialyzed, and lyophilized as above.

Synthesis of Fluorescein–Dextran Tracers (42)

Dichlorotriazinylaminofluorescein dihydrochloride (30 mg; Research Organics, Cleveland, OH) and 100 mg of either amino-dextran (to make the fixable tracer FDA) or unsubstituted dextran (to make the nonfixable tracer FDX) are dissolved in 3 ml of distilled water at room temperature and the pH is adjusted to 11 with 1 N NaOH. After 2 hr, this reaction mixture is poured dropwise into 50 ml of rapidly stirred, 100% ethanol at room temperature to precipitate the product, FDA or FDX. The solution is centrifuged and the pellet is lyophilized.

Synthesis of Tetramethylrhodamine–Dextran Tracers

Tetramethylrhodamine B isothiocyanate isomer R (40 mg; Sigma) and 100 mg of either amino-dextran (to make the fixable tracer RDA) or carboxy-dextran (to make the nonfixable tracer RDX) are dissolved in 3 ml of dimethyl sulfoxide at 97°C in a waterbath. Two drops of pyridine and 2 μl of the catalyst dibutyltin dilaurate (practical grade; Fluka, Ronkonkoma, NY) are added. After 2 hr, the mixture is poured dropwise into 50 ml of rapidly stirred, 100% ethanol at room temperature to precipitate the product, RDA or RDX. The solution is centrifuged and the pellet is lyophilized.

Synthesis of Fixable Texas Red–Dextran Tracer

Dextran–amine (100 mg) is dissolved in 5 ml of a solution of 0.15 M NaCl and 0.2 M Tris-HCl buffer, pH 9, at 4°C. Texas Red powder (20 mg; sulforhodamine 101 acid chloride, Research Organics; not preexposed to atmosphere) is added with stirring. After 4 hr, the mixture is poured dropwise into 50 ml of rapidly stirred, 100% ethanol at room temperature to precipitate the product, TxRDA. The solution is centrifuged and the pellet is lyophilized.

Purification of Tracers

Approximately 100 mg of lyophilized tracer is dissolved in 1 ml of 100 mM ammonium carbonate buffer, pH 9, and chromatographed on a BioGel P-4 column (10 g, 50 cm by 10 mm; Bio-Rad, Richmond, CA). The tracers are heterogeneous in molecular weight, and elute in a broad, intensely colored peak extending from the void volume through the initial postvoid fractions. These fractions are collected, frozen in a beaker immersed in dry ice and 95% ethanol, and lyophilized until all the ammonium carbonate has sublimed. The lyophilized tracer is stored at $-20°C$ until it is used to make the stock solutions.

Estimation of Fluorophore/Dextran Ratio

The number of fluorophores bound per dextran molecule is estimated by comparing the absorbance of a given concentration of the tracer to the absorbance of known concentrations of the free fluorophore at its wavelength of maximal absorbance. For these estimates, the molecular weight of the tracer is assumed to be the same as the average molecular weight of the dextran starting material. The procedures given above generally bind 1–3 fluorophores per dextran molecule.

Acknowledgments

We thank Kathryn A. Halpin and Muoi Loi for technical assistance and Gerald P. Keleher for contributions to the injection procedures. This work was supported in part by research grants NS 12818 and HD 17088 from the National Institutes of Health and BNS 8309564 and 8820033 from the National Science Foundation, as well as by grants from the March of Dimes Birth Defects Foundation MOD 1-738 and the Rowland Foundation.

References

1. C. O. Whitman, *J. Morphol.* **1,** 105 (1887).
2. J. E. Sulston, E. Schierenberg, J. G. White, and J. N. Thomson, *Dev. Biol.* **100,** 64 (1983).
3. J. E. Sulston and J. G. White, *Dev. Biol.* **78,** 577 (1980).
4. A. Garcia-Bellido and J. R. Merriam, *J. Exp. Zool.* **170,** 61 (1969).
5. G. S. Stent, D. A. Weisblat, S. S. Blair, and S. L. Zackson, *in* "Neuronal Development" (N. Spitzer, ed.), p. 1. Plenum, New York, 1982.
6. D. A. Weisblat, R. T. Sawyer, and G. S. Stent, *Science* **202,** 1295 (1978).
7. D. A. Weisblat, S. L. Zackson, S. S. Blair, and J. D. Young, *Science* **209,** 1538 (1980).
8. R. L. Gimlich and J. Braun, *Dev. Biol.* **109,** 509 (1985).

9. R. L. Gimlich and J. Cooke, *Nature (London)* **306,** 471 (1983).
10. H. Balakier and R. A. Pederson, *Dev. Biol.* **90,** 352 (1982).
11. C. B. Kimmel and R. D. Law, *Dev. Biol.* **108,** 94 (1985).
12. H. Nishida and N. Satoh, *Dev. Biol.* **99,** 382 (1983).
13. T. Komminami, *J. Embryol. Exp. Morphol.* **75,** 87 (1983).
14. M. Bronner-Fraser and S. E. Fraser, *Nature (London)* **335,** 161 (1988).
15. J. Sanes, *Trends NeuroSci. (Pers. Ed.)* **12,** 21 (1989).
16. M.-M. Mesulam, "Tracing Neural Connections with Horseradish Peroxidase." Wiley, New York, 1982.
17. R. D. Streck, S. T. Bissen, and D. A. Weisblat, *Soc. Neurosci. Abstr.* **13,** 1139 (1987).
18. R. K. Ho and D. A. Weisblat, *Dev. Biol.* **120,** 520 (1987).
19. A. P. Kramer and D. A. Weisblat, *J. Neurosci.* **5,** 388 (1985).
20. J. A. Titus, R. Haugland, S. O. Sharrow, and D. M. Segal, *J. Immunol. Methods* **50,** 193 (1982).
21. J. D. Spikes, *in* "Photophysiology" (A. C. Giese, ed.), p. 33. Academic Press, New York, 1968.
22. M. Shankland, *Nature (London)* **307,** 541 (1984).
23. J. Braun and G. S. Stent, *Dev. Biol.* **132,** 486 (1989).
24. J. Braun, Ph.D. thesis. University of California, Berkeley, 1985.
25. M. Martindale and M. Shankland, personal communication.
26. J. P. Miller and A. I. Selverston, *Science* **206,** 702 (1979).
27. J. G. White, W. B. Amos, and M. Fordham, *J. Cell Biol.* **105,** 41 (1987).
28. H. Giloh and J. W. Sedat, *Science* **217,** 1252 (1982).
29. G. D. Johnson, R. S. Davidson, K. C. McNamee, G. Russell, D. Goodwin, and E. J. Holborow, *J. Immunol. Methods* **55,** 231 (1982).
30. P. H. Taghert, M. J. Bastiani, R. K. Ho, and C. S. Goodman, *Dev. Biol.* **94,** 391 (1982).
31. N. A. O'Rourke and S. E. Fraser, *Dev. Biol.* **114,** 265 (1986).
32. H. Khalfan, R. Abuknesha, M. Rand-Weaver, R. G. Price, and D. Robinson, *Histochem. J.* **18,** 497 (1986).
33. S. A. Torrence and D. K. Stuart, *J. Neurosci.* **6,** 2736 (1986).
34. D. K. Stuart, S. S. Blair, and D. A. Weisblat, *J. Neurosci.* **7,** 1107 (1987).
35. J. Braun and G. S. Stent, *Dev. Biol.* **132,** 471 (1989).
36. D. K. Stuart, S. A. Torrence, and M. I. Law, *Dev. Biol.* **136,** 17 (1989).
37. S. A. Torrence, M. I. Law, and D. K. Stuart, *Dev. Biol.* **136,** 40 (1989).
38. M. J. Karnovsky, *J. Cell Biol.* **27,** 137A (1965).
39. M. Shankland and D. A. Weisblat, *Dev. Biol.* **106,** 326 (1984).
40. K. Mosbach, P.-O. Larsson, and C. Lowe, *in* "Methods in Enzymology" (K. Mosbach, ed.), Vol. 44, p. 859. Academic Press, New York, 1976.
41. A. F. S. A. Habeeb, *Anal. Biochem.* **14,** 328 (1966).
42. A. N. de Belder and K. Granath, *Carbohydr. Res.* **30,** 375 (1973).

[25] Methods for Clonal Analysis and Tracing Cell Lineages of Vertebrate Central Nervous System

Marcus Jacobson

Introduction

In this chapter, I adopt an essentially practical approach to clonal analysis of the vertebrate central nervous system (CNS). The emphasis is on the techniques, not on the theories, which are dealt with elsewhere (1–3). The methods adopted will be determined by the specific aims of the investigation. Therefore, the scope and limitations of clonal analysis are reviewed briefly here.

A *clone* is a cell population that is descended from a single ancestral cell. A *polyclone* is a cell population that is descended from a small group of ancestral cells. Such small groups of cells have been shown to become committed to a specific morphological fate (i.e., to form a specified domain of the final structure), but single cells within the group are not necessarily committed to form any type of cell (4).

Clonal analysis aims at a complete description of the growth of a clone or polyclone from identified ancestral cells, including the number of descendants, their states of determination at progressively later cell generations, and their final states of differentiation. The *lineage* of any specific type of cell, for example, spinal cord motor neurons, can be traced as part of a clonal analysis. Fate maps can be deduced from regular relationships between the positions of ancestral cells and the positions and types of their descendants. Clonal analysis includes more than tracing cell lineages and constructing fate maps, which are merely descriptive. Clonal analysis also aims at finding clonal restrictions of the developmental potentials of cells. For clones or polyclones to be of significance they must show developmental singularities. Clonal singularities may take the form of either expression or restrictions of developmental activities of cells determined by their origin from specified ancestral cells, and shared by all cells descended from the same progenitors. Clonal singularities may be morphological or histological. Morphological clonal restrictions involve segregation of clones or polyclones in separate spatial domains or compartments (4). Histological clonal singularities involve expression or restrictions of cell differentiation determined by origins from specified ancestral cells.

To study morphological clonal restrictions, it is necessary to initiate labeled clones at early stages of developmental, before and during the period of morphogenesis, i.e., starting before gastrulation. By contrast, to study the relation of cell lineages to final states of cell differentiation, it is necessary to initiate labeled clones at or before the stages at which cells become committed to specific fates, which may be delayed until at or near their terminal cell cycle.

The techniques of clonal analysis all require a means of labeling a single ancestral cell, at a chosen time in development, with a label that is not found normally in the cell lineages being traced, that does not alter normal development, and is passed on to all the progeny, and can be detected at later stages. Several methods are available for initiating a labeled clone from a single ancestral cell: (1) by introducing a heritable lineage tracer into the cytoplasm; (2) by insertion of a retrovirus carrying a reporter gene into the genome; (3) by means of a radiation-induced somatic mutation that results in a nonlethal phenotypic alteration, usually a change in pigmentation, that can be easily detected in the progeny; and (4) by introducing one or more ancestral cells, labeled with an heritable intracellular lineage tracer or with a genetic marker, into an unlabeled or wild-type embryo. The methods which are chosen will be dictated by the aims of the investigation and by the species and stage of development. It should also be emphasized that tracing cell lineages cannot, by itself, show the times of commitment of cells to different fates. To study the role of cell lineage in cell determination (commitment, specification) it is necessary to combine lineage tracing with grafting cells (or ideally, a single cell) to different positions. In that way, it can be shown whether fates are determined by lineage from specific progenitors (i.e., are cells autonomous), or whether cell fates are determined by extrinsic factors that are position-dependent, such as cell interactions and induction, or by a combination of factors.

In principle, genetic markers should be ideal for clonal analysis or lineage tracing in vertebrates because they are expressed in all the progeny of the originally marked cells regardless of the number of cell generations or of cell differentiation and growth. Genetically marked cells can be grafted to produce genetic mosaics or aggregation chimeras. This has been done in amphibian, avian, and mammalian embryos. Retroviruses have been used as a means of inserting a genetic marker into dividing cells in avian and mammalian embryos. Another significant advantage is that retroviruses enter cells in the S-phase of mitosis, without requiring intracellular injection.

In vertebrate embryos, the inherent difficulties of clonal analysis arise from the following factors, which have to be taken into consideration when deciding on the most advantageous techniques.

1. Access to the embryo is limited in amniotes and mammals, which may make it necessary to perform the experiment *in vitro*. For example, Calof and Jessell (5) cultured midgestation rat embryos *in vitro* and infected them with a retrovirus injected in the amniotic cavity. They were able to trace clones for several days, which was the limit of survival *in vitro*. Muneoka *et al.* (6) have successfully operated on mouse embryos delivered from the uterus into the abdominal cavity, attached to the placenta. After closure of the abdomen, these fetuses developed normally to the end of gestation and were delivered by cesarean section.

2. Variability of cleavage patterns during blastula stages will result in variability of the sizes and positions of clones initiated from early-stage blastomeres. It may be advantageous to select embryos with regular patterns of cleavage or to initiate the labeled clone at small-cell blastula stages, at a time after which the earlier patterns of cleavage are not significant (Fig. 1).

3. Many cell generations are produced before the stages of final cell differentiation, so that any clone initiated at blastula stages will finally consist of thousands of cells of many histotypes. During the time between initiation and final characterization of the clone, cell mingling and cell death are likely to occur. To take these into account, it is necessary to look at intermediate stages in clonal development. This requires using fluorescent labels which enable cells to be traced *in vivo,* and studying the states of the clone at progressively later stages in a series of fixed embryos.

Clonal Analysis Using Intracellular Injection of Tracers

Intracellular injection of a heritable cell lineage is the method of choice in cases where the size of the cells is large enough, and where repeated cells divisions and cell growth do not result in dilution of the tracer below limits of detectability.

Two classes of molecules are available for tracing cell lineages of the vertebrate CNS: enzymes, of which horseradish peroxidase is the most useful (7), and fluorescent probes, such as rhodamine or fluorescein coupled to dextran about 10,000 MW, to prevent permeation of gap junctions, and lysinated to enable fixation in histological preparation (8–10). These tracers are readily available commercially (Molecular Probes, Eugene, OR). To be useful as intracellular lineage tracers, these molecules should not be present in the injected cells, or endogenous levels should be very low relative to injected amounts. The former holds for the fluorescent dextrans, the latter for HRP. The molecules should not permeate gap junctions (i.e., they should be larger than 5000 MW), and should be nontoxic at initial injected levels that can be detected in the progeny after 10- to 30-fold dilutions. Both HRP and fluorescent dextrans satisfy these criteria when injected intracellulary in

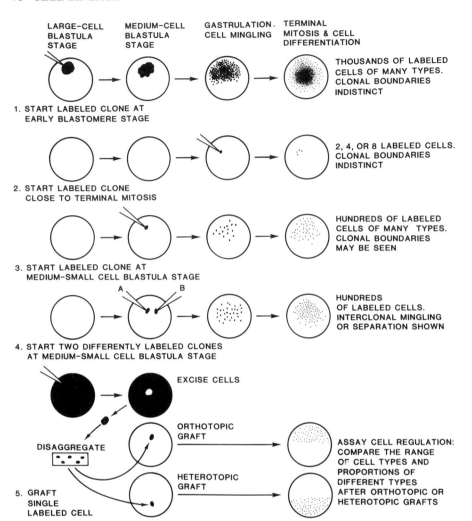

LARGE-CELL
BLASTULA
STAGE

MEDIUM-CELL
BLASTULA
STAGE

GASTRULATION.
CELL MINGLING

TERMINAL
MITOSIS & CELL
DIFFERENTIATION

THOUSANDS OF LABELED
CELLS OF MANY TYPES.
CLONAL BOUNDARIES
INDISTINCT

1. START LABELED CLONE AT
EARLY BLASTOMERE STAGE

2, 4, OR 8 LABELED CELLS.
CLONAL BOUNDARIES
INDISTINCT

2. START LABELED CLONE
CLOSE TO TERMINAL MITOSIS

HUNDREDS OF LABELED
CELLS OF MANY TYPES.
CLONAL BOUNDARIES
MAY BE SEEN

3. START LABELED CLONE AT
MEDIUM-SMALL CELL BLASTULA STAGE

HUNDREDS
OF LABELED CELLS.
INTERCLONAL MINGLING
OR SEPARATION SHOWN

4. START TWO DIFFERENTLY LABELED CLONES
AT MEDIUM-SMALL CELL BLASTULA STAGE

EXCISE CELLS

ORTHOTOPIC
GRAFT

DISAGGREGATE

HETEROTOPIC
GRAFT

5. GRAFT
SINGLE
LABELED CELL

ASSAY CELL REGULATION:
COMPARE THE RANGE
OF CELL TYPES AND
PROPORTIONS OF
DIFFERENT TYPES
AFTER ORTHOTOPIC OR
HETEROTOPIC GRAFTS

FIG. 1   Methods of initiation of labeled clones from a single, identified ancestral cell, labeled with an intracellular cell lineage tracer in the frog embryo. (Method 1, Ref. 7; method 2, Refs. 23 and 24; method 3, Ref. 7; method 4, Ref. 9; method 5, Ref. 37.)

the appropriate volume (0.1–5 μl, proportional to the size of the cell) or diluted (HRP, <10 mg/ml, in sterile distilled water). Larger amounts frequently result in blockade of mitosis and cell death.

The main advantages of the technique of intracellular injection are positive identification of the initially labeled ancestral cell and the ability to monitor the developing clone, using a fluorescent label (Fig. 1, method 1, and Fig. 2). Another advantage is that two or more labels can be used in a number of different combinations. For example, a fluorescent labeled dextran can be coinjected with horseradish peroxidase to obtain the combined advantages of both tracers: the ability to monitor the clone continuously as well as the greater sensitivity and resolution of histological details afforded by HRP. Sheard and Jacobson (9) have injected two different fluorescent dextrans (lissamine–rhodamine–dextran and fluorescein isothiocyanate–dextran) into two ancestral cells in the same frog embryo in order to study the amount of mingling between the clones (Fig. 1, method 3). Another possible application, not yet published, is to inject one fluorescent tracer into a single ancestral cell at an early stage and another fluorescent tracer into one of the labeled progeny, thus producing a doubly labeled subclone. The purpose of such a double-fluorescent labeling technique would be to study the times of divergence of different lineages in the same clone. By using two fluorescent labels with well-separated absorption peaks, it would be possible to photoablate the subclone by exposing the embryo to the peak absorption wavelength of the second fluorescent label, effectively killing the double-labeled cells, but not those labeled only with the first label.

Injection of tracers into single cells requires microinjection to control the dose delivered, and the micropipette needs to be guided to the selected cell by means of a micromanipulator which is under direct vision through a microscope, or indirectly viewed with a television camera and video monitor. The apparatus should be rigidly fixed, preferably on antivibration mountings. However, the embryo is always the least rigid part, and it may not be possible to hold it securely. A holder made of soft modeling clay, which can be molded quickly to the desired form, provides stability without impairing the viability of the embryo or fetus.

Injection may be either by means of pressure or iontophoresis. Equipment for this purpose is available commercially. The viscosity of an aqueous solution of HRP greater than 20 mg/ml or of fluorescent dextran greater than 200 mg/ml may make it difficult to fill the micropipette, and may result in blockage of the tip. However, the maximum concentrations recommended are about half those amounts. The tracers can be injected iontophoretically, using positive current pulses (200 msec, 5 nA, 2 Hz, 10 sec are typical parameters, but these should be determined empirically for specific applications). Measurement of a resting membrane potential provides the assurance that the pipette tip is intracellular before and after expelling the tracer. The pneumatic injection devices provide a holding pressure to prevent slow leakage of the tracer from inside the micropipette and to prevent influx of fluid from outside, and a short pulse of pressure is given for the injection of tracer into the cell. It is useful to be able to monitor the injection of HRP or any other enzyme by coinjection of a fluorescent tracer such as lissamine–rho-damine–dextran. After injection, the embryo can be viewed under a fluorescence microscope equipped with a sensitive television camera and video monitor as described below. In order to avoid phototoxic damage (11), it is necessary to use very low levels of exciting wavelength and to avoid the use of ultraviolet.

Micropipette fabrication requires a brief comment. Micropipettes are pulled on a standard device available for this purpose, either a vertical or horizontal puller (12). Standard glass (aluminosilicate) thin-walled capillary tubing used for intracellular recording is utilized, preferably containing a glass filament to assist filling the micropipette with the tracer (13). Glass capillary tubing should be washed and then sterilized before pulling. The ideal configuration of the micropipettes used for intracellular injection is a short, sharply tapered shank, to provide maximum rigidity. This is easily made by a double-pull technique (12): the capillary is heated initially, without pulling, to a temperative at which the glass softens, then, after a short pull, an air puff cools the glass, which is quickly reheated and finally pulled to a fine tip. For pressure injection, the inner diameter of the tip should be about 1 μm; smaller diameters result in frequent blockage of the tip. It is usually necessary to break the tip under a compound microscope, which requires considerable practice, or to bevel the tip of the micropipette (14, 15). For iontophoresis, the microelectrode tip diameter should be below the resolution of the light microscope, so impedance measurements are used instead, aiming for an impedance of about 10 to 20 MΩ when filled with 1.2 M LiCl.

The labeled cells are finally visualized by reacting the tissue, either as a whole mount or in histological sections, with the substrate, hydrogen peroxide, and a suitable chromagen (tetramethylbenzidine or diaminobenzidine tetrahydrochloride) which forms an insoluble reaction product (16). One of the advantages of HRP is that the reaction product can be detected by electron microscopy as well as light microscopy. With the electron microscope, the HRP reaction product can be shown to be relatively uniformly distributed in the cell, not associated specifically with any cellular components. Greatly increased sensitivity of HRP as a cell lineage tracer can be achieved by using biotinylated HRP. The labeled cells are finally reacted with avidin complexed with a fluorescent molecule (17) or with an enzyme that can be detected histochemically. Avidin has a very high affinity for biotin, to which it binds irreversibly. Avidin has four binding sites for biotin and most proteins, including HRP and other enzymes. This allows macromolecular complexes to be formed between avidin and biotinylated HRP. Jacobson and Huang (18) have made use of this technique for tracing lineages of spinal cord neurons in *Xenopus*. The enhanced sensitivity of the

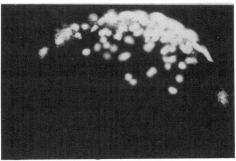

FIG. 2   (A and B) Mixing and dispersal of the labeled clone in the zebrafish embryo. A single blastomere was injected with a fluorescent cell lineage tracer at the 64-cell stage, and the photographs show the resulting clone 5 hr later in the living gastrula. (B) Epifluorescence alone is shown. [From Kimmel and Warga (10).]

final reaction between the injected biotinylated HRP and the avidin–HRP complexes resulted in staining that gave excellent histological resolution of, for example, outgrowing neurites and filopodia on growth cones (Fig. 3).

Clonal Analysis Using Retrovirus as Vectors for Gene Transfer

Almost any gene can be cloned into a retrovirus vector by standard recombinant DNA techniques (Fig. 3). However, there are several specific requirements for constructing a retroviral vector suitable for tracing cell lineages in the vertebrate nervous system. (1) The virus must be infective in the species under investigation but should not infect humans. This is ensured by using suitable vectors, for example, those which have an envelope protein of the ectotropic class which allows entry only into rat and mouse cells. At present, suitable retroviruses are available that infect mammalian and avian cells, but retrovirus vectors suitable for clonal analysis have not yet been constructed for use in fish or amphibians. (2) A suitable packaging cell line is used for producing quantities of the retrovirus. (3) The vector should be constructed to contain a promoter that is expressed specifically in neural cell lineages, or which is not tissue specific. The expression in neural progenitor cells of the Moloney murine leukemia virus long-terminal-repeat (MMLV-LTR) promoter, and the SV40 early promoter, transduced by a retrovirus, has been demonstrated in chick, mouse, and rat (5, 19, 20). (4) The reporter gene transduced into the retroviral vector should provide a gene product that is easily identifiable by immunohistological or histochemical methods. Furthermore, the gene product should be harmless and should either be absent

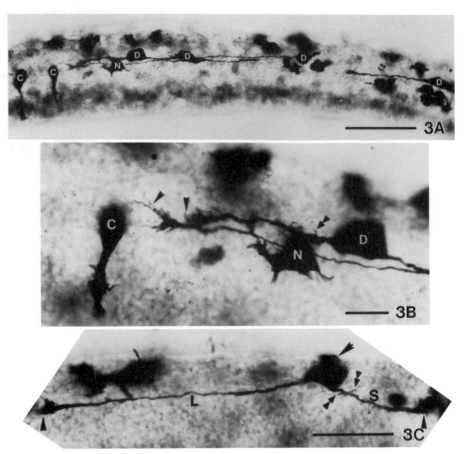

FIG. 3 Whole mount of trunk spinal cord of *Xenopus* embryo at stage 24 after injection of HRP into blastomere V1.2.1 at the 32-cell stage. N, Neuron at stage of initiation of neurite outgrowth, with filopodial processes on the cell body. D, Dorsal longitudinal neurons with neurites extending rostrally and caudally, terminating in growth cones with filopodia (arrowheads in B). Double arrowheads in C point to filopodia on the neurite shaft. C, Commissural neurons with short, broad neurite extending ventrally, terminating in a growth cone with filopodia. Rostral is to the left, and dorsal to the top of the photographs. Bar, 100 μm (A); 20 μm (B); 50 μm (C). [From Jacobson and Huang (18).]

from the normal tissue or be overexpressed relative to the endogenous levels. The *Escherichia coli* β-galactosidase gene (*β-gal*) satisfies these criteria: it is expressed at high levels in cells after infection with retrovirus, either from the MMLV-LTR promoter (13) or SV40 early promoter (20). The β-galactosidase activity is easily detected histochemically, as it produces an intense blue precipitate after hydrolysis of the substrate X-Gal. However, the histological resolution obtained by this method, while it may be adequate for easily identified types of cells, is inferior to that obtained with HRP or fluorescent tracers, as comparison between Figs. 2, 3, and 4 shows.

The retrovirus is injected extracellularly in a small volume (0.1–1 μl) containing a virus titer of 10^6–10^8 colony-forming units (cfu)/ml into the region containing neural ancestral cells. A dye such as Trypan blue (0.05%) can be injected with the virus to aid in monitoring the injection site. Retroviruses enter cells by interaction between the viral envelope and receptors on the host cell surface, so that intracellular injection is not required. Virus enters cells rapidly and is cleared from the extracellular space within a few hours. Virus infects both postmitotic and mitotic cells, but only integrates with the genome of cells in the S-phase. It is important to inject the virus close to dividing cells, and to use a dose low enough to result in infection of very few, well-separated cells, to ensure that isolated labeled clones are produced. Cells are infected at random, so that this method does not permit identification of the progenitor cell.

The advantage of the retroviral method is that it permits labeling of cells that are too small to be injected directly with a lineage tracer, which is usually the case for cells near their final mitosis. The retroviral method is most useful when applied to problems related to the terminal branches of lineages, for example, whether the same progenitor gives rise to more than one nerve cell type or to both nerve cells and glial cells (21, 22). The main disadvantage is that the ancestral cells initially labeled with retrovirus cannot be identified. Therefore, intracellular injection of tracers is the preferable method, when it is possible to do at or close to the termination of the lineage (23, 24).

Clonal Analysis by Means of Mosaics and Chimeras

Mosaics or chimeras can be produced by several different techniques: (1) fusion of two or more embryos of different genotypes, (2) grafting of one or more cells of one genotype into an embryo of a different genotype, or (3) grafting of one or more cells labeled with a heritable cell lineage tracer into an unlabeled host of the same species.

The cells of two embryos of different genotypes can be combined so that the progeny of both genotypes form parts of the adult animal. From the numbers of cells and their spatial configuration, the initial numbers of ancestral cells may be deduced (25). Several cell-autonomous markers have been

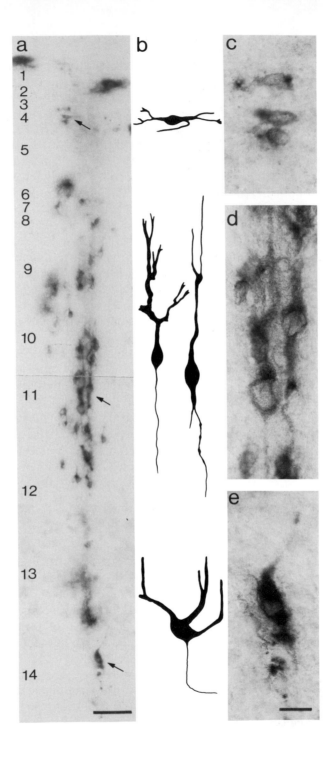

used, such as chromosomal marker and enzyme variants, which can be detected histologically.

Chimeras made by introduction of rat inner mass cells into mouse blastocysts have been made, and the rat and mouse cells can later be identified by staining with Hoechst dye (26) or by *in situ* hybridization with species-specific DNA probes (27). However, this has proved to be useful for short-term analysis only, because most rat cells were selectively eliminated in such chimeras as development proceeded (28). Interspecific chimeras of *Mus musculus* and *Mus caroli* have been made by embryo aggregation or insertion of cells of one species into the mass cells of an embryo of the other species (29). The cells of the two types can be identified in tissue sections by *in situ* hybridization with species-specific DNA probes. A reliable technique that gives adequate preservation of histological details after denaturation of DNA (required for *in situ* hybridization), and uses a biotinylated DNA probe, is given in Ref. 29.

A method of producing genetic mosaics by radiation-induced somatic cell mutations, first used for clonal analysis in *Drosophila* (30), has been adapted for use in the zebrafish (31). Zebrafish embryo heterozygous for the golden mutation are γ-irradiated from a cesium-137 source (dose about 1000 R per min, for 0.1–1.0 min) to result in homozygous, labeled blastomeres. The progeny of the labeled blastomeres are phenotypically distinguishable from wild-type darkly pigmented cells in showing golden pigment in the pigmented retinal epithelial cells. The frequency of induction of labeled clones varies with the dose of gamma rays and the stage of development, and a single clone is produced at doses that generate mosaic eyes in less than 10% of embryos. This type of clonal analysis has to be done retrospectively, and requires statistical analysis of the number of cells in labeled clones in a large sample of animals. The limitations of retrospective analysis of chimeras and mosaics are well known (1, 25). Some of the problems that can arise from analysis of genetic mosaics are piquantly shown by a recent debate about the validity of conclusions drawn from lineage analysis of cerebellar Purkinje and facial nucleus neurons of the mouse CNS (32, 33).

Interspecific cell transplantation between quail and chick embryos has been particularly successful in tracing migrating cells of neural crest origin (34). Identification of cells derived from quail or chick is possible because of

---

FIG. 4 (a) A clone of *lacZ*-positive cells in the optic tectum of a chick embryo that was injected at stage 17 and fixed at stage 45 (embryonic day 19). Laminae are numbered from the surface to the ventricle. Arrows indicate cells shown at higher magnification in c–e. (b) Tracings are based on the known appearance of cells in the respective lamina, as shown after Golgi staining. Bar, 100 μm (a); 20 μm (c–e). [From Gray *et al.* (20).]

the characteristic differences between their interphase nuclei when stained with the Feulgen technique: the nucleolar heterochromatin is finely dispersed in the chick but forms large clumps in the quail. A similar nuclear marker can be used in the frog, *Xenopus:* quincrine staining results in punctate fluorescence of nuclei of cells of *Xenopus borealis,* while nuclei of *Xenopus laevis* show a uniform fluorescence (35). These techniques of interspecific cell grafting can show the fates of groups of grafted cells, but it is much more difficult to graft a single labeled cell (36). That has been accomplished by Jacobson and Xu (37), who grafted a single cell from a *Xenopus* embryo totally labeled with HRP to an unlabeled embryo. The technique involved surgical excision of a small cluster of cells from the totally labeled embryo, disaggregation of the cluster, and transfer to the host embryo of a single labeled cell by means of a micropipette (Fig. 1, method 4). The transplanted cell continued to divide and produced labeled, differentiated progeny of a wide range of cell types. Single-cell grafts offer the opportunity of studying cell regulation that may take place after heterotopic grafting, as well as tracing cell lineages after orthotopic grafting. Grafting between embryos at different stages of development can show when cells become committed to specific fates, and analyze the conditions required in the host environment versus the cell-autonomous conditions.

Summary of Requirements of an Ideal Cell Lineage Analysis

1. The method should satisfy the main aims of any clonal analysis, which are (a) tracing cell fates, (b) showing when commitment to specific fates occurs, (c) showing whether cell fates are lineage-dependent, and (d) showing whether cell fates are cell-autonomous or are modified by external factors. These aims cannot be accomplished by cell lineage tracing alone, but in addition require cell transplantation and cell ablation experiments, and unambiguous identification of the cell types that differentiate under experimentally altered conditions, using cell-type-specific antibodies.

2. The lineage should be traced from a single ancestral cell at a selected position. This requirement is satisfied by intracellular injection of a lineage tracer or by grafting a single labeled cell. It is not satisfied by the methods of retroviral infection or radiation-induced somatic mutation, in which the number and positions of initially labeled cells cannot be controlled.

3. The lineage tracer should be detectable after many cell generations and after cell differentiation and growth. Tracers that are injected into the cell are diluted with successive mitoses and cell growth and may be degraded, so that their application is limited to short lineages and to lineages in which cell division is rapid and occurs without much increase in cell volume.

Those conditions occur in amphibian and fish embryos, in which lineages have been traced for up to 20 cell generations, using intracellularly injected HRP, or biotinylated HRP, or fluorescent dextrans.

4. The clonal analysis should proceed prospectively: all descendants should be traced through successive generations until final differentiation of all descendants has occurred. Only fluorescent tracers enable continuous observation of the labeled clone, and, in practice, this is limited to cells at or near the surface of the embryo. When other means of clonal labeling are used, clonal development can be examined in a series of embryos fixed at different intermediate stages and in a series in which the clone is initiated at progressively later cell generations.

5. The tracer should not alter normal development and should be transferred exclusively to all the lineal descendants of the initially labeled ancestral cell. Controls are necessary to show that the method does not result in cell death.

6. The types of labeled progeny should be identifiable. Within the limits of light microscopic histology, HRP allows most definitive identification and provides permanent histological preparations, which can also be used for electron microscopic studies. Fluorescent tracers give the poorest resolution and, as the label fades, the preparations are not durable. Ideally, the labeled cells should also be identified by means of cell-type-specific antibodies.

References

1. M. Jacobson, *Annu. Rev. Neurosci.* **8**, 71 (1985).
2. M. Jacobson, *Trends NeuroSci. (Pers. Ed.)* **8**, 151 (1985).
3. G. S. Stent, *Philos. Trans. R. Soc. London B* **312**, 3 (1985).
4. G. Morata and P. A. Lawrence, *Nature (London)* **265**, 211 (1976).
5. A. L. Calof and T. M. Jessell, *Soc. Neurosci. Abstr.* **12**, 183 (1986).
6. K. Muneoka, N. Wanek, and S. V. Bryant, *J. Exp. Zool.* **239**, 289 (1986).
7. M. Jacobson and G. Hirose, *J. Neurosci.* **1**, 271 (1981).
8. R. L. Gimlich and J. Braun, *Dev. Biol.* **109**, 509 (1985).
9. P. W. Sheard and M. Jacobson, *Science* **236**, 851 (1987).
10. C. Kimmel and R. Warga, *Trends NeuroSci. (Pers. Ed.)* **4**, 68 (1988).
11. J. P. Miller and A. I. Selverston, *Science* **206**, 702 (1979).
12. K. T. Brown and D. G. Flaming, *Neuroscience (Oxford)* **2**, 813 (1977).
13. L. B. Haberly and J. M. Bower, *J. Neurosci. Methods* **3**, 251 (1981).
14. T. E. Ogden, M. Citron, and R. Pierantoni, *Science* **201**, 469 (1978).
15. D. J. Baldwin, *J. Neurosci. Methods* **2**, 153 (1980).
16. M.-M. Mesulam and D. L. Rosene, *J. Histochem. Cytochem.* **27**, 763 (1979).
17. M. Wilchek and E. A. Bayer, *Immunol. Today February* (1984).
18. M. Jacobson and S. Huang, *Dev. Biol.* **110**, 102 (1985).

19. J. Price, D. Turner, and C. Cepko, *Proc. Natl. Acad. Sci. U.S.A.* **84,** 156 (1987).
20. G. E. Gray, J. C. Glover, J. Majors, and J. R. Sanes, *Proc. Natl. Acad. Sci. U.S.A.* **85,** 7356 (1988).
21. D. L. Turner and C. L. Cepko, *Nature (London)* **328,** 131 (1987).
22. J. R. Sanes, *Trends NeuroSci. (Pers. Ed.)* **12,** 21 (1989).
23. R. Wetts and S. E. Fraser, *Science* **239,** 1142 (1988).
24. C. E. Holt, T. W. Bertsen, H. M. Ellis, and W. A. Harris, *Neuron* **1,** 15 (1988).
25. A. McLaren, "Mammalian Chimaeras." Cambridge Univ. Press, London and New York, 1976.
26. G. R. Cunha and K. D. Vanderslice, *Stain Technol.* **59,** 7 (1984).
27. U. Muller, L. Singh, S. Grund, and K. W. Jones, *Differentiation* **22,** 138 (1982).
28. R. L. Gardner and M. H. Johnson, *Ciba Found. Symp.* **29,** 183 (1975).
29. J. Rossant, *Philos. Trans. R. Soc. London B* **312,** 91 (1985).
30. P. J. Bryant and H. A. Schneiderman, *Dev. Biol.* **20,** 263 (1969).
31. G. Streisinger, F. Coale, C. Taggart, C. Walker, and D. J. Grunwald, *Dev. Biol.* **131,** 60 (1989).
32. C. G. B. Jennings, *Trends NeuroSci.* **11,** 46 (1988).
33. K. Herrup, *Trends NeuroSci.* **11,** 49 (1988).
34. N. Le Douarin, "The Neutral Crest." Cambridge Univ. Press, London and New York, 1982.
35. C. H. Thiébaud, *Dev. Biol.* **98,** 245 (1983).
36. J. Heasman, A. Snape, J. C. Smith, and C. C. Wylie, *J. Embryol. Exp. Morphol., Suppl.* **97,** 65 (1986).
37. M. Jacobson and W. L. Xu, *Dev. Biol.* **131,** 119 (1989).

Index